ANTHROPOLOGY

A to Z

UNIVERSAL REFERENCE LIBRARY

Published:

NON-CHRISTIAN RELIGIONS

MUSIC

PHILOSOPHY

ANTHROPOLOGY

In preparation:

ASTRONOMY

CHEMISTRY

SOCIOLOGY

CLASSICAL ART

Universal Reference Library

Anthropology

A to Z

EDITED BY

CARLETON S. COON

Professor of Anthropology, the University Museum,
University of Pennsylvania

AND

EDWARD E. HUNT, JR.

Assistant Professor of Anthropology,
Forsyth Dental Infirmary,
Harvard School of Dental Medicine

BASED ON THE WORK OF
GERHARD HEBERER, GOTTFRIED KURTH,
AND ILSE SCHWIDETZKY-ROESING

GROSSET & DUNLAP, INC., *Publishers*

NEW YORK

Based on *Anthropologie* of the Fischer Lexikon series,
published by the Fischer Bücherei K.G.
Frankfurt-Main-Hamburg. Translation, adaptation and
new material arranged under the supervision of
Grosset & Dunlap, Inc.

TRANSLATION BY:

HANS GUNTHARDT

GERTRUDE HIRSCHLER

BENITA LUCKMANN

ALAN NEWHAM

ERIC PROTTER

E. M. VALK

SOPHIE WILKINS

INTRODUCTION

THIS VOLUME REPRESENTS the efforts of a group of distinguished German scientists of several related disciplines to bring together and coordinate our knowledge of man's origins and evolutionary history, his distribution into races, and the biological aspects of human behavior. It is, for example, the first book I know in which a reader can find essays on human growth, paternity diagnosis, constitution, and social biology along with human paleontology and serology.

The subject matter of this book is international in scope and Edward Hunt and I, who have worked together before, have done our best (1) to bring as fully up to date as possible the few articles covering subjects in which new discoveries are being made almost every day, (2) to present the volume as a whole in terms familiar to Americans, and (3) to preserve the essence and flavor of the original while making it particularly applicable to New World as well as Old World problems.

—CARLETON S. COON

ANTHROPOLOGY

Anthropology is the science of man. The term goes back to Aristotle, and we find it employed once again in 1655, by an anonymous writer who understood it to denote anatomy and physiology. Modern anthropology, still young as a science, has not yet been defined to the mutual satisfaction of workers in all countries, and what is legitimately embraced by this discipline is still subject to international debate. On the continent of Europe anthropology means what British and Americans call physical anthropology. In Britain and the United States, anthropology also embraces comparative sociology and the study of cultures in time and space.

Anthropology in the European sense and physical anthropology in the American sense cover areas that can be analyzed by the methods of natural science (see Methods of Anthropology). Thus it would include morphology (the descriptive study of somatic forms), physiology (the science of the functions of the body)—inclusive of biological processes (chromosomal duplication) and hereditary variations (mutation)—modes of inheritance, the mechanisms of evolution (selection, genetic drift, etc.), the origin of groups, and the origins of the hominid family (the formation of species and their geographic distribution). As the closest relatives of the hominids, non-hominid primates, particularly the Pongidae (great apes), are given consideration. However, this highly complex, still incompletely delineated content of what Rudolf Martin, in 1914, called the "natural history of the hominids" comprises but a fraction of what a scientific study of man must investigate. Although such areas as the study of twins, genealogy, ethnography, ethnology, and racial psychology are basically scientific in their methods, they are also related to the humanities.

Anthropology does have a humanistic aspect, and hence can no longer simply be defined as the "natural" history of the hominids. This circumstance has made it possible for disciplines other than those of theoretical science, which likewise seek to grasp the nature of man, to make use of the traditional designation of anthropology; for example, philosophical anthropology, cultural anthropology, Christian anthropology, and medical anthropology. The last-named, incidentally, demonstrates impressively that these areas cannot be sharply distinguished from the natural science of anthropology. The possibility of combining these two separate approaches to the study of man—the scientific and the humanistic—into one unified discipline called anthropology derives from the fact that man is a physical-intellectual entity, and can be approached methodically from either point of view. The aim is to obtain a picture of the nature of man. Egon von Eickstedt has termed anthropology "the biology of man," as a "third biological science" alongside that of animals (zoology) and of plants (botany).

ANTHROPOLOGY

Eugen Fischer proposes the term "anthropobiology" for this study, since, in his view, it has gone outside the conventional concept of anthropology as the natural history of the hominids. He would have the term "anthropology" denote the study of man in broad, general terms, in keeping with its literal translation. The term would then embrace both branches of inquiry—the scientific and the humanistic.

In this encyclopedia the traditional concept of anthropology as a scientific discipline has been retained, while taking into account, however, the areas in which it dovetails with humanistic fields of study. This apparently has not adversely affected the concept of "true" anthropology, for the layman will hardly look for philosophers, theologians, or even clinical medical practitioners in an "Institute of Anthropology." After all, the science of zoology, too, has transcended its old boundaries by virtue of its intensive occupation with such fields as "behavioral study" (the psychology of animals), and yet it has not been renamed "zoobiology." Of course, this is not a good analogy, for since human beings are distinguished from animals by reason of their intellect, special considerations are involved in the study of man. Anthropologists do not, by any means, claim to have obtained an exhaustive picture of the nature of man.

Modifying the scheme of Eugen Fischer, the scope of anthropology, as the term is used here, may be broken down as follows:

1. *Hominid Morphology:* Comparative anatomy of the body, systems of organs, and individual organs of the Hominidae.

2. *Racial Studies:* Racial morphology, racial taxonomy, and racial history.

3. *Human Paleontology:* The morphology of the fossil hominids (in the order of Primates) and the history of human evolution (anthropogenesis).

4. *Human Genetics:* Hereditary mechanisms, variability, selection, population genetics, and the laws of racial differentiation.

5. *Comparative Human Physiology:* A comparative investigation of the functions of the body.

6. *Comparative Human Psychology:* Investigation of behavioral differences.

7. *Comparative Human Pathology:* Morphological and physiological aberrations; references to human genetics.

8. *Social Biology:* Group selection, social assortment, group anthropology.

9. *Applied Anthropology:* The application of human biology to problems of forensic classification (paternity diagnosis), the genetic improvement of man (eugenics), and the use of body measurements in design and engineering.

To obtain its results, anthropology makes use of the methods of study employed in general biology, accommodated to the object of its investigation—which, of course, is man (see Methods of Anthropology).

THE CONCEPT OF RACE

Human races are classified as zoological subspecies of *Homo sapiens*. The term "race" designates major groups, or populations, consisting of individuals who propagate their kind by sexual reproduction and possess certain common characteristics of form, color, etc., which distinguish them from the other subspecies. It should be noted, however, that the races of a species are interfertile, and that the effective barrier to interbreeding arises only on the next higher level, between species themselves. Under natural conditions, a geographical area, for the most part, ordinarily is inhabited only by the members of a single race, so that although in principle there is no limit on interbreeding among the individuals of a species, in practice the choice of mates is restricted to individuals in the immediate area. Hence every race is phylogenetically a potential starting point for a new species (see The Formation of Races) if it is sufficiently isolated for many generations. Accordingly, race is of considerable taxonomic importance, for it serves as a preliminary phase in the evolution of every higher category.

Before the basic factors of heredity were known, the division of species into races was grounded empirically on the observable differences in the characteristics of the various groups. After Gregor Mendel, in 1866, experimentally demonstrated the distribution pattern of inherited traits (his second law), and after his researches were rediscovered forty years later, when they were used as the basis for extensive controlled experiments, it became possible to establish that the hereditary genotypic differences among individuals of a genetic population are quite significant. As a rule, the genotype of an individual is fundamentally different from that of every other individual of his genetic population, as it must be, in view of the fact that each human being is estimated to have between 24,000 and 42,000 genes, some of which have undergone mutation. Yet the apparently high individual variability of heritable characteristics does not affect distinguishing marks that are shared by all the members of a genetic population. These distinctive common traits continue to set such a population apart from the others. On the basis of such observations, supported by certain genetic theories, Eugen Fischer was the first to arrive at the following, still valid, definition of race, as applied to man: "Races are groups (in a breeding community) that have in common certain genes which are lacking in other groups."

This was the first scientifically valid, precise concept of race as applied to man. It was greatly needed, for the "race problem," since the turn of the century, had been a subject of lively discussion although no one then possessed sufficient knowledge of the biological factors involved. The concepts "race," "peoples" (such as Germanic or Latin), and "language groups" (such as Aryan or Semitic) were carelessly tossed about and used interchangeably, although "race" is the only one of these that can be strictly defined in a genetic and biological sense. Moreover, "race" as such cannot be correlated with national or language groups. This confusion, regrettably, brought the scientific concept of race into discredit from the start, the more so as it was linked, in public discussions, with philosophical and non-scientific valuations. Such abuses, however, cannot alter the fact that there are genetically determined racial differences, and that, therefore, the existence of races cannot be ignored by biologists, nor, certainly, by those studying such a biological entity as man.

After World War II, in which the various philosophical-political controversies over race had reached their climax, UNESCO published two "Statements on Race." The first, issued in 1950, was formulated without consulting biologists and still reflected the influence of philosophical-political discussions. When this statement was rejected by scientists all over the world, in 1951 the second formulation was promulgated: "In its anthropological sense, the word 'race' should be reserved for groups of mankind possessing well-developed and primarily heritable physical differences from other groups."

The few biologists who took part in this convention at once protested that the new definition restricted itself to physical differences and excluded psychological aspects. From a genetic point of view, the psychological realm cannot be given a separate and special status. Experimental studies of heredity have established that the psychology of man in particular is subject to the laws of heredity which are valid for all living beings (see Human Genetics). Such behavioral studies conducted on animals have also proved beyond a doubt that in some behavioral features no sharp distinction can be made between lower animals and men. The UNESCO declaration of 1951, which is more restrictive than Fischer's definition, is not the fruit of scientifically provable facts. It is best seen as evidence that the non-biologist still has reservations about accepting the idea that man is completely subject to the same laws of heredity that apply to all of life's forms and expressions. It is difficult, after all, to give up all the customary distinctions between man, as a thinking, cognizant, creative being, and the animal world.

In regard to both definitions of race given above, there is another essential point to be made: As both seek primarily to set apart living genetic populations, their function is a static one. But race is, from the biological point of view, not a static, but a dynamic condition. Within the constantly changing movement of "life" it represents a breeding unit continuously modifying itself, by infinitesimal degrees, through mutations. This mobile condition was most aptly formulated by the American geneticist Dobzhansky, who said: "Race is a process." His statement at last fits the concept of race meaningfully into the history of life, and at the same time makes race understandable as the smallest ever-changing taxonomic unit (genetic population) by which we can interpret the total course of organic evolution.

To identify a race, it is theoretically sufficient to note the prevalence of a new gene and the consequent characteristic trait or traits that occur predominantly in a particular genetic population and distinguish it from neighboring populations. But the one-trait basis of differentiation, considering the vast numbers of genes in mammals alone, would lead to an unjustifiable multiplicity of taxonomic units such as species and subspecies. Therefore, Fischer's early postulate—of the gene groups in man which unite to produce certain characteristic patterns of traits, thus permitting a clear differentiation of the various genetic populations of a species within a large framework—has been used as a basis for the determination and classification of races. The foregoing remarks in connection with Dobzhansky's definition of race also serve to show that under natural conditions in the course of the evolution of life, there can be no "pure races," but only transitional forms having more or less characteristic combinations of hereditary features. "Pure" racial strains were first created by man himself through the planned breeding of animals.

There is some disagreement concerning the numbers of races, even though the races are always differentiated in accordance with the same basic principles of genetics. The differences in the estimated numbers result mostly from differences in emphasis. Some writers tend to base their estimate on the number of observable regional genetic populations (see The Formation of Races); others are concerned with more general considerations. Of course, the more local races that are subsumed under related super-regional entities, or "major races" (i.e., Caucasoid, Mongoloid, Congoid), the smaller the number of single traits within each characteristic combination that can be taken into consideration. At the same time, authors will differ in assigning local groups to one or the other major race, especially in the contact zones. These differences in taxonomy and in point of view do not militate, however, against the validity of the definition of race itself; they arise solely from the fact that various writers evaluate racial traits differently and assign a different significance to them. Such conceptual differences also underline the fact that in talking about races we are dealing with developing life, with processes not easily subsumed under the necessarily rigid schemes which our need for methodical classification demands.

About the actual inheritance of racial traits in man, we know only what we can learn from observing spontaneous racial mixtures (for example, Caucasoid-Congoid, Caucasoid-Mongoloid, Caucasoid-Capoid), since we cannot conduct experiments in hybridization on human beings. But modern human genetics, through studies of twins and paternity problems, has by now accumulated an almost unmanageable profusion of data on the heritability of the subtlest morphological-physical traits and their corresponding psychological tendencies. The scientific knowledge we now have leaves no doubt that man, with all his physical characteristics and functions as well as his psychological powers, is subject to the same laws of heredity as all the other organisms on earth, and that only a concept of race which embraces man in his entirety is valid.

CONSTITUTION

The term "constitution" refers to the whole form and functioning of an individual, as influenced by his heredity and environment, and is concerned with permanent rather than ephemeral characteristics of the organism. Constitutional patterns are those which show prolonged continuity throughout the individual's life rather than poorly predictable, transient alterations. There are as many constitutions as there are individuals. The scientific study of constitution deals with this diversity in two ways:

1. Groups of similar individual constitutions are designated as constitutional types.

2. Constitutional characteristics of different kinds are examined and compared; in fact, Ernst Kretschmer maintains that "the study of constitution is the study of correlations." In particular, correlations are of special interest to the anthropologist.

Factor Analysis

Since the beginning of constitutional research, increasingly exact quantitative methods have been used to evaluate the covariation of different somatic and psychological characteristics. Studies of physique have progressed furthest in this direction.

The most intricate and widely used quantitative method in this field is factor analysis, which was originally developed by psychologists. Using this procedure, one attempts to isolate factors which are shared by all traits in a particular study (common factors), as well as those which affect particular regions or dimensions of the body (special or group factors). In addition, one may calculate factor saturations, which specify the extent to which factors express themselves in the physique of a particular person.

In the analysis of physique, the major advantage of factor analysis is its objectivity. The number and kind of selected factors, however, depend on the measurements and indices that are to be correlated, and may also vary according to which of several alternative methods the investigator chooses to employ. Despite these shortcomings, however, several modern studies have been able to develop a number of acceptable general principles in regard to the factorial variation of human physique.

1. A general size-factor appears in all absolute somatic measurements.

2. Factors of somatic elongation and girth, or corpulence, vary independently of each other. The factor of somatic elongation is expressed particularly in the length of the trunk and legs, whereas that of circumference is revealed both by the girth of the abdomen and chest and by direct measurements of the thickness of the subcutaneous adipose layer at different standardized sites. Adipose thicknesses in different parts of the body show high correlations with one another. Measurements of body

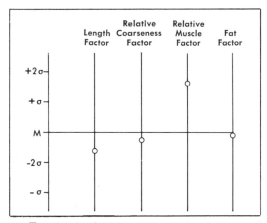

FIG. 1 An individual diagnosis of physique, using Lindegård's method, for four dominant factors, expressed in standard deviation units (after Lindegård, 1953).

breadth, on the other hand, are far less clearly correlated with this factor of adiposity, or bulkiness of physique.

3. Factor analysis indicates that the measurements of the head show generally no relation to those of the trunk and limbs. When non-overlapping dimensions of the head are determined, they show notably low correlations with one another.

4. For the upper and lower trunk, a common determinant of breadth has been found, as well as tendencies toward an independent variation of the transverse dimensions of these two regions.

When a factor analysis has been completed on a set of measurements from a sample of individuals, these measurements can be applied to a single person to evaluate the magnitude, or "saturation," of each factor in his physique.

For diagnoses of individuals, Lindegård and Parnell independently developed the use of three indicators of physique by the following factorial methods: the score in standard deviation units of a length factor, a factor of adiposity, and a factor for muscular development. Schlegel uses the size of the hand for classifying individuals on a scale from asthenic to athletic, and the breadth of the pelvis as the major feature on a masculine-feminine scale.

Types of Physique

Most of the older research on human physique did not exhaustively analyze the correlations between somatic traits. Instead, they were estimated on sight, and described, in terms of supposedly correlated features, as types of physique.

Many of the older typologies emphasized variations between a long-narrow and a short-broad pole of physique (macroscelic and microscelic, according to Manouvrier in 1902; microsplanchnic and megalosplanchnic, according to Viola, 1909; asthenic and sthenic in the terminology of Mills, 1917; sthenoplastic and euroclastic, according to Bunak, 1923; linear and lateral types, according to Stockard, 1923; etc.).

At the same time, correlations of these types with psychological and functional traits, especially disposition to illness, were often investigated or at least assumed. Kretschmer called these two extremes of physique leptosome (earlier also asthenic) and pyknic, but he added the athletic type as a third distinct and independent "syndrome of correlations."

Kretschmer's system marks a new phase in the study of physique, for he and his followers went beyond mere classification and tried to establish new correlations. He used small samples of "pure" types and compared data on leptosome, pyknic, and athletic physiques.

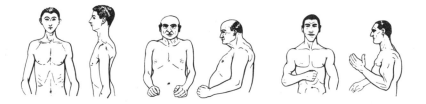

FIG. 2 Types of physique after Kretschmer. Left: leptosome. Center: pyknic. Right: athletic.

A catalogue of dominant physical traits was established for the typological diagnosis of physiques (but these traits per se were not tested statistically in terms of correlations) (see Table p. 9). Body measurements supported and helped to clarify the diagnosis of physique by visual observation alone. The differences between leptosome and pyknic types emerged more clearly as a result of these measurements; but the athletic type was placed between the other two.

Conrad therefore attempted to translate the tripartite typology of Kretschmer into two bipolar scales of somatic variation. As a primary continuum he distinguishes the leptomorphic-pyknomorphic scale, and secondarily he recognizes an asthenic-sthenic, or asthenic-athletic, scale. The primary variants are regarded as forms of growth: the pyknomorphic type represents in all its proportions the childish "conservative" type; the leptomorphic represents a further differentiated "propulsive" growth form (see Growth). Since growth is influenced greatly by endocrine secretions and by the sensitivity of immature tissues to these agents, one can assume that different types of physique correspond to different hormone systems. Actually, the relative weight of the endocrine glands of pyknics and leptosomes does show characteristic variations. The weight of the thymus gland of pyknics, which is relatively large and active during childhood, is above average, whereas the relative weight of all other endocrine glands is lower than that of leptosomes.

The Italian school of constitutional study has made use of evidence of the effects of endocrine glands on both normal and abnormal physique and growth. The results have become the basis for their system of normal types of physique. It established an extended classification system based on the hyper- or hypo-functioning of the thyroid gland, the pituitary, the

MAJOR CHARACTERISTICS OF KRETSCHMER'S EXTREME BODY TYPES			
	PYKNIC	ATHLETIC	LEPTOSOME
Proportions of Trunk	Short, deep rounded rib cage; obtuse angle of lower ribs.	Broad, strong shoulders. Trapezoidal trunk with relatively narrow hips.	Flattened, elongated thorax. Acute angle of lower ribs. Relatively broad hips.
Body Surface	Round, soft form resulting from well-developed subcutaneous fat deposition.	Strongly developed, plastic muscle prominence on massive skeletal structure.	Lean or sinewy with meager deposition of subcutaneous fat.
Extremities	Soft, relatively short limbs; fine-boned, short and broad hands and feet.	Crudely modeled, powerful arms and legs; large hands and feet. Eventual cyanosis distally.	Long, lean extremities with long, narrow hands and feet.
Head and Neck	Relatively large, rounded head, with flattened crown. Short, massive neck.	High, coarsely modeled head. Upright, powerful neck with sloping, tightly stretched trapezius.	Relatively small head. Long, thin neck.
Face	Soft, plastic, broad, florid face. Slight anterior convexity of profile.	Coarse, angular, bony modeled face. Shape a steep-sided oval.	Pale, narrow face; a foreshortened oval. Pointed, narrow nose. Usually an angular profile.
Head and Body Hair	Fine head hair. Tendency to baldness. Moderate to extreme hairiness of body.	Strongly developed head hair. Body hairiness moderate.	Coarse head hair. Usually shaped like a fur cap. Slight development of body hair.

gonads, and the adrenal glands. This school of thought, however, has received little attention outside Italy.

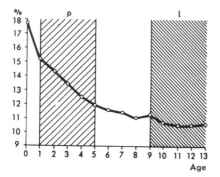

FIG. 3 Types of physique as forms of growth. The average relative depth of the thorax (sagittal depth of the chest as a percentage of stature) from the pyknic to the leptosomic stages of development (after K. Conrad, 1949).

In Great Britain and the United States, Sheldon's method of somatotyping, which is derived from Kretschmer's system, is the predominant system. Sheldon distinguished three components of physique, which he relates to the embryonic germ layers. These components combine in separate individuals in varying mixtures. The dominant traits of the endomorphic component are the predominance of the trunk over the extremities and the pelvis over the shoulders, as well as a soft roundness of the body contours, weak musculature, delicate bones, and relatively small hands and feet. The mesomorphic component is characterized by predominance of muscle and bone: the physique is hard and rectangular, the musculature is pronounced, the extremities are long and robust, and the shoulders predominate over the abdominal trunk. The ectomorphic component is characterized by linearity and delicacy of physique: the limbs are long in comparison with the trunk, so there is a decentralization of the body mass; the chest and pelvis are flat, the face recedes strongly in comparison with the back of the head. The endomorphic, mesomor-

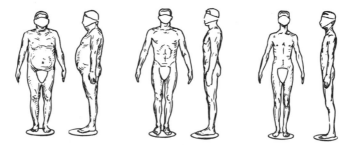

FIG. 4 Body types after Sheldon. *Left:* predominantly endomorphic components (711). *Center:* predominantly mesomorphic components (171). *Right:* predominantly ectomorphic components (117).

phic, and ectomorphic components correspond respectively to the pyknic, athletic, and leptosome constitutional types of Kretschmer. Each component is expressed on a scale of 1 to 7; the individual is designated by a three-digit figure. Somatotype 326, for example, would indicate medium, weakly, and strongly marked endomorphic, mesomorphic, and ectomorphic components, respectively. The individual diagnosis is based on measurements of length taken from standardized photographs. Endomorphic and ectomorphic components show a high negative correlation, which indicates the existence of a continuum. The continuum is related to a factor that can be isolated by factorial analysis, whereas the mesomorphic component corresponds to a different and ill-defined factor.

Sexual Types

The most pronounced differentiation of physique in all ethnic groups is that between the male and the female. It is based not only on autosomal differences, as is the case with all other constitutional variants, but on the difference in the sex chromosomes: the male possesses an X chromosome and a Y chromosome, the female two X chromosomes (see Human Genetics). The chromosome pattern is set at the moment of conception; during the period of individual development, however, autosomal genes also influence sexual characteristics. The gonad in either sex is potentially bisexual; the preponderance of one sex over the other derives from a repression of the predisposition of the opposite sex. A residue of potential bisexuality in adults is evident in the production of both sex hormones by every individual, although hormones of the opposite sex are produced in smaller quantities. The approximate daily production of male sex hormones (androgens) is 12–70 units in the male and 10–20 units in the female. The production of the female sex hormone (estrogen) is 30–1,500 units daily for the female (with strong fluctuations within the menstrual cycle) and 80–150 units for the male. The sexes therefore do not differ absolutely; their ranges of variation overlap. What is true of hormonal structure is equally true of physique and psychological make-up. The most obvious differences are those between the primary sexual characteristics, i.e., the sex organs directly involved in procreation. Genuine intermediate sexes (intersexes and hermaphrodites) are rare. Secondary sexual characteristics such as differences in size, proportion, hair, and psychological make-up do show overlapping between the sexes.

Most differences between men and women can be traced back to two basic facts: the different reproductive functions and the earlier maturation of women (see Growth). The reproductive functions determine above all the form of the pelvis; the female pelvis is broader and lower, the inferior rami of the pubis have a more obtuse angle, and the angle of the ischiatic notch is greater. The opening of the pelvis is broad and oval as compared with the rounded form of the male pelvis. Comparative pelvic measurements of skeletons establish the correct sex in 98 out of 100 cases. The broader pelvis together with the narrower shoulders of the female clearly establish sexual differentiations as reflected in the trunk index (breadth of shoulders × 100 divided by breadth of pelvis). Next to the pelvis, the female breasts are the most obvious sexual characteristic.

Many characteristics in the female remain in an infantile stage due to her early maturation. This holds true particularly for the absolute size and strength of the limbs. In all absolute measurements the male is larger than the female except for the breadth of the pelvis in some human stocks; his larger muscles attached to a more rugged bone structure produce more pronounced muscle markings. The bones of the cranial vault are thicker, the brow ridges are larger, and the forehead more sloping. The mastoid process is larger, and the nuchal surface of the occipital bone has more conspicuous muscle markings. All these traits make it possible to determine the sex of most skulls, frequently even after cremation. Sex can be correctly established in 95 out of 100 cases through measurements of the upper thigh bone; the combination of pelvic and femur measurements

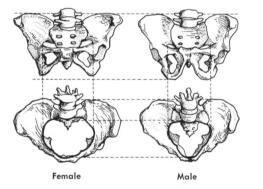

Fig. 5

Female and
male pelvis.

Female   Male

produce even more reliable results. The differences in the development of the locomotor apparatus result in differences between the sexes in performance and efficiency, particularly in sports.

Differences in absolute size are not the only distinguishing characteristics; men and women also differ in body proportions. The male thus exhibits a tendency toward a larger head, a longer face, a flatter chest, and a shorter trunk in proportion to his stature, and a higher proportion of upper arm and thigh length to the total length of the extremities. On the other hand, the female exhibits the corresponding opposite, infantile traits: a rounder head, a shorter, rounder face, a deeper thorax, a larger relative trunk length, and a greater relative length of the upper versus the lower extremity. The absolute brain weight of the female is lower, though the brain is relatively larger than that of the male. The more pronounced development of subcutaneous fat in the female, which determines her softer body form, is an infantile trait. Among American and European populations, there are sexual differentiations of pigmentation, particularly a more pronounced pigmentation of eyes and hair in the female, as well as a differentiation in hair distribution: longer head hair, but sparser body and face hair in the female; an extension of body hair from the pubic region toward the navel in the male, and a horizontal upper boundary of pubic hair in the female.

The development of secondary sexual characteristics shows marked individual variations; members of both sexes will therefore be classified in accordance with their proximity to a masculine or feminine extreme. Recent studies in constitution have attempted to define this phenomenon more precisely.

Sheldon developed the gynandromorphic index, which determined the strength of opposite sexual characteristics in the physique. The following feminine characteristics are classified and listed in condensed form for the male: round and delicate shoulders, relatively short and delicate arms, broad hips, hourglass-shaped body form in posterior view with high-set waist, fully rounded waist-knee contours and round buttocks, sparse body hair, straight borderline of pubic hair, soft body surface due to subcutaneous fat tissue, predominance of the lateral over the medial curve of calves, rudimentary development of breasts. Schlegel developed an andromorphic-gynecomorphic scale for men: large, relatively long frontal trunk wall, thick adipose development of the buttocks, and large diameter of the areola of the breast are characteristics of the female extreme which are somewhat correlated in individuals.

The distinctiveness of secondary sexual characteristics and the differences between the sexes vary from race to race. The sexual dimorphism of the African Congoids is thus negligible in pelvic breadth and body hair, whereas it is marked in most Caucasoids. The physiques of more infantile racial stocks, such as the Veddas and the small, gracile Mongoloids of Southeast Asia, have a more feminine character than the coarsely built, "masculine" stocks, such as the Northwest Europeans and the robust tribes

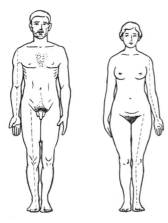

FIG. 6

Sexual differentiation of physique
(after A. Scheinfeld, 1940).

13

of North American Indians. In the former, more "feminine" races, the women are therefore more typically representative of their groups, while the men are correspondingly more representative of the latter, more "masculine" groups.

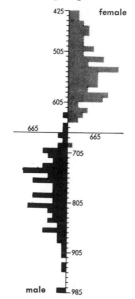

Fig. 7 Determination of sex from skeleton. Selective analysis on the basis of four traits (length of femur, diameter of femur head, length of ischium, length of pubic bone) of 198 Negro skeletons of known sex (after Thieme and Schull, 1957).

Psychophysical Correlations

The basic problem of an anthropological inquiry into constitution is the relationship between physical and psychological traits. Westphal states that the largest such project is still the 8,100 cases which were the core of Kretschmer's researches in constitution. In particular, Kretschmer studied the correlations between body build and mental illness. He found good statistical evidence of a predisposition of the leptosomes toward schizophrenia, of the pyknics toward manic-depression, and of the athletics toward epilepsy. Kretschmer regards these psychotic conditions as extreme variants of normality. He developed his more normal character types on the basis of studies of different representative types of physique. The schizoid temperament which corresponds to the leptosome physique exhibits the following psychological traits: a concern for shape rather than color, an analytic perception which enables the individual to grasp the structural parts of phenomena (i.e., an ability to discern between component parts of a whole), a tendency toward conservatism and perseverance in thought and behavior. Schizoids like isolation and are considered emotionally cold. The cycloid temperament of the pyknic exhibits contrary traits· an emphasis on color rather than on shape, a holistic world view, and a weaker tendency toward perseverance. The cycloid is

ADULT PSYCHOPHYSICAL CORRELATIONS

SOMATIC CHARACTERISTIC	PSYCHIC CHARACTERISTIC	r
I. Stature		
(a) 2,257 Swedish recruits	Intelligence Test	+0.22
(b) 567 French soldiers	" " (Penrose)	+0.29
(c) 80 Otomi Indians	" " (Minnesota)	+0.31
(d) 80 Otomi Indians	" " (Form Board)	+0.35
II. Endomorphy	Visceratonia	+0.79
"	Somatotonia	−0.29
"	Cerebrotonia	−0.32
Mesomorphy	Somatotonia	+0.82
"	Cerebrotonia	−0.58
Ectomorphy	Cerebrotonia	+0.83
"	Intelligence (Ia)	+0.19
III. Endomorphy	Manic-depressive components	+0.54
"	Schizoid "	−0.25
Mesomorphy	Manic-depressive "	+0.41
"	Paranoid "	+0.57
"	Schizoid "	−0.68
Ectomorphy	Manic-depressive "	−0.59
"	Paranoid "	−0.34
"	Schizoid "	+0.64
IV. Coarseness factor	Vocabulary test	−0.14
Muscle factor	Vocabulary test	−0.18
"	Validity	+0.21
"	Stability	−0.29
Fat factor	Stability	−0.33
Relative weight	Stability	−0.44

GROUP I = (a) 2,257 Swedish recruits (after Husen, 1947). (b) 567 French soldiers (after Schreider, 1956). (c) & (d) 80 Otomi Indians (after Schreider, 1956).
GROUP II = 200 students (after Sheldon, 1942).
GROUP III = 155 patients of Elgin State Hospital (after Sheldon, 1949).
GROUP IV = 287–295 Swedish recruits (after Lindegård and Nyman, 1956).

sociable and emotionally warm. The normal traits of the athletic type were reduced to the common denominator of a viscous or sluggish temperament.

Sheldon arrived at similar conclusions. He discerned three groups of correlated character traits. The viscerotonic complex of traits include: a need for human contact, love, and recognition, and inertness and slowness of bodily movements. In the somatotonic complex, activity and vigorous bodily movements are the chief characteristics. Representatives of the cerebrotonic complex react swiftly but are restrained in expressive movements; their adaptability is poor; they are antisocial. Corresponding to the classification of types of physique, seven temperamental components were distinguished. The indicator of tested individuals was again a number with three digits: 225 thus indicates a weakly viscerotonic and somatotonic, but markedly predominant cerebrotonic component. The endomorphic component shows a high correlation with viscerotonia, the mesomorphic and ectomorphic correspondingly with somatotonia and cerebrotonia. Similarly, three "psychiatric components" show correlations with components of physique: the manic-depressive complex predominantly with endomorphy, the paranoid with mesomorphy, and the hebephrenic (schizoid) with ectomorphy. The viscerotonic-cerebrotonic variability scale is described as stable by Nyman, who also regards it as directly correlated with Lindegård's fat factor.

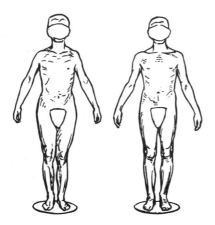

FIG. 8 Gynandromorphy. Figures at left and right respectively indicate higher and lower gynandromorphic index of men having the same type of body structure (442) (after W. H. Sheldon, 1940).

Conrad demonstrated that the traits of primary variations can be interpreted in terms of biological development: children differ from adults in the same direction as pyknomorphics from leptomorphics. Accordingly, leptosomes do better in school than pyknics; there is, further, a correlation, albeit a weak one, between body length and intelligence quotient, as well as between ectomorphy and intelligence.

The constitutional study of sexual dimorphism has similarly revealed valid psychological correlations. They provide a foundation and elaboration of the numerous intuitive descriptions of male and female characteristics which refer them to polar dominant traits (e.g., *Homo faber* and *Homo curativus,* according to Buytendijk; the male's interest in artifacts versus the female's interest in persons, according to Klages; male behavior dominated by noetic, or intellective, functions, as opposed to the more visceral, or vegetative, functions of the female, according to Lersch and others). An exhaustive study of sexual personality differences has been made by Terman and Miles. The results of many test questions show clear differentiations, and individual diagnosis is reached through the summation of "masculine" and "feminine" responses.

Male and female are definitely differentiated in the average values and the distribution of the M-F index; however, as in the case of secondary sexual characteristics of the physique, there exist intermediate scores attained by a minority of both sexes. Factor analysis of test batteries yielded a factor of emotionality and a factor expressing specific interests. The frequency distribution of intellectual ability is lower in the female in that there are fewer female geniuses. There are also differences in specific abilities: boys on the average show more ability in mathematics, girls in the learning of languages. There is a weak intra-sexual correlation between the M-F index and traits of physique: a somewhat higher masculinity in

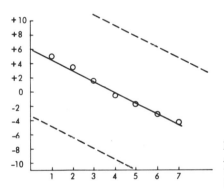

FIG. 9 Psychophysical correlatives. Average values of the fat factor on the 1–7 scale of psychological stability (after Lindegård and Nyman, 1956).

males with tall stature and those with deep voices. On the other hand, Schlegel found a relatively high correlation between dominant traits on the andromorphic-gynecomorphic variability scale, i.e., the diameter of the pelvic opening and the answers to specific test questions. The men with feminine physique accordingly exhibited a greater interest in color rather than in form as compared with the more masculine ones, a more holistic than analytic appraisal, stronger sociability, higher adaptability, and a stronger attachment to living creatures. "Man is of major interest to the gynecomorphic, things to the andromorphic."

Psychological sexual differentiation in test scores, as well as the intuitive appraisals, is related, to a considerable degree, to physique. Unlike the psychological correlation with different types of physique, the influence of social and cultural determinants has to be taken into consideration here: boys and girls are trained for specific social roles from early childhood. It is not yet possible to differentiate with exactness between cultural and genetic determinants of masculine and feminine behavior.

A key to the understanding of psychological correlations is provided by both normal and abnormal endocrine conditions. Excesses or deficiencies of endocrine function are manifested in physical as well as psychological symptoms. Overproduction of the thyroxins of the thyroid gland accelerates all vital functions from metabolism to emotional irritability, and is associated with a lean physique (Basedow's syndrome). Inadequate secretion of these hormones leads to developmental disturbances, stocky, infantile proportions, sluggish intellectual functioning, and even mental deficiency. Treatment with the androgen testosterone (a hormone produced by the testes) will accelerate a slow rate of physical maturation in some boys. Older men with inadequate androgenic functions may also benefit in some cases from treatment with this substance. The complicated interplay of hormones and the nervous system gives rise to a variety of patterns of endocrine function, and thereby to behavior.

In physical and psychological characteristics, the child differs from the adult in the same way that woman differs from man, the gynaecomorphic from the andromorphic man, and the pyknic from the leptosome.

Many of an individual's characteristics, then, depend on the way he looks at the world: whether his approach is holistic or analytic; whether he makes social contacts easily and likes to do so, or whether he finds it difficult and thus obtains little enjoyment from it.

Adaptability

The individual constitution may vary according to changes in the environment (see Human Genetics). If whole populations or parts of them are exposed to such modifications, their average character changes; genetically similar populations in different environments can then be distinguished by different phenotypes. This adaptability is well established for a series of somatic traits through various comparative scales.

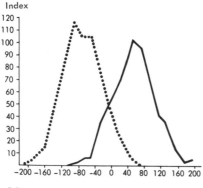

Fig. 10 Psychic-sexual differences. The distribution of the M-F Index among women is indicated by the dotted line, among men by the solid line (after P. Hofstätter, 1944, based on the material of L. M. Terman and C. C. Miles, 1936).

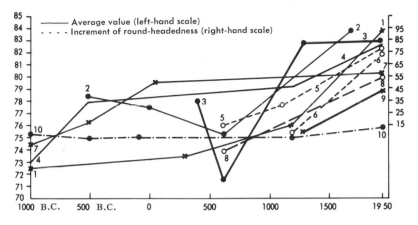

FIG. 11 The rounding of the head. 1. Silesia 2. Switzerland and Southern Germany 3. The Palatinate 4. Auvergne 5. Bavaria 6. Bohemia-Moravia 7. Brittany 8. Lower Saxony 9. Japan 10. Sweden (data from Giot, 1949; Hug, 1940; Martin, 1928; Schwidzky, 1939 and 1954; Suzuki, 1956).

1. In the case of colonial populations, the second generation frequently differs from the emigrant generation, or the population of the motherland. Investigations in this field were first undertaken by Boas in his studies of immigrants to the United States; later investigations distinguished more clearly between modification and characteristics that may have singled out particular groups for emigration in the first place (see Social Biology). Immigrants to Venezuela from Baden in the second generation showed features of body build and facial form which closely resembled those of the population of the village they had come from; in this case, differences in heritable characteristics were unlikely to occur and changes in body size and proportions (especially an increased stature and a narrowing of the head and face) must be regarded as plastic modifications. Children of Japanese immigrants in Hawaii showed no significant deviations from their parents in shape and pigmentation, but differed in size and proportional measurements.

2. In cities the indigenous population can frequently be distinguished from new settlers; i.e., children born in cities differ from parents born in the country. The city-born have narrower heads and faces.

3. Racially identical populations exhibit differences in size and proportions in relation to the environment—according to whether they live on the plains or in the mountains, or on loamy or sandy soil. In all cases, smaller sizes and narrower proportions are observable in the less favorable environments.

4. In many countries stature has increased considerably in the last century (see Growth).

19

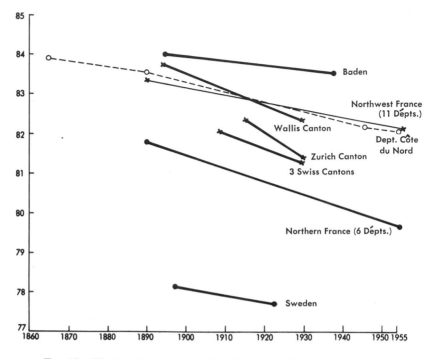

Fig. 12 The lengthening of the head in recent decades (data from Giot, 1956; Gloor, 1958; Oliver, 1957; Schaeuble, 1954; and Schlaginhaufen, 1946).

5. An increased roundness of the head (brachycephalization) can be observed in many European countries (Denmark, Germany, France, Austria, Switzerland), and also in Japan. This development can be traced back to the Middle Ages, in part even to the Neolithic Age. This process occurs even where no racial changes can be expected. In recent times—according to the oldest available dates (in Brittany), approximately since the middle of the nineteenth century—an opposite tendency toward long-headedness, i.e., a reduction in the length-breadth index of the head, is taking place (Germany, France, Italy, Sweden, Switzerland).

A clear-cut analysis of the causes is impossible in most cases, but a few contributing factors can be listed:

a) Differences in nutrition—a better nutrition, particularly a larger intake of fats and meats, promotes growth (see Growth).

b) Allometric growth changes occur in body size and proportions; thus all absolute length and height measurements are positively allometric, but the breadth measurements are negatively allometric in relation to body height. The increase in long-headedness of the last century can therefore be considered a part of the pattern of the increase in stature.

c) Climatic factors are also influential. For example, mice raised under a low average temperature with wide temperature fluctuations, were found to be larger than those of a comparable test group raised under a higher temperature with a narrower range of temperature fluctuations.

d) Domestic animals, as well as wild animals in captivity, often exhibit proportions different from those of their ancestors; animals in zoos, as one example, showed shorter and rounder heads. If this trend is caused by nutritional or climatic factors, or the limitations imposed on freedom of movement, it has not yet been clarified. According to this interpretation, it is, however, possible that man's "self-domestication" led to changes in size and proportion; brachycephaly has therefore been described as the cultural shape of the skull.

External factors, such as nutrition and climate, influence the growing organism by way of the endocrine glands. Adults therefore possess only a limited physical adaptability. Bodily changes are caused either by differences in the fat and water content of the tissues, or possibly through changed modes of movement and posture. During the famine of 1921–22 in the Ukraine, it was observed that the head measurements of adults who were measured frequently during progressive starvation decreased in breadth more than in length. Exercises can produce changes in muscle thickness and tone, vital capacity, chest breadth, hand width, and length of arms even in adults. These, however, cannot compare in scope with the changes possible during growth. We know more about collective modifications of physiological functions and modes of behavior than about

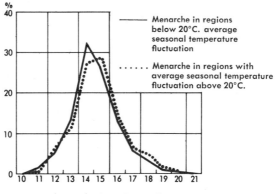

Age at the time of menarche

FIG. 13   Climatic modifications of physiological functions. The menarcheal age of Norwegian girls in regions with seasonal temperature fluctuations above and below 20°C. (after Škerlj, 1939).

21

changes in body form. The beginning of the menses (menarche) shows a relation to climate, i.e., to temperature as well as humidity (see Growth).

The basal metabolic rate is ordinarily measured from the oxygen consumption of an individual as related to his body surface area after hours of rest and fasting. This rate varies among different races; it depends not only on size, age, and sex but also on nutrition, temperature, and occupation. For most non-European populations it is smaller than the average European metabolism; it decreases among Europeans in the tropics, where it approaches that of the Negroids. One population adapted to a cold climate, the Alacaluf of Southern Chile, have a basal metabolism 160 per cent of that of Europeans of the same height and weight.

CULTURAL ANTHROPOLOGY

Man lives in a cultural environment of his own making; this is his one unique feature. Hence it is not possible to characterize man without defining and analyzing this aspect of human behavior. It is the task of cultural anthropology as defined in this book to obtain and to interpret whatever information is essential for this purpose from available scientific data. Cultural anthropology describes cultural variants as behavioral variants, and thus becomes part of the study of human behavior. Its most important functions are: (1) to investigate the variability of cultures and cultural elements, distinguishing between constants and variables; (2) to compare and, if opportunity arises, to correlate human and animal modes of behavior; (3) to explore the role of instinctual (inherited) and acquired modes of behavior and to determine the general biological foundations of man's capacity for civilized living.

Cultural Constants and Cultural Variables

The refinement by culture of human behavior affects every functional sphere, a term used by ecologists to denote specific spheres of life, with a fixed systematic ordering of organs, functions, and modes of behavior on one side and specific parts of the environment on the other. The functional spheres of nourishment, sex, hostility, etc., exist for humans, but they are so greatly complicated by culture that there is no longer a direct contact between the organism and its natural environment; there is an "expansion of functional spheres." In the functional sphere of nourishment, for example, the act of direct procurement of food is expanded by division of labor in the production of food and by barter or purchase. In part, tedious and complicated techniques of preparation have come between the procurement of food and its actual ingestion. Again, man has no specific organs for fighting his enemies, but even in his most primitive cultural stages we find him using weapons of his own making. Interjected into the functional sphere of sex are tradition-bound customs of courtship, engagement and marriage, the social standardization of sex roles, and so forth. This construction of a specifically human environment of things made or invented is called self-domestication, because it is comparable to the "artificial," arbitrarily influenced environment of the domestic animal. In both instances, there are, first and foremost, arbitrary changes in the conditions governing nourishment and reproduction, which give rise to similar biological consequences, particularly to an increase in variability of the species, because of the reduction of selective pressures.

There is a multitude of cultures, both living and extinct, of typical forms into which men have shaped and arranged their lives. Their number is estimated at 3,000 or more, depending on the number of elements used as criteria to distinguish one culture from another. Only the aggregate of cultural behavior variables represents what is specifically human behavior, which is characterized precisely by this extraordinary variability. Only a relatively small number of generalized traits are common to all living cultures: (1) In every culture, natural environment is altered by technical means in order to satisfy the need for food, shelter, and protection. (2) In every culture, there is thought in terms of symbols, and a language of auditory symbols which links fixed sound configurations with certain specific meanings and which manipulates these abstract symbols. (3) In every culture, there are rules for male and female behavior, not only for sexual behavior, but also regarding the care of children and other roles in the division of labor. (4) In every culture, there is a drive for artistic expression and interpretation through music and dance, the plastic arts, poetry, or related aesthetic efforts. (5) In every culture, there are concepts of order regarding group life, and standards for right and wrong, good and evil, proper and improper conduct; in general, the need for reciprocity comes into play in the determination of these norms.

Fig. 14 Chimpanzee putting together bamboo canes (after Wolfgang Köhler, 1921).

Comparison of Human and Animal Behavior

Degrees of relationship that can be interpreted phylogenetically can be determined not only by somatic traits but also by behavioral modes which increasingly gain in significance in the area of zoological taxonomy (homologous behavior).

A number of behavioral modes in man may be traced back to more general forms of primate, mammal, or even vertebrate behavior. The specifically human variations of these more generalized behavior patterns are of particular significance for cultural anthropology.

Sexual Behavior

The most important variables in the satisfaction of human sex drives are found also in other primates. Along with heterosexual intercourse are found homosexuality, onanism, foreplay preliminary to coitus, and the sexual play of childhood. The initiative may be taken by either the male or the female. In addition, as we advance in the systematic order from lower primates to humans, we note a number of progressive variations: especially decreased influence of sex hormones and increased influence of cerebral control on sexual behavior. Within the species, the forms of behavior become increasingly variable and plastic, and the learning component grows in significance. Sexual play in the pre-puberty period serves increasingly as an exercise in sexual forms of behavior. The seasonal oestrous cycles are obliterated. Sexual interest and activity continue at all seasons in all the higher primate forms, including individuals that are not living in captivity; hence their young are born in any month of the year. Indiscriminate mating declines, to be replaced by preference for one specific partner (as clearly noted, for instance, in chimpanzees). Sexual activity increases in all domesticated animals and animals living in captivity; it is possible, therefore, that the strong sexualization of man has some connection with his self-domestication.

The main features of the refinement of sexual behavior by human culture are: (1) The development of a sphere of intimacy which, of course, is circumscribed in a great variety of ways. Among the other primates, sexual play and mating take place in the open; in nearly all human cultures, however, the norm is that this is done in seclusion. This may be due to the greater personal bonds involved in human sexual relationships. (2) The neutralization or inhibition of sexual drives with regard to certain persons (incest, see below), or in certain roles in life (for example, celibacy in priests), or at certain times (for example, premarital chastity). (3) The sublimation of excess sexual energy into some other sphere of activity (such as art).

The institutionalization of sexual behavior takes a great variety of forms. The attitude toward means for the satisfaction of the sex drive vary from culture to culture. Attitudes toward homosexuality range from

24

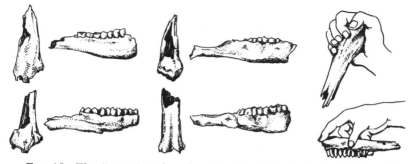

FIG. 15 The "osteodontokeratic culture" of the Australopithecines. Two types of Makapansgat bone fragments and their possible use (after R. A. Dart, 1957).

stern prohibition, with threat of punishment, through toleration or indifference to positive valuation and even furtherance. Toward pre-pubertal sex play, attitudes range from complete freedom to strictly enforced prohibition. In one culture, sex initiative is viewed as exclusively or preferably male; in other cultures, the taking of the initiative by the female may be permitted or even preferred (though this is not frequently the case either in humans or primate animals). The delineation of the sphere of intimacy includes every degree of rigidity: it may extend from taboos on everything having to do with sex, through the neutralization of every degree and tendency in sexuality, down to complete asceticism. In no human society, however, will the sexual norm cover every actual variation; in this connection, the role of "abnormal" or "immoral" forms of behavior may vary greatly, even to the extent that it undermines the "norm." Therefore, the wide variations in sexual norms throughout history are just as typical of man as is his great racial variability.

The Family

The basis of the family is the relationship between mother and child. In mammals, this relationship deepens in stability, closeness, and content as the period of youth lengthens and the young are dependent on the mother's care for a longer time. In no animal does this relationship extend beyond the time the young attain full sexual maturity. In many instances, however, it lasts beyond the period when the young are directly dependent on the mother for nourishment. Here, the nucleus of the family, in addition to the mother, includes several young of varying ages, making for greater differentiation of relationships, both between the mother and her young and between the siblings. In human beings the "psychological weaning process" is greatly retarded and in many instances is never completed at all. This gives rise to dual family relationships: the relationship of the individual to his family of orientation and to his family of procreation. It is only among humans that there is the possibility of an individual being a link in a chain of three generations, obviously an important requisite for the maintenance of a tradition based on experience and knowledge.

In nearly all primate animals, the male has a personal relationship to the female, but not to his offspring; he is the begetter, but not the father. The domestication of the male constitutes the final step in the establishment of the human family. Although in primate animals the familial and extra-familial interests (the procurement of food in particular) coexist without being interrelated, these two spheres of interest become closely related in the human family. The transition from a preponderantly vegetarian mode of living to a more mixed diet, and particularly to big-game hunting, may have had an important part in this change. Among primate animals, an adult individual seldom shares any of the food he has gathered (an exception to this, however, can be seen among zoo monkeys; females have been observed to "prostitute" themselves to a male in return for a portion of some desired delicacy). Hunting, an activity probably known to the Australopithecines in a crude form, must have made for a sexual differentiation in the search for nourishment (see Social Biology). It was the male, rather than the female, who engaged in the procurement of meat, to feed the female as well as the young. Thus, to the function of the male as a protector, which is a form of general mammalian behavior, there was added a new function, which contributed to the integration of the family as a social unit. Certain beginnings of this may be noted among the wide variations of social capacity in the great apes. Male chimpanzees give protection to the young of their own group first and foremost. In a group of chimpanzees living in captivity, consisting only of a male, a female, and one offspring, it was possible to observe "fatherly" behavior by the male in the form of positive, personal attention to the one offspring.

Another characterizing feature of the human family is the tendency toward monopolization of sexual relationships. "For reasons of protection and livelihood, the father is included" in the long-lived relationships between the mother and her offspring. "This prolonged relationship, based on biologically required care in humans, makes for new emotional ties and reciprocal activity, kindred relationships and moral obligations. . . . The permanent ties deriving from the prolonged collaboration of male and female for the welfare of their young are carried over into their relationship as sexual partners" (H. Schelsky). Among primitive peoples, marriage and the family are primarily economic institutions; the greatly diversified forms of marriage depend to a large extent on the society's economic structure. Tendencies toward monopolization of sexual relationships take root, in varying degrees, in the social and religious institutionalization of marriage. However, polygamy, which prevails among the primate hordes, still survives in all human societies, regardless of whether the society officially sanctions or condemns it. Where monogamy is rigorously upheld, polygamy survives in the form of prostitution, which the society views with contempt.

Still another characteristic trait in all human family systems is the incest taboo. In fact, the human family has been defined as "a group in which sexual intercourse is expected to take place between the principals, but in which such intercourse between any of the other members of the group is forbidden" (E. W. Count). Despite the wide diffusion of this taboo, it is hardly likely that it is derived from instinct, for there is no such instinct in primate animals, among whom there is uninhibited mating between fathers and daughters, mothers and sons, brothers and sisters. Moreover, in many instances, the incest taboo is applied not only to the community of biological origin, but extends also to relatives other than blood relations. Insight into the biological relationship between fathers and offspring—i.e., into the connection between sexual intercourse and birth—is a relatively recent acquisition which may still be lacking in a number of present-day primitive peoples. The incest taboo has two social functions which may be able to explain both its origin and its widespread diffusion. First, it stabilizes the family as a unit in the struggle for survival by excluding those sexual rivalries that make for a good many of the social disputes that go on, at least among primate animals living in captivity. Second, the law of exogamy (which makes it mandatory to marry someone outside one's own group) tightens the various family bonds, and thus is a contributing factor in the integration of larger social communities.

Territoriality

The demarcation and defense of territory is a pattern of behavior common to all vertebrates. Among the lowest vertebrate forms (as with fish, for instance), there are only breeding or family territories. In more highly organized forms, there are also group territories, which may be subdivided into family grounds. The nearer the attacker comes to the central nesting site, the more violent and successful will be the defender's struggle to retain that territory. Hence, as density of population increases, territorial fights become increasingly numerous and violent, as, for example, among animals living in captivity. Among the social functions of territoriality are the safeguarding of the young, the even distribution of population, reduction in the incidence of fights involving sex and rank, and integration of groups. Identification with a specific place also favors individualization; since all vertebrates have a well-developed memory for places, identification makes it easier for them to recognize other creatures of their kind. The area of the territories, as well as the distances of attack and retreat, vary from species to species and also within these categories. They depend on such factors as the individual's body size, need for food, and kind of nourishment taken.

Primates, too, have territories. The great apes have group territories of comparatively large area and move relatively far away from the group habitations when they go out to gather food. The amount of space allotted to individuals is related to social status, particularly among baboons. However, there is no inflexible division of the group territory; whenever individuals of high rank move to a new place, existing spaces are reallotted.

Territoriality still plays an important part in the social organization of man. Group territories range from the hunting grounds of individual bands of hunters, which as a rule are respected by the other small groups, to the demarcation and defense of territorial boundaries of highly civilized nations. Individuals and families, too, endeavor to secure and demarcate territories for themselves (as observed, for instance, in prisons and refugee camps).

Hostility to neighbors and the endeavor to demarcate one's own nesting site develop in direct proportion to the density of population. Among mental patients, a fixed distance of retreat, varying from individual to individual, has been observed. If an outsider transgressed these limits, behavior changed abruptly to patterns of panic and aggression. Obviously, territoriality and aggression against outsiders are factors basic to the "pluralism of culture"; they oppose the diffusion of cultural traits and favor the development of forms of behavior specific to the group.

Hierarchical Order

Many groups of animals, including primates, are structured upon hierarchical orders, even as human societies are. The status of individuals in the hierarchical order may be decided by fights. Such fights, however, may eventually evolve into ceremonial acts, such as sham battles, in which poses and gestures symbolizing threats or aiming to impress and gestures of humility and submission take the place of actual fighting. Forms of behavior which inhibit aggression against members of the same species are particularly well developed among those carnivorous species, such as

Fig. 16   Tools of the early Chou Kou Tien period (after Grahmann, 1952).

Fig. 17   Tools of the Upper Paleolithic Age. Bifaces, points, and scrapers from the Kiik Cave, Crimea, and from Ilskaya, Kuban Territory (after Grahmann, 1952).

ULTURAL ANTHROPOLOGY

wolves, which are capable of killing other individuals of the same size. In primates, such inhibitions were present once transition was made to hunting and the invention of tools. However, protective measures to prevent the killing of a creature of the same species now were no longer based on instinctive forms of behavior, but on acquired behavior patterns. Only creatures alien to the group or territory were attacked; as a rule, members of the same group, personally known to the other members, were left unmolested. "Personal acquaintance," a learning process, plays a part even in battles for status and territory waged among animals. In either instinctive or acquired patterns of behavior, the control of the aggressive drive is a mechanism that can easily be upset.

Each species has its own gestures symbolizing threats and submission, the wish to impress or a show of humility. In every species, the mannerisms meant to impress others involve a rise in tonus, accompanied by gestures symbolizing self-enlargement (inflation, ruffling of feathers, strutting, spreading of tail, raising of fins, ears, or tail); mannerisms of humility involve a lowering of tonus, accompanied by gestures of self-diminution (contraction, ducking, lowering of tail, keeping ears close to head, etc.). These basic forms of behavior specific to position are still recognizable in the status gestures of humans, even though they have been refined by culture, and have been taught and prescribed by etiquette. Bowing and curtsying, removal of headgear, kneeling and prostration, make the inferior seem smaller. The body positions of individuals of higher rank are supported by technical aids. Masks, crowns and tiaras, stilts, raised seats, and conspicuous clothing—to make one appear taller and larger—all serve to make the person of high rank impressive.

In vertebrates, superior physical size facilitates the attainment of high rank or of a large territory. Hence, large, strong individuals who have proven successful in the fight for mate and territory are favored also by natural selection. However, experience and vitality may compensate for inferior size. In primates, with their distinct sexual differences in body size, the male dominates, as a rule; indeed, the female gesture indicating readiness to receive the male may be used as a general gesture of submission even by the male (particularly among baboons). Frequently, the rank of the female is determined by her male partner; thus, she can rise or descend on the social ladder by mating. Physical size and sex have a significant part also in human societies (see Social Biology). In all likelihood, however, with increasing differentiation in social structure, physical size as a means of impressing others has yielded to experience. In modern society, correlations between social rank and physical size arise only indirectly, through the correlation between physical size and the ability to learn. Furthermore, in humans there are new factors besides individual endowments which determine rank—family origin, occupation, and property, which have only a loose connection with the individual's biological character. Hence, although in animal societies, as a rule, there is only a single hierarchical order—or, at most, a double order, one for males and

9

one for females—in which every individual has one fixed status, human societies have multiple hierarchical orders. Human society is structured into a number of hierarchies, and an individual may occupy different rank positions in his family, in his occupation, and in his public life.

The Use of Tools

The use of tools has a special role in cultural anthropology, since it not only permits us to make comparative studies of living species, but also serves to bridge the gap between primate animals and humans by providing us with finds dating back to prehistoric times. Tools are objects other than the body which are used for certain purposes and which are replaced by similar objects when lost. Hence, they are part of a continuously maintained set of technical equipment. As a rule, only objects that have undergone adaptation of some sort are classified as tools. Alterations of environment by "technical" means occur among many animals; occasionally, these even entail the use and adaptation of objects other than the body, but the objects are not kept after use. The most elaborate technical achievements such as beehives, termite labyrinths, spiders' webs, and birds' nests are based preponderantly on the instinct component; the learning component is either limited or entirely absent. Occasionally, the use of stones (for the opening of nuts) and of branches has been noted among primates, whose behavior is greatly modified by learning, even among animals not living in captivity. Wolfgang Köhler conducted systematic experiments with captive chimpanzees. They used various objects other than their bodies (e.g., boxes, sticks) in order to reach for desired morsels. Biting a hollow cane to the proper size to fit into another hollow cane, so as to make it longer, involved the adaptation of an existing object for a specific purpose. When this experiment was repeated, a cane previously used was readapted and used with greater dispatch than in the original effort. Even without training, there obviously was a beginning at constancy in the knowledge of an object (object constancy).

The alleged "osteodontokeratic culture" of the Australopithecines consists of bone fragments found in the breccias along with Australopithecine remains. Few anthropologists now recognize them as tools. Since the Australopithecines engaged in hunting small animals, such as lizards and rodents, it is likely that they made use of simple stone tools, if only because neither their hominid teeth nor their primate hands were suited to the dissection of animals with thick skins.

It has been established with certainty that Sinanthropus adapted objects from nature for his use; it is highly probable that all the other representatives of *Homo erectus* also did so (Southern Asian chopping-tool cultures, etc.). In the course of the Paleolithic Age, stonework becomes increasingly refined; in addition to multiple-purpose tools, such as the hand-ax (*coup de poing*), we find a variety of specialized tools made of stone and bone (points, scrapers, drills, harpoons, etc.). These tools indicate not only ingenuity but also a great deal of perseverance and patience. They imply also a certain detachment on the part of the maker from the end for which the tool was made—i.e., the product became something of an object in itself. Among the chimpanzees mentioned above, technical achievements occurred only under the immediate pressure of the stimulus situation. In the course of continuous technical evolution subsequent to the Paleolithic Age, no natural raw material has remained untreated, and multiple adaptive techniques have introduced an infinite variety of artifacts into man's environment for his constant use.

Language

Of the various functions of human language, communication and expression is clearly shared by animals. Many animals are capable of expressing joy and anger, terror and fear, by sounds or mannerisms that will be understood by members of their own, and often also by related, species. The communicative and interpretative functions of language are demonstrated particularly in the "bee language," which can give detailed information concerning such facts as the nature, direction, and abundance of

FIG. 18 Indication of the existence of language in the Aurignacian period: the "magician" of Trois Frères.

a source of nourishment. However, this language is based purely on inherited patterns. Of the sounds emitted by primate animals, the best known are those of the chimpanzee. Pitch and stress of sound, rhythm, kind and sequence of available vowel and vocal sounds, are extraordinarily variable and allow the expression of a great many different moods and emotions through multifarious combinations. There are also sounds related to one particular situation, as well as a number of individual variations. However, articulation is not distinct—this is because of the anatomy and physiology of the larynx—and there are no fixed vocal configurations,

31

but only "chain words," the length of which depends on the intensity of the excitement expressed. In a very few instances, it has been possible by arduous training to teach chimpanzees isolated human words, which, though narrowed down to mean certain definite complexes of significance, are still not closely associated with specific meanings. The highly developed imitative ability of chimpanzees is almost exclusively visual; it does not extend to auditory phenomena. However, they may be able to understand up to 50 words; in isolated instances, it has been possible to teach them to separate constituent parts of learned sentence formations and to re-form these into new combinations.

Human language, which is closely linked with human thought and must have developed concomitantly with it, is characterized particularly by its symbolic character. Sound configurations are initiated, objectified, and defined in their meaning by the situation they are employed to express. In this manner, they become symbols for the elements of reality. Only with the help of symbolic thought and language is it possible to form abstract concepts and to manipulate these, rather than objects, in order to express not only relationships but also relationships between relationships. The reciprocal control of behavior through language is infinitely more precise and economical than that by other mannerisms. Energy can be budgeted more economically, affording more opportunities for the physical leisure that is requisite for creative thought. Moreover, the symbol system of language can comprehensively store up and communicate experiences and information. It represents the final means by which the intellectual horizon of man may be expanded beyond the limits of direct personal experience. The extension of the dimensions of time from the immediately experienced present into the past and the future extending beyond one's own life span is bound as much to symbolic language as is the construction of an "inner world of images" which constantly molds human behavior and frees it from the immediate confines of specific situations.

The languages of man are based on acquired patterns only. The ability to speak, however, is a hereditary predisposition in the species, and there are inherited elements in the babbled monologues of infants, in some of the sounds emitted by deaf-mutes and the mentally ill, and in the expressive characteristics of language. The fact that languages are modifiable in character makes for a multiplicity of languages, and thus for considerable difficulty in making oneself understood even within the species. Gesticulative language, too, is extensively modified and subdivided into a multitude of ethnic, social, and historical variants, in which only a few instinctive elements (for example, gestures meant to impress others or to show submission) may be recognized.

Only indirect conclusions can be made concerning the phylogenetic development of language. One may ask what psychical structures were at the basis of the ways of life and of the achievements of fossil man, and to what extent these presuppose language or at least indicate the existence of language. The philological history of language dates back to about the year 3000 B.C. (to the Sumerians). It is presumed that man in the Upper Paleolithic Period already had a well-developed symbolic language.

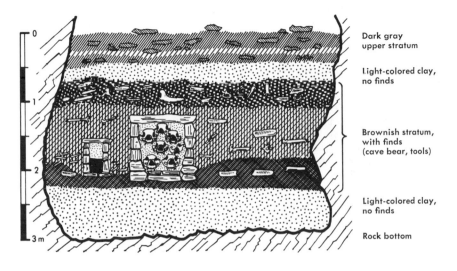

Dark gray upper stratum

Light-colored clay, no finds

Brownish stratum, with finds (cave bear, tools)

Light-colored clay, no finds

Rock bottom

FIG. 19   Indications of the existence of language in the Neanderthal period. Cave bear cult in Drachenloch site.

The cave art dating from the Upper Paleolithic Period shows a flair for pictorial representation; it is quite free in its treatment of objects and combines them into pictures not corresponding to reality (for example, the "magician" of Trois Frères with the legs of a human, the face of an owl, and the antlers of a stag). It is also assumed that the men of the Middle Paleolithic Period, particularly the Mousterians (Neanderthal men), used language too. This is indicated by the tools from that period, which show a high degree of constancy in the use of objects, a detachment from the end for which the tools were made, and an objectification of the achievement. It is also indicated by the fact that the world concept held by these men extended beyond the range of immediate personal experience. Burial customs—for example, the companion offerings deposited in burial places—attest to the fact that they thought about death. The forces of nature were invoked by magic through the cave bear cult at such sites as Drachenloch and Petersstein. If Neanderthal man indeed had a human symbolic language, this language must have been "invented" by *Homo erectus* (Pithecanthropus and related forms) at the very latest. The permanent association of specific sounds with specific meanings may already have begun with the Australopithecines, so that their calls and cries were one-word sentences, much like those with which the human infant also

33

begins to talk. Somewhere in the development of the hominid line, the predisposition for the understanding of sounds must have been joined by a predisposition for the ability to imitate sounds, which is absent in primate animals now living, but without which the acquired language of humans would not be possible.

Instincts and Institutions

In human behavior shaped by culture, we may still recognize a number of survivals of instincts in such areas as the relationships between the sexes and between mother and child, dominance and submissiveness, and in the general urge for expression and interpretation which includes speech. However, in man, instinct determines only the amount of energy to be expended and the general direction of the behavior pattern, not the specific, definite development of such patterns, as it does in animals relying upon instinct alone. Instead, each culture selects certain variants from the infinite variety of possible human behavior patterns and elevates them to the status of socially sanctioned models upon which to pattern behavior, which are then binding upon all the members of the group. Such culturally imposed behavior patterns or institutions relieve the individual from the necessity of making an excessive number of decisions. They afford him a guide through the multiplicity of impressions and stimuli with which man is swamped, and thus make a secure bond between man and his environment. However, institutions do not function with the same dependability as do instincts. In instincts, the triggering key stimuli and the appropriate reactions are precisely attuned to one another, unless, of course, the instincts are disturbed, as is frequently the case in domesticated animals. "The animal plays the game according to the rules; man can do likewise but does not always do so. . . . It almost seems as if culture 'knew' of its inadequacy in this respect, and therefore was eager to set up as many protective institutions as possible" (W. E. Mühlmann). In humans, stringent laws ascribed to divine precepts, and threats of stern punishment (as severe as eternal damnation), must be employed to enforce the observance of the rules set up by culture—rules which, in instinctive behavioral forms, function of themselves.

Biological Bases of the Capacity for Culture

Human behavior is preponderantly determined by learning processes. The superimposition of acquired forms of behavior on instinct-controlled forms may be noted in the phylogenetic-taxonomic orders of animals. It is particularly far advanced in the Primate order, from the prosimians to the great apes. Wherever learning processes are active, behavior becomes more plastic and variable. Thus, great learning ability constitutes a basic factor in human behavior. Important in this connection is memory, which is increasingly perfected in the Primate order: in prosimians, the longest period of time after which a source of food, once shown, is remembered and immediately sought out at the next opportunity is five seconds; in catarrhines and gibbons, it is fifteen seconds; in the great apes, it extends up to two hours and longer; in man the period may be delayed practically indefinitely. The ability to analyze the field of perception and the ability to combine its components in a variety of ways is also basic to intelligence —i.e., to the ability to learn by the use of experience. Beginnings of the comprehension of components—a prerequisite for all abstraction and ideation—are found as far down as the invertebrates. This has been studied with particular thoroughness in connection with the ability to count in birds, and has been well documented also for higher primates. However, in all animals, there still is difficulty in recognizing an object once the outer and inner circumstances under which it was originally perceived have changed; that is, when the object reappears in an environment of other objects, or in an emotional context other than that in which it was first perceived. In the course of ontogenetic evolution, too, the ability to analyze spatial, temporal, and emotional configurations is the first to mature. Its development varies not only with age groups but with different constitutional types (see Constitution). *Homo sapiens* is greatly superior to all primate animals now living in his ability to analyze perceptions and to grasp the constancy of objects; realization of the constancy of objects is an important foundation for symbolic language, with its fixed relationships between sound configuration and meaning.

The storage of memories, the analysis of perceptions and associations, are primarily a function of the cerebral cortex, which in the Primate order shows a progressive increase, due partly to the increase in cranial capacity and partly to the folding of the cortex itself. The gap in knowledge of how this occurred between the primate animals and *Homo sapiens* is being bridged by means of fossil finds (see The Descent of Man). There is also a progressive differentiation in the cortical areas, which can be distinguished histologically. Further up the primate scale, the so-called secondary cortical areas, which serve for purposes of association, grow more in size and number than the primary cortical areas for sensory

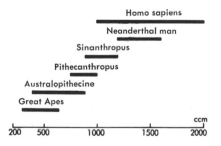

Fig. 20 Cranial capacity (brain volume) in the course of the development of the human family.

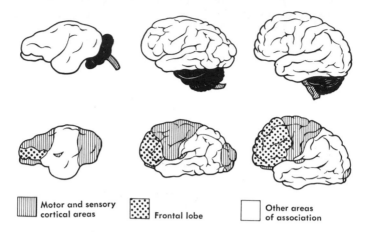

| | Motor and sensory cortical areas | | Frontal lobe | | Other areas of association |

FIG. 21   The brain as the organ of cultural capacity in man. Cerebral folds and cerebral areas, in, from left to right: tarsiers, great apes, and man. Diagrams all drawn in identical length (after Portmann, 1948; Scharrer, 1936; and Ashley Montagu, 1951).

perception and motor control. Thus, in prosimians, the frontal lobe, which is of particular importance in higher mental achievements, is 8 per cent of the total cerebral cortex; in chimpanzees it is 17 per cent, and in man the average is 29 per cent. New in humans are such areas as the speech center in the third convolution of the temporal lobe (Broca's area), and close by it the center for knowledge and its practical application, which is important in technical skills. Next to the brain, the organ most important for the development of culture is the working hand, freed from its

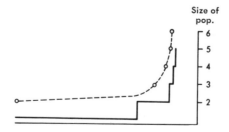

FIG. 22   Development of culture and size of population. Duration of cultural phases (Middle and Upper Paleolithic Age, Mesolithic Age, Neolithic Age, .Metal Age) and the growth of population in France (based on estimates by Nougier, 1954).

locomotive functions. This organ developed when man acquired erect posture, and thus it is phylogenetically older than the capacity of the human brain. Not only is the free grasping hand essential for the use and adaptation of tools, and thus for the technical alteration of natural environment, but it also aids in the comprehension of the constancy of objects and thus supports symbolic thought and speech. The idea of grasping in the construction of the mental world image is still clearly evident in spoken language (mental grasping, a grasp of things, taking up, etc.).

Although the general capacity for culture in man is based on his constitution, which is characteristic of his genus, the growth and differentiation of cultures cannot be wholly explained by his hereditary make-up. By the Middle Paleolithic Age, man's cranial capacity had already reached the size typical of living *Homo sapiens*. Yet, since that time, civilization has not only advanced quite considerably, but its progress has accelerated increasingly. Culture grows by accumulation. In many instances, the old survives alongside the new, and the number of possible combinations and variations grows with every new invention. The special character of cultural evolution, which works through addition more often than through substitution, allows for the existence, side by side, of many cultures. A prerequisite for the process of accumulation is a tradition of knowledge and experience. In this process, the long and close connection between older and younger generations, through a prolonged period of youth and a drawn-out senescence, plays an important role. The capacity for accumulation was greatly augmented by language, which, being a purely acquired trait, must itself be passed on through tradition, and it was greatly accelerated by the invention of writing.

Size of population and density of population (see Demography) also have a part in the growth of culture by accumulation. The chances for new inventions by individuals with creative talent increase as population grows; the chances for the diffusion of new culture traits grow with increased population density. In small communities with low economic levels and only slight technical control of natural environment, the division of labor is not complex; every individual is faced with the task of procuring nourishment by direct action. Thus, there is hardly any leisure time, and people with special talents can exercise them less often than they might in larger communities with greater economic and cultural differentiation. Division of labor and specialization increase the ability of the species to adjust and to achieve. Man not only occupies an infinite variety of natural environments, but he alters them by means of specific cultural variants and thus renders them humanly habitable. Within ethnic groups or communities, inner differentiation, by natural selection, of those of higher civilization is manifested by larger populations (see Social Biology). We can assume man's general capacity for culture is also favored by natural selection. This would explain the progressive elaboration of the human way of life, and the rise of man to a dominant form in the Primate order.

DEMOGRAPHY

From time immemorial, population, as the sum total of all people living within the confines of a given area, has acted as an economic, political, and military factor for nations and governments, but primarily as a static concept. The fact that the natural elements of reproduction, that is, the basic biological phenomena of birth and death, display in their frequency of occurrence and in their relationship to each other a certain rhythm and constancy, was first recognized by the political arithmeticians Graunt (1620–74) and Petry (1623–87) in the study of London's records of christenings and deaths. Shortly thereafter, the Prussian theologian Johann Peter Süssmilch (1707–67), on the basis of more extensive material, saw the "divine order in the changes in the human race due to births, deaths and propagation occurring therein." The era of Mercantilism also recognized the relationship between an economy based on a marginal food supply and population growth. The ideas of Thomas Robert Malthus (1760–1834) formed the basis of much demographic discussion for more than a century. His theory was that the population constantly tends to increase more rapidly than the means of subsistence; "positive" and "preventive" checks, that is, death and misery and the fear of both, are continually needed to keep procreation within bounds. Charles Darwin incorporated Malthus's ideas into his theory of evolution by linking them with a qualitative viewpoint—the survival of the fittest. Demography is therefore, on the one hand, an important foundation of human biology and, on the other, a full-fledged branch of that science.

Sources and Methods

The basic demographic events of birth, copulation, death, and migration represent mass phenomena that can be comprehended in their totality and structure only statistically. Demographic statistics is therefore the basis of the science of population. This valuable research tool covers both the status of populations and population trends. The most reliable records are derived from censuses, which establish for a given period of time the number of people and, depending on the extent of the census pattern, the age, sex, occupation, family status and family size, length of marriage of married couples, and so forth. Changes in the status of a population can be established by registering births and deaths, marriages and divorces, emigration and immigration, or by comparing various censuses. However, only highly developed countries regularly collect statistics, and even these countries have been doing so only since the second half of the nineteenth century at the earliest. Roughly 5 per cent of the world's population is today regularly and extensively registered statistically. For some 40 per cent, there exist only undocumented statements and sometimes only estimates of the number of people. Through international cooperation, particularly within the framework of the United Nations, efforts are being made to organize an over-all statistical service for the entire population of the world in order to obtain fully comparable detailed data from all countries.

For the period before any regular census was taken, demographic history serves to probe statistically valuable sources; the reliability of such sources must be critically weighed in each instance. Among these are occasional censuses taken for a specific purpose, for determining the needs of the population in case of war, or for tax and death records, citizens' rolls, army strength, and the like. If only part of the population is included —such as men fit for military service— that figure can be used to estimate the entire population on the basis of conversion codes derived from other sources. Frequently, indirect data can also be used, such as the number of houses or dwellings, the size of a city's built-up area, the amount of land under cultivation, the consumption of wheat, etc.

When written sources are exhausted, the science of paleodemography must be relied on. The methods of this science have been developed by combining physical anthropology with archaeology. Its most important sources of information are human remains found in prehistoric settlements, graveyards, and isolated graves. From these bones it is possible to determine age and sex, and thus estimate the age of death, how it differed between the sexes, and, if the archaeological search is particularly rewarding, the age and sex structure of the population, the size of the settlement, and the population trend. In many cases, even the ashes remaining after cremation permit the determination of age and sex. The drawbacks in the usefulness of paleodemography lie in the fact that there is a paucity of preserved human remains in proportion to the head count of prehistoric populations, and that the quality of preservation varies. Skeletons of children and adolescents disintegrate more quickly in the ground and many archaeologists do not keep them, particularly in view of the fact that a child's skeleton can only be compared with that of another of the same age and there would be too few of each age group to make a significant series; they are therefore infrequently seen in collections and museums. This is also true for female skeletons, which, in comparison with the more robust male skeletons, are delicate. Indirect sources for determining population size and population density are the amount and abundance of artifacts and structures. Also, population figures can be estimated from the type of economy and the size of the area inhabited by correlating them with present-day conditions, particularly with those prevailing among primitive peoples.

Demographic statistics are compiled by a special set of measurements and methods. The most basic statistic concerning any population is the head count. It is all we know about more than 40 per cent of the earth's population, and even this compilation is at times quite inaccurate. Most historical statistics are concerned only with the head count. Population density (the number of inhabitants per square mile) depends on the resources of the region and the economic use to which they are put. For hunters in tropical-forest regions it is estimated that 1.2 square miles are

POPULATION AND POPULATION DENSITIES, 1961

	Estimated Population	Approx. Land Area (sq. mi.)	Density (per sq. mi.)
WORLD (excludes Antarctica)	3,060,800,000	52,191,200	59
Africa	261,000,000	11,695,400	22
Egypt	26,578,000	386,200	69
Ghana	6,943,000	91,800	76
Kenya	7,287,000	225,000	32
Morocco	11,925,000	174,000	69
Nigeria	35,752,000	373,000	96
Republic of South Africa	16,122,000	472,400	34
Asia (excludes U.S.S.R.)	1,714,000,000	10,397,700	165
Burma	21,527,000	261,800	82
China (includes Formosa)	657,501,000	3,780,000	174
India	440,316,000	1,266,900	348
Indonesia	96,385,000	575,900	167
Iran	20,678,000	628,100	33
Iraq	7,085,000	171,600	41
Israel	2,183,000	7,800	280
Japan	94,053,000	142,700	659
Jordan	1,690,000	37,400	45
Korea (North and South)	31,400,000	85,300	368
Pakistan	94,601,000	364,800	259
Philippines	28,727,000	115,800	248
Turkey	28,602,000	296,500	96
U.S.S.R.	218,000,000	8,649,400	25
Europe (excludes U.S.S.R.)	430,000,000	1,912,400	225
Austria	7,081,000	32,400	219
Belgium	9,203,000	11,800	780
Bulgaria	7,906,000	42,800	185
Czechoslovakia	13,776,000	49,400	279
Denmark	4,617,000	16,600	278
France	45,960,000	212,700	216
Germany (East and West)	70,147,000	137,600	517
Hungary	10,028,000	35,900	279
Ireland	2,815,000	27,100	104
Italy	49,455,000	116,300	425
Netherlands	11,637,000	12,500	931
Norway	3,611,000	125,100	29
Poland	29,965,000	120,400	249
Portugal	9,146,000	35,500	258
Rumania	18,567,000	91,700	202
Spain	30,559,000	194,400	157
Sweden	7,520,000	173,400	43
Switzerland	5,470,000	15,900	344
United Kingdom	52,925,000	94,200	562
Yugoslavia	18,607,000	98,800	188

North America	273,000,000	8,300,800	33
Canada (1962)	18,508,000	3,851,800	5
Mexico	36,091,000	758,300	48
United States	183,043,000	3,549,000	51
South America	148,000,000	7,930,900	19
Argentina	21,078,000	1,072,500	20
Brazil	73,088,000	3,286,300	22
Colombia	14,443,000	439,500	33
Peru	10,365,000	482,300	22
Venezuela	7,590,000	352,200	22
Oceania (includes Hawaii)	16,800,000	3,304,600	5
Australia	10,508,000	2,974,600	4
New Zealand	2,420,000	103,400	23

From *Population Index* (Jan., 1963), U.N. Statistical Office, and other sources.

required for each member of the population and in deserts an even larger area (Bushmen 21.2, Australians 42.5 square miles per person). Primitive races with rudimentary agriculture and cattle raising attain population densities up to 26 per square mile. However, countries in which the economy is based on intensive agriculture have a population density many times that figure (China 174, India 348, Korea 368). But such figures are greatly surpassed by countries that have an industrial economy (Belgium 780, Great Britain 562, West Germany 565, Italy 425). Overpopulation and underpopulation are therefore relative terms. They are based on the productiveness of a region with a particular economy, natural resources, and living standards.

The most important biological features for classifying the members of a population are sex and age. Their distribution is represented graphically by a frequency polygon, the so-called age pyramid, which also reveals something of population dynamics. A broad base of children and adolescents (the pyramid shape proper) shows a growing population, a narrower base a stationary one, and a still narrower base a shrinking population. A balanced proportion of the sexes is expressed by the symmetrical structure of the polygon. Asymmetries can be caused, for example, by the high death rate among males during wars, or by the scarcity of women in countries with a high immigration rate.

The methods for determining the population trend are highly developed. The simplest measures of mortality are the general mortality statistics (death rates). They indicate the number of deaths in one year per 1,000 of the population in the middle of the census period, and provide quick comparisons between various populations and countries. However, they do not take into account the considerable group differences in mortality within the population. This is done by means of special mortality figures

41

according to age and sex, in which the rate of deaths in one age group is expressed as a proportion of 1,000 living persons of that group. Infant mortality, which plays a major role in mortality as a whole, is, however, not a rate based on 1,000 infants alive at the age of one, but on 1,000 infants born in the period involved.

Another method not based on death frequency calculates actuarial life expectancy for each age group; survivors of the age group involved are subject to the actuarial life expectancy of the group immediately following, and so forth. The mortality table combines all these death probabilities according to age and sex in tabular form. The figures always refer to a group of persons of the same age that pass through the various actual life expectancies of the age groups, and they must therefore be recalculated for each census period. They reveal the changes in mortality conditions which become apparent as the group, taken from the start, passes through the various death probabilities. The advantage of this method is primarily that mortality can be represented as one continuous process, that is, as a life table. Furthermore, average life expectancy can be calculated from the life table. For each age group it shows the total number of years still to be lived divided by the number of survivors.

As in the case of deaths, the simplest measure for births is the birth rate, which relates the number of births in one year to 1,000 of the population in the middle of the census period. But this measure does not take into account the age and sex structure of the population, for only women of a certain age group are significant for this basic demographic phenomenon. Thus, the general fertility rate refers the number of births in one year to the number of procreative women, which, as a rule, is taken to be the number of women between the ages of 15 and 45. This measure of fertility can be further broken down, particularly according to age, length of marriage, and family status.

Other measures of fertility are the so-called reproductive rates. These take into account only the female births, from which the procreative women of the next generation will be recruited, and they measure the average procreativeness of the female population. The gross reproductive rate (GRR) indicates how many female offspring a woman brings into the world during her period of procreation, that is, whether or not she fulfills the procreative probabilities peculiar to her age in any given year. The net reproductive rate (NRR) takes into account the mortality based on life tables for women. In contrast to the GRR, it is really a measure of reproduction, since it indicates to what extent the female births in one year under given fertility and mortality conditions are replacing the parental generation. A value of 1 means that the parental generation is being exactly replaced; values over 1 indicate growth; values under 1 indicate a shrinking population. The NRR is today the most frequently used standard of measure for a population's fertility and reproduction. To calculate it, however, sophisticated statistics are required, that is, statistics must be available on fertility and death rates based on age and sex. A coarser method of expressing the balance between births and deaths is the rate of excess of births over deaths, established as the difference between birth and mortality rates.

Migration statistics are not yet as highly developed as those for natural population trends. They differentiate between immigration and emigration beyond a nation's borders on the one hand, and internal migration on the other. In the latter case, country-to-town migration is of particular importance. To establish internal migration requires a well-organized resident registration system, which even some advanced nations (the United States, for example) do not have.

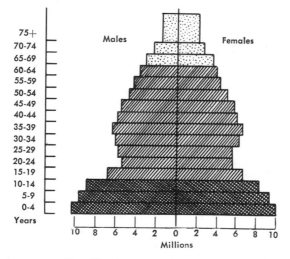

Fig. 23   Age pyramid. Age and sex groups for the United States in 1960 (in millions).

Population Status

The world's population for the year 1961 has been estimated at 3,060,800,000 inhabitants. Comparison with earlier censuses shows a considerable increase. If this growth trend continues, about 3,860,000,000 can be expected by 1980 and 6,280,000,000 by the year 2000.

Distribution and density of the world's population differ greatly. In Central and Western Europe there are huge masses of people, and in no country does the population density fall below 185 persons per square mile; mainland China, despite her primitive agriculture and low state of industrialization, has 174; Japan 659; India 348; and Pakistan 259, according to the 1961 figures. In the continental United States, exclusive of Alaska, the figure is only 51, although in the eastern states it rises to more than 518.1. Other large regions throughout the world, on the other hand, are very thinly populated, partly because climate and soil conditions create natural barriers (polar regions, high mountain ranges), and partly because economic development is still in its primitive stages in such areas.

The population trend prior to the beginning of the modern era can be determined only by comparing estimates of population statistics for various historical periods. The enormous population growth during the history of man has not run an even course. In the early Paleolithic period, there were perhaps only a few thousand people alive on this earth at the same time, and in the late Paleolithic period at the most a few hundred thousand. This is one of the reasons why civilization developed so slowly in the beginning. The Neolithic Age produced the first "demographic revolution" through the development of agriculture and sedentary life. In France, which has undergone thorough archaeological study, the population in the early Paleolithic Age, based on the wealth of prehistoric discoveries, is estimated to have been a few hundred people, at the end of the Paleolithic Age (10,000 B.C.) about 50,000; in the next 6,000 years the population multiplied tenfold and in the next 1,000 years it again multiplied tenfold. By 3000 B.C., the population has been estimated to have been 5 million, but that figure is probably too high rather than too low.

Even the great empires and civilizations of antiquity were developed and maintained by amazingly small populations. Sumer—and similarly later in America the old Mayan empire—had hardly more than half a million inhabitants. Under the last Pharaohs, ancient Egypt had 7 million people, and the Early Empire at the time of its creative surge could not have numbered more than one million. In the Golden Age of Greece, there were about 3 million Greeks, but fewer than one and a half million in the Peloponnesus and central Greece, the core of Greek habitation and civilization. At the time of Augustus, Italy's population was about 6 million, after an undoubtedly large population increase since the beginning of the Republic.

In Western and Central Europe, population increased tremendously after the period of migration. The excess of births over deaths was counterbalanced by clearing the land and by colonization to the east. In the late Middle Ages, one of the signs of a population shrinkage was the numerous deserted villages, the result, in part, of the great plagues of that era. The economic development and the increase in prices point to a growth in population in the late Middle Ages and the sixteenth century. Europe's population in 1650 has been estimated at about 100 million, that of the world at about 515 million. In modern times, Europe's population, despite heavy emigration to overseas areas, had multiplied five times by 1930, while the world's population quadrupled. Africa's population increased the least. European colonization resulted in a sudden jump in population in America and in Australia. Thus, since the beginning of the history of man, population growth has been accelerated considerably as civilization progressed.

Period	Total Number of Adults	Age at Death (in per cent)			Life Expectancy at Birth	Source
		20–40	40–60	Over 60		
Early Paleolithic Age	9	89.9	11.1	—	—	Vallois, 1937
Late Paleolithic Age	67	82.1	17.9	—	—	"
Neolithic Age, Cyprus (Khirokitia)	97	78.4	21.6	—	21	Kurth, 1958
Neolithic Age, Silesia	60	70.4	29.6	—	—	Euler & Werner, 1936
Bell-beaker people	102	30.4	64.7	4.9	—	Gerhardt, 1953
Early Bronze Age, Lower Austria	208	52.6	37.7	9.7	20	Franz and Winkler, 1936
Greece, Middle Bronze Age, Early Iron Age	175	50.9	46.3	2.8	—	Angel, 1947
Greece, classic period	75	38.7	53.3	8	—	"
Egypt, in Roman times	98	62.2	23.5	14.3	22	Pearson, 1902
Rome (mostly during the Empire)	3676	68.3	18.6	13.1	21	Macdonell, 1913
Provinces of Hispania and Lusitania Hispania	1587	49	26.5	24.5	—	"
Province of Africa "	8879	32.3	23.6	44.1	—	"
Early Canaries, Total Population	1179	29.4	53.7	16.9	—	Schwidetzky, 1958
Early Canaries, Upper Class	265	19.6	58.1	22.3	—	"
Spanish West Goths 5th–6th century	180	38.9	45	16.1	—	"
Vikings of Haitabu	65	60	35.4	4.6	—	Schäfer, 1956
10–12th century, Hungary	932	34.4	40.6	25	30.6	Acsádi and
France, 1896–1905	—	16	24	60	—	Nemeskéri, 1957

Table title: AGE AT DEATH AND LIFE EXPECTANCY OF PREHISTORIC AND ANCIENT PEOPLES

Phases of the Population Trend

Aside from the particular differences, a typical phase pattern can be recognized in the natural population trend resulting from births and deaths. This pattern is most advanced in Europe and also best established there statistically, but it is also recognizable, although not coinciding in time, of course, in all other countries that have the proper statistical data.

Phase I is characterized by high birth and death rates with a small excess of births over deaths—that is, slow population growth. The population adapts to the food supply mainly through mortality. This is the type of population regulation that also predominates in the animal kingdom and applies to by far the greatest part of human population history. Infant mortality is high. There are figures that go as high as 80 per cent. Female mortality is higher than that of the male, mainly because of deaths in childbirth. Pestilence, not yet under control, takes many victims. Prior to the development of world-wide communications, starvation in the wake of a bad harvest or some other catastrophe of nature constituted the most drastic means of adapting the population to the food supply. It is estimated that during the years of the plague of 1348–49, Europe lost one third of its population. Ireland's potato famine of 1845–47 took the lives of 800,000 to 1,000,000 people, at least 10 per cent of the population. In 1918–19, famine and an epidemic of grippe raged simultaneously in India and wiped out 15 per cent of the population.

In Phase I, average life expectancy is therefore low. In India, at birth, it is 32.5 years (1960), in the eleventh century in Hungary it was 30.6 years. Population is organized in relatively closed marriage and propagation circles (isolates), in which close marriages and even incest prevail. Abortion and infanticide are known as means of interfering with natural fertility, whereas contraception plays a minor role. Within the population, marriage frequency and marriage age are tuned to the socioeconomic level of the classes. The economically poorer groups form families less frequently or later in life. Insofar as there is any differentiated propagation, the tendency is for the upper social classes to produce more children.

Phase II is characterized by a drop in the mortality rate because of the development of medicine and hygiene, particularly through the elimination of deadly plagues (the last great plague in Europe was 1709–11), and through the improvement in infant care. The birth rate, on the other

POPULATION TREND SINCE 1650, IN MILLIONS								
Continent	1650	1750	1800	1850	1900	1920	1940	1960
Europe	100	140	180	270	400	450	530	603
Asia	300	450	575	730	920	1010	1185	1698
Africa	100	100	95	100	125	140	153	244
North America	7	6	15	39	106	143	183	265
South America	6	6	8	20	38	64	89	140
Oceania	2	2	2	2	6	8	10	16
	515	704	875	1161	1595	1815	2150	2966
Annual growth rate (per 1,000)	3.2		4.3	5.7	6.3	6.5	8.4	13.4

(After Landry, 1949, and *World Almanac,* 1960)

hand, falls less, not at all, or even rises, because of the increase in the procreative age groups. A population pincer comes into being. Birth rate and death rate diverge and between them there remains a growing excess of births over deaths. This phase is therefore characterized by rapid population growth. It began in Western Europe around the start of the nineteenth century. The result was a surging population trend. With increasing population density, the isolates begin to break up and the classes begin to mix more freely. This is to be observed, along with other phenomena, in the drop in consanguine marriages and in the territorial broadening of marriage circles.

The population adapts to the subsistence means by increasing the food-supply area, by intensification of agriculture, by urbanization and industrialization, and by emigration. In 1801, France had 253 towns with a population of more than 5,000 each, whose total population was 3.7 million, which amounts to 13.6 per cent of the national population; by 1901 it had 648 towns, with 14.4 million, or 37 per cent of the country's total population. In the United States in 1790, the farm population (i.e., those living in communities under 2,000) was 94 per cent; in 1840, it was still 88 per cent, but by 1910 it was 54 per cent, and by 1959, only 12.5 per cent. In Germany, the share of communities with less than 2,000 inhabitants dropped from 63 per cent to 30 per cent between 1871 and 1939 (in 1900, it was 44 per cent). Furthermore, in the nineteenth century, about 40 million Europeans emigrated to foreign countries, roughly 20 million of them to the United States.

Wherever there are social differences in population growth, higher fertility among the higher social levels is to be expected, for their mortality rate is always lower and they are the first to profit from progress in medicine and hygiene. These differences, however, are partially counterbalanced by the fact that in a modern industrial society the regulating effect of marriage age and marriage frequency does not come into play. The marriage age begins to adjust to the commencement of a business career, which reverses the relationship between social rank and marriage age. The more uneducated a social group is, the lower its average marriage age. Because of the more rapid sequence of generations, unfavorable mortality factors are offset. As urbanization increases, the country-city differences in reproduction play a more important role, particularly in Europe where propagation in cities has always been less than in the country. But in the United States, with the recent increase in suburban industrialization (along with other post-war developments), early marriages are again coming into vogue.

According to paleodemographic research, the mortality trend has shown a constantly downward tendency ever since the dawn of history. In the Paleolithic Age, few people lived beyond their fiftieth birthday. In the Neolithic Age and in the Bronze Age, on the other hand, people died at an older age and there is proof that some lived beyond sixty years of age. In later epochs, the proportion of older people in the population continued to grow, but by no means regularly and not to the same degree in all areas. Where infant and child mortality can be established (late Iron Age in Sweden, early Middle Ages in Hungary), it is not substantially above Phase I of modern European times in the case of sedentary populations. In most prehistoric populations, female mortality is higher than male mortality. The fact that the life span extends far beyond the sexually and reproductively active years is a specifically human phenomenon and represents a result of advancing civilization.

In Phase III, the birth rate follows the mortality rate in its downward trend. The population pincers close again. As in Phase I, population increase is small—until a decline in population sets in—but there is much less population turnover. Once the mortality rate has been brought under control in Phase II, the same thing happens to the fertility rate. Family planning and rationalization of propagation come into their own. The regulating factors here are the rapidly spreading methods of contraception, rather than the primitive and crude methods of abortion and infanticide. The physiological differences in fertility are now completely smothered by the social and cultural metamorphosis.

Birth and death rates affect each other in many different ways in Phase III. One strong motive for family planning results from the falling mortality rate and from the economic problems which a rapidly growing population must face. Lower infant mortality and a higher maturation rate make it possible to attain the desired family size with fewer births. The progressive extension of life expectancy also reduces the birth rate. This is due to the fact that the proportion of older age groups increases, and they are a segment of the population that contributes little to reproduction. On the other hand, the lower birth rate and the wider spacing of births favorably affect the mortality rate. This applies primarily to infant mortality. In the most advanced countries, it drops to less than 3 per cent (Sweden 2.3; New Zealand, whites 2.2; Australia 2.8; Netherlands 2.9 per cent) and thus approaches the limit of endogenous mortality based on hereditary and constitutional defects, which is estimated to be 2 per cent. Furthermore, whereas female mortality, particularly that of the procreative age groups, formerly exceeded male mortality, it is now lower in all age groups. With the increase in life expectancy, the percentage of the higher age groups in the population as a whole increases, and such superannuation leads to new economic and social problems which create a new branch of human biology, the science of gerontology. The probability of death continues to display a first peak in the infant age group, then a sharp drop to the very low levels of the 5- to 35-year-olds, and then a slow rise, which increases after the age of 50.

In the social differentiation of fertility, the relationships finally reverse themselves in Phase III. The desired restriction as to the number of children, as well as the drop in the mortality rate, begin to appear in the upper classes, which, despite more favorable mortality rates, attain a lower reproductive rate than the lower classes. The latter adopt family-

BIRTH RATE, DEATH RATE, AND EXCESS OF BIRTHS OVER DEATHS IN VARIOUS COUNTRIES FOR 1959			
	Birth Rate	Mortality Rate	Excess of Births over Deaths
I. High Birth and Mortality Rates			
Guatemala	49.8	17.3	32.5
Union of South Africa (colored)	46.3	15.2	31.1
Ecuador	45.9	15.1	30.8
Egypt (1958)	45.6	19.3	26.3
II. High Birth Rate and Falling Mortality Rate			
Venezuela	49.9	8.7	41.2
Costa Rica	47.5	9.0	38.5
Mexico	46.9	11.9	35.0
El Salvador	45.9	11.9	34.0
Iran	44.3	8.7	35.6
China (Taiwan)	41.2	7.2	34.0
Panama	40.8	9.1	31.7
Dominican Republic	39.8	10.5	29.3
Jordan	38.9	7.4	31.5
Chile	35.4	12.7	22.7
III. Falling Birth Rate and Low Mortality Rate			
Canada	27.5	8.0	19.5
Syria	25.0	5.1	19.9
U.S.S.R.	25.0	7.6	17.4
Poland	24.7	8.9	15.8
United States	24.3	9.4	14.7
Portugal	23.5	10.8	12.7
Argentina	23.0	8.3	14.7
Yugoslavia	23.0	9.8	13.2
Australia	22.6	8.9	13.7
Spain	21.8	9.0	12.8
Rumania	20.2	10.2	10.0
Greece	19.4	7.4	12.0
Italy	18.4	9.3	9.1
Norway	17.7	8.9	8.8
Bulgaria	17.6	9.5	8.1
Japan	17.6	7.5	10.1
IV. Low Birth Rate and Medium Mortality Rate			
France	18.4	11.3	7.1
Switzerland	17.7	9.6	8.1
Austria	17.6	12.5	5.1
West Germany	17.6	10.8	6.8
Belgium	17.4	11.4	6.0
East Germany	17.1	13.1	4.0
Great Britain	16.9	11.7	5.2

Figures from *Demographic Yearbook*, 1960

planning methods later. The cities, particularly the large metropolises, intensify even more the limitation of births, with the result that the differences in reproduction between city and country are increased. The drop in the birth rate is closely associated with high social mobility in the highly industrialized society and with the drive toward social advancement, in which small families are favored. As birth control gradually reaches the broad lower classes, differences of social fertility are again brought into balance. The unskilled-worker class, now underpopulated due to the general drive toward social betterment, is often brought up to strength by immigration from less-developed countries.

In Western Europe, there are indications of the onset of a Phase IV. The drop in the mortality rate through extension of the life span has, it is true, not yet reached its natural limit, but it is proceeding much more slowly. With the increase in the higher age groups in the structure of the population, the mortality rate again increases. Once reproduction has gone through all stages of rationalization at every level of the population, it frequently happens that a positive relationship between social status and family size recurs. However, the social differences in marriage age, which shorten the generation span in the less-educated classes, remain. Once the industrial economy is completely developed, social drive slackens. The standard of living is high at all levels and this leads to a renewed increase in the birth rate, which, however, never again attains the high values of Phase I and Phase II.

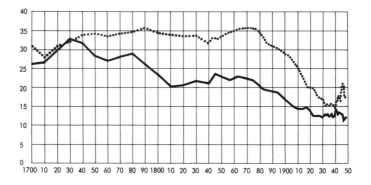

FIG. 24   Phases of the population trend. Birth rate (dotted line) and mortality rate (solid line) in England and Wales 1700–1949. Drop in the mortality rate since 1730 with the birth rate remaining almost stationary (Phase II of the population trend: opening of the "population pincers"). Since 1880, a sharper drop in both the mortality and the birth rate (Phase III of the population trend: closing of the "population pincers") (after Mackenroth, 1953).

Phase Differences

At present, the various peoples and countries of the earth find themselves in different demographic phases. These differences are mainly a function of the degree of industrial maturity and of the modernization of their way of life. As soon as demographic statistics are reasonably reliable in a given country civilization has already advanced so far that the mortality rate has begun to drop. Relatively high mortality rates along with high birth rates prevail today, particularly in a number of South and Central American countries (Guatemala, Colombia, Ecuador). According to official figures, India follows some distance behind them, but such figures, both with regard to births and deaths, are probably too low.

The majority of populations for which no figures on the natural population trend are available are most likely in Phase I—slow population growth with a high mortality rate. However, the birth rate among primitive peoples is by no means as high as that of the Europeans prior to industrialization. Knowledge of abortion appears to be universal and it is often practiced to a considerable extent among primitive peoples. Even physiological fertility appears to be higher among civilized peoples than among primitive tribes. Deprivation and heavy physical burdens affect not only mortality but also fertility. Thus the Negro regions of Africa report low birth rates for the most part, resulting from female sterility due to overwork, abortion, and premature senility. In the animal kingdom, also, fluctuations in fertility contribute to a small degree in adapting the population to the food-supply area.

In the European colonial regions, the natives, without exception, continued to represent Phase I of the population trend for some time after the arrival of the whites (for example in the Union of South Africa, New Zealand, and the United States). The first contact most primitive tribes had with Europeans led at first to a sharp drop in population. The factors here are a high mortality rate—through the introduction of diseases, through brutal decimation, and through the natives' being driven into poverty-stricken and retreat areas—as well as a falling birth rate. Such a drop is caused by, among other things, venereal disease, enlisting the male population as migrant laborers, as well as mental depression brought on by the dissolution of the tribal order and ethnically ingrained systems of values. As a result, a number of smaller primitive groups died out (Tasmanian, some American Indian and Melanesian tribes); others, however, survived the adaptation crisis and returned to the group of stationary populations or even became growing populations by adopting certain elements of the colonists' culture, thus causing their mortality rate to drop. This holds true for numerous Melanesian groups, for the Maori in New Zealand, and for North American Indians.

However, these are relatively small groups. The large population blocks that today represent the rapidly growing populations of Phase II—falling mortality rate with high birth rate—are the Latin American countries with a large Indian population; the Islamic countries of the Near East and North Africa; and parts of South and Southeast Asia and China. In the Latin American countries, development is being pushed forward by the white population, which, just as in the colonial countries proper, represents a later phase of demographic development. However the native population also shared in the cultural advance and, in doing so, entered the phase of falling mortality rates. In various parts of Asia, the former colonial governments also improved living conditions, successfully fought contagious diseases, intensified agriculture and health service, and thereby reduced the mortality rate. Java, in particular, with its 50 million inhabitants, densely settled thanks to its rice cultivation, is of great importance as such a growth cell, as is the Philippines.

The Islamic countries report especially high birth rates, however only in part from official sources. Wherever demographic data within those countries are divided into religious communities, the Moslems show the highest birth rate (Egypt, 1956: 40.6 as compared with Christians 34 and Jews 21). Many of these countries are in the midst of rapid economic development, which supports the trend toward a falling mortality rate.

Israel, due to the constant influx of young and vital colonists, has a particularly low mortality rate but very great differences in fertility among the various groups of foreign origin, which reflect the demographic differential of the countries of origin.

China represents the largest growing population bloc. However, the official mortality rate is improbably low and, because of incomplete registration, it should be corrected, as should the rate for India. However, the birth rate is undoubtedly high and a comparison of various censuses reveals a strong population growth. The 1962 census registered 650 million mainland Chinese, whereas the 1950 population was estimated to be 450–500 million. Since 1878, heavy Chinese emigration has been colonizing Manchuria, and all of Southeast Asia serves Chinese laborers and merchants as a migration area.

Most European countries and countries settled by Europeans, including the U.S.S.R., are in Phase III, with falling birth rate and low, but, to a large extent, stabilized mortality rate. However, in Europe there is a differential from east to west and from north to south. The highest birth rate and the highest rate of excess births over deaths are in Poland and in Russia, while the southern and southeastern European countries have higher rates than the northern and northwestern European countries. The relationship with the degree of industrial maturity and with the level of the population's standard of living is here very distinct. In the overseas countries settled by Europeans, both the birth rate and the excess of births over deaths are for the most part higher than are those of the countries of origin, but such statistics also include the non-European members of the population. Among the non-European countries, highly industrialized

Japan entered the phase of falling birth rate relatively early—that is, between World War I and World War II—and today, from the standpoint of demography, counts itself among the European countries.

Fɪɢ. 25   The effect of demographic political measures on the birth trend. The birth rates in Germany, France, and England, 1901–1952: sharp rise in Germany after 1933, in France after 1940; but also a rise in England after 1940, and this without any demographic political measures (figures from *Population,* 1953).

The countries of northwestern and central Europe represent Phase IV, again with a slightly increased mortality rate and thus a particularly low excess of births over deaths. At times, the net reproductive rate sank below 1, but since the renewed increase in births, which began in the 1930's, it is again in some areas above that figure.

The consistent correlation between the manner of population and the economic level promises the so-called underdeveloped countries, now in Phase I and Phase II, a transition to Phase III sooner or later. In most of those countries, there are already indications, some distinct, others less so, which point to a drop in the birth rate. The later a population enters this phase, the more rapid the tempo of development tends to be and, thus, the sharper the drop in the birth rate. The leveling of the vast cultural and techno-economic differences, just getting under way now among the peoples of the earth, also promises to assimilate natural population growth and thus stabilize demographic conditions to a certain extent.

53

Population Policy

Numerous political measures affect the population either directly or indirectly. All measures that change the standard of living, hygienic conditions, and medical care influence the mortality rate; political pressure and economic distress further the trends toward emigration. Rapid economic growth can act as a kind of immigration suction, while marriage and family laws are contributing factors with respect to marriage age and to marriage and divorce frequency, and, thus, also with respect to fertility in the marriages. Demographic political measures in the narrower sense have primarily to do with the birth rate and the migration trend. Many European countries and many overseas countries settled by Europeans pursue a positive policy with regard to births and have done so ever since the reproductive rates dropped to 1 or even to below 1. This is done first of all by granting families with children economic relief, either through direct gratuities or else indirectly, through graduated tax rates and other preferential treatment. This system has found its widest application in France, as embodied in the 1939 *Code de Famille.* Starting in 1933 the Nazi government of Germany issued political decrees encouraging parents to produce large families, offering as inducements financial aid and such prestige items as maternity medals and honorary godparenthoods. Out of 41 constitutions adopted or amended by various nations after World War II, 35 contain clauses on family protection or benefits, mother care, and similar clauses.

Political measures aimed at influencing the birth rate, however, are known to have existed in antiquity. Emperor Augustus (27 B.C.–A.D. 14) introduced the *lex Papia et Poppaea,* which increased the taxes of bachelors, childless couples, and even of widows, and also limited their inheritance rights. He awarded poor citizens prizes for having children, publicly commended large families, and introduced badges of honor for mothers. Under later emperors, dependency allowances for indigent citizens came into being under the alimentation system. There is some doubt as to whether or not such purposeful measures are successful. The laws of Augustus obviously failed to halt the population decline in Italy; after the passage of such laws in France and Germany, the birth rates did rise considerably, but that was also true in other countries, although to a lesser extent, without any direct demographic political legislation. However, economic and social security are undoubtedly weighty factors in family planning, though by no means are they the only factors determining family size.

On the other hand, Japan and India, by fostering family planning and contraception, pursue policies whose purpose is to curb population growth. In Japan, where the birth rates had already begun to fall prior to World War II and the concept of family planning could be made compatible with earlier traditions, this policy has thus far achieved greater success than in a less-developed country like India. The same problems exist in China and other "underdeveloped" countries, but so far no demographic political conclusions have been drawn from this fact. Every form of economic aid that raises the standard of living and thus lowers the mortality rate remains an illusion, so long as the birth rates do not also fall, and so long as the population fails to attain a state of balance adapted to the economic potential. Rapidly growing populations, for which additional means of subsistence cannot be created at the same rate, face potential catastrophes and become areas of unrest. Demographic policy is therefore an essential part of general world politics. From the outset, the United Nations has focused its attention on demographic questions, not only in the sections dealing with social and economic affairs but also in the United Nations Office of Statistics and in the World Health Organization (WHO).

Migration policy is also becoming increasingly a problem for international regulation. Most countries place practically no restrictions on emigration; on the other hand, virtually all countries have immigration laws, which limit the number of immigrants and exclude certain categories —in particular, invalids, criminals, and the disabled. The large-scale migrations in the wake of World War II broke through many of these regulations but the International Refugee Organization and the United Nations High Commissioner for Refugees have again taken in hand the problem of resettlement, which is frequently connected with new international migration trends. Numerous political measures in respect to migration are known from demographic history: resettlements and evacuations frequently served to keep the peace in conquered territories (the Babylonian exile of the Jews; the resettlement policy of the Assyrians, Incas, and Chinese emperors; the deportation of the Vandals after the siege of Belisarius in A.D. 533, among others); the settling of aliens to increase the economic or military strength of nations (the Teutons in the Roman Empire; the resettling measures during the Age of Mercantilism: the Huguenots in Brandenburg, colonists from Salzburg in East Prussia). Migration policy is also an important component of world politics in that it settles uprooted groups and creates a balance between overpopulated and underpopulated areas.

THE DESCENT OF MAN

The theory that man is descended from lower primates postulates the general evolution of all living beings in the course of the history of the world. Evolution began with a transition from inert to living matter in which inorganic-chemical aggregates were organized into organic-chemical aggregates capable of propagating themselves in identical form. The beginning of such a process of duplication marks the first step toward the living world and leads in progressive complexity to typical organisms and their further development into today's world of living beings. The rise of the hominids was, of course, part of these evolutionary events. The hominids have formed a separate evolutionary line ever since the separation of these primates from their non-hominid ancestors. The objective of the general theory of evolution is to prove that evolution occurred, and hence to clarify the course of evolutionary history in general as well as in respect to specific lines of descent. A further objective is to analyze the complex causes of these historic patterns.

After a few unsuccessful attempts (Lamarck, *Philosophie zoologique,* 1809) to popularize and prove one theory of evolution, another was scientifically launched a little over one hundred years ago. On November 24, 1859, the classic work of Charles Darwin, *The Origin of Species,* was published. This book contained such an overwhelming amount of evidence in support of evolution and especially its causes, that the genetic-dynamic concept of life began to replace the hitherto dominant static theory of immutability. There were, of course, setbacks for the new theory, but the consequences it held for man were obvious to Darwin and others. Ernst Haeckel formulated it first at the famous convention of German scientists and physicians in Stettin in 1863, stating that man had to look for his ancestors among the apelike mammals of the Tertiary period. In the same year Huxley's classic *Zoological Evidences as to Man's Place in Nature* appeared. Darwin himself waited until 1871 before publishing his comprehensive and characteristically thorough and careful study *The Descent of Man.* Thus, since Darwin, Huxley, Haeckel, and others there has been no reason to regard the descent of man as an unsolved mystery. It has basically been solved. The hominids descend from—in Darwin's own words—"ancient members" of the great apes. In regard to specific details of this descent many questions remain, although the phylogeny of the hominids comes into clearer and clearer focus as the tools of modern research increasingly permit us to pinpoint the problems.

We shall now attempt to demonstrate a proof of the general theory of evolution. It is primarily a historical theory and can be verified only indirectly—inductively, not experimentally. However, in the field of experimental genetics, a new branch of evolutionary research has been opened up—experimental phylogenetics, or evolutionary genetics—in which present-day evolutionary changes are measured by exact inductive methods and are also analyzed experimentally. The findings in regard to the causes of changes are then extrapolated into the past. Fossil research affords insights into actual, documented changes and certain regularities or patterns followed by these changes, but it does not yield direct information about the underlying causes at work in remote times. The extrapolation of present causes into the past is methodologically admissible and can be supported in numerous ways. We might just mention here that the trilobites, three-lobed arthropods related to spiders, lived during the Cambrian, 500 million years ago. These organisms were composed of cells and these cells had nuclei containing chromosomes.

These trilobites occurred in rather extensive populations, not singly—something that has been true of all organisms, at all times, even back to the beginning of life (the abiotic-biotic transition), 3 billion years ago. At any rate, cells—i.e., highly complex organic systems—have been in existence as long as 2 billion years. With its experimental and statistical methods, modern evolutionary genetics examines changes which take place in the genetic codes of the chromosomes and in the populations. There are no grounds for assuming that the processes involved could have been materially different in the evolution of organisms of the geologic past.

In the past, some biologists have disputed the theory of evolution through mutation and natural selection on the grounds that such a haphazard process could never have produced complex functional units whose individual parts cannot function independently. Such a system is the human eye. The explanation of this apparent paradox is that the eyes of all vertebrates represent the end products of a long evolutionary process that began long ago with the origin of vertebrates, and the eye is virtually identical in all primates.

All these concepts, of course, stand or fall with the evidence for, and the general proof of, evolution. This proof, however, has been available since Darwin. He provided it through observations made on his trip around the world from 1831 to 1836, observations which have been verified by an extensive mass of data collected in our day. Darwin noticed similarities between fossils and living mammals in South America; he observed that related species of South American rodents occupied the same ecological niches (vicariism); and, most decisive, that forms of animals that emigrated to some isolated island groups (the Galápagos Islands) tended to segregate into species and races (Darwin's finches).

Today we possess infallible proof of the progression of species through time. The vertical sequences of geological formations represent successions of related types of organisms in ever-increasing complexity of organization (anagenesis). At any rate, biology is based upon the old axiom of Harvey—"Omne vivum e vivo"—and not upon statics and creation. The young Darwin, of course, was still convinced of the latter; before his trip he had believed in the immutability of organisms, but on the basis of his own observations he formulated an evolutionary concept of nature. The progressive sequences of forms not only strongly suggest an evolutionary type of development but also leave no doubt as to the continuity of the life chain. The special structural arrangement of organic systems, with their graded variability, is that much more proof. Why do organisms have these built-in kinds of order, or why doesn't some other kind of order prevail, or chaos for that matter? Thus, the theory of special creation has been replaced by the concrete actuality of transformation.

Beyond this demonstration of basic proof, there is at present an abundance of further so-called supplementary evidence. One is comparative morphology, studied by means of comparing homologies: Homologous organs have a common origin even though they may differ in structural details. In the past it was assumed that homologies in structure bore no implication of common origin. Many morphological structures were analyzed from this conceptual point of view, and many morphogenetic problems were recognized. This approach stimulated research but did not lead to valid conclusions. It is essentially an ahistoric, Platonic concept which offers no truly concrete explanations of causation. Just the same, it has provided many fruitful ideas useful in the study of evolutionary causation. The so-called rudimentary organs—the series showing the gradual absorption of extremities in lizards, the traces of limbs in snakes, the rudiments of the pelvis in manatees, the rudimentary teeth of right whales —are witnesses of the real course of evolution as it slowly and gradually brought about enormous changes in form. The snakes go back to tetrapod reptiles, the manatee to tetrapod hoofed animals, the toothless whales descend from toothed ancestors which secondarily adapted to life in water. For all this there are fossil records. The changes of form seen during the embryonic development would not be conceivable without this historic background. This provides the solid ground for Haeckel's so-called "biogenetic law" (1866), although he formulated the relationship as a slogan and with a slight misconception when he stated: "Ontogenesis is a shortened and often secondarily altered recapitulation of phylogenesis." It is a fact that basically the structure of the ancestral type is recapitulated, although this recapitulation in most cases only encompasses its embryonic arrangement. Comparative physiology, psychology and analysis of behavior, biogeography, and the presently still expanding documentary racial history, paleontology, and the findings of all these disciplines make sense only in their historical context: the organisms are in every way historical living beings derived genetically from ancestral forms and conditions.

Today the theory of evolution is accepted in biology and anthropology as a verified as well as a working theory on the grounds stated above, and is progressing in two directions. Accordingly, evolutionary research can be subdivided as follows: historical phylogenetics, which deals with the formal phylogenetic events, and experimental phylogenetics, which deals with the causes for the actual phylogeny. Experimental phylogenetics obtains its results through exact inductive methods. These results are then extrapolated over the phylogeny as it has been reconstructed by and with the aid of comparative methodology. Thus, it also studies the causes of this phylogeny by means of a comparative method, but does so equipped with a complete knowledge of the causes at work in our contemporary phylogeny. This is admissible on the premise that Harvey's dictum is generally reliable—nothing contradicts it—and assuming that from the beginning the basic processes of life have always been the same.

Historical Phylogenetics

The reliability of the reconstructed picture of formal phylogeny depends upon the amount of fossil information available. Often such information is lacking. For some animal groups the locale of the phylogenetic sequence is still unknown. Just the same, paleontology has made impressive strides since Cuvier (1769–1832), since Darwin's work in the second half of the nineteenth century, and especially since the beginning of the twentieth century.

On the whole, we can conclude that the phylogeny of organisms is not in serious conflict with the postulated evolutionary mechanisms (the causalities established by experimental phylogenetics); at any rate, there is no need to assume additional unknown mechanisms.

Previously, the lack of intermediate forms within the paleontological records—and who does not think of the missing link in the ancestry of the hominids?—was cited. At one time there appeared to be no forms at all connecting groups of higher taxonomic categories. This lack of bridges was first explained by saltations—i.e., macrophyletic changes which would lead abruptly to a new type without any transitional individuals. This concept was based upon an assumed continuous sequence of geological strata, a stratigraphic continuity which seemed to support a saltation hypothesis.

This assumption has been weakened by modern stratigraphic research which has shown more and more that geologic continuity is often lacking, and that there are corresponding disturbances of strata which might have contained the connecting bridge animals (or plants). Neither the apparent lack of bridge forms nor the lack of stratigraphic layers between the fossil types constitutes concrete evidence. On the other hand, the actual existence of the bridge animals as they are discovered becomes increasingly important and illuminating as the fossil collection nears completion. We shall continue to gain more knowledge, and it will become clearer that evolutionary history is not characterized by abrupt leaps or saltations but that phylogeny is a product of continuous minute changes. Sir Julian Huxley has illustrated this difference in his statement that evolution does not proceed in steps, as though climbing a staircase, but rather moves smoothly along an ascending, oblique plane. The hypothesis of major mutational changes within phylogeny proves more and more mistaken, aside from being questionable from the point of view of genetics. Occasionally intermediate types are found. They are rarely the real genealogical bridges, but they can be used as structural ancestors, or models of ancestors (Ichthyostega, Archeopteryx, Oligokyphus, etc.; for the primate phylogeny: proconsulines, Kenyapithecus, Australopithecines). Certain regularities in the course of the phylogenetic changes occur in the paleontological records: the chronologically arranged progressive sequences of form, for instance the equid series going from small size to large size, from four toes to one toe, from low teeth to high teeth (hypsodonty), etc.; in the hominids, especially, the increasing brain size (cerebralization). There was an attempt to explain this directionality as the work of special inherent mechanisms which guided evolution toward a definite goal (orthogenetic directional factors). Even here evolutionary genetics, together with paleontology's gradual completion of its fossil collection, has shown that such teleologically active, orthogenetic factors are not required to produce the phenomenon of orthogenesis (to be understood descriptively). It would seem better not to use the theoretically colored word "orthogenesis" any longer and to replace it with "trend," which is not theoretically weighted. Darwin and his theory of the survival of the fittest leave no room for any teleological causality factors in the generation of adaptive modifications. Thus, in the descent of man as well, saltations and teleological factors seem improbable.

Experimental Phylogenetics

As previously mentioned, certain regularities can be seen in the history of form phylogenesis, often leading to anagenesis through numerous additive adaptive changes, which in themselves, however, cannot indicate any operative causes. In fact, their occurrence has led to faulty speculations (the teleological nature of evolution, special orthogenetic factors, saltations from type to type). Experimental phylogenetics tests these results as far as possible by means of fossil documentation. Essentially, however, it applies or extrapolates insights obtained through studying living organisms, animals or plants, which may reveal the operative causes of evolutionary changes over the entire phylogeny. Experiments have yielded a very important result, namely, that there is no basis for the controversial Lamarckian theory of inheritance, which states that somatic changes during the lifetime of the individual could be transmitted through the sex cells, so that they would reappear in similar or even heightened fashion in the offspring although the originally causative environmental conditions no longer would exert themselves. Such an inheritance of acquired characteristics was never verified, and at any rate does not play any role in the phylogenetic evolutionary history of organisms. Darwin did not yet know about Mendel's work and the mechanism of inheritance, and had no insight into the physico-chemical basis of the genetic variability of organisms. He still took the inheritance of acquired characteristics into consideration. Today both the inheritance of acquired factors and the autogenetic factors (orthogenesis, etc.) are equally unacceptable in evolutionary theory.

Primarily, phylogenetics must take into account changes in the genetic make-up. This applies equally to plants, animals, and man. Such inherited changes are called mutations (see Human Genetics), a word which was already used by Darwin. Mutability is the original phylogenetic process; it produces the elementary evolutionary material. Both major and minor changes can originate through mutations; but only the minor ones do not necessarily damage the evolving organism.

The small, very limited mutations, not the saltations (macro-mutations which produce drastic effects), form the material for phylogeny. In spite of the very low frequency (an average of 1 in 100,000) and in spite of the varying damage caused by many mutations, there are enough positive constructive mutations. The history of phylogeny is extensive enough (perhaps three billion years have elapsed since the cell stage was reached) to provide these building blocks of evolution, the positive mutations, to make the history of organisms the reality it is. Mutations are subject to certain limitations, but they never show bias toward certain goals; they are not usually adaptive (i.e., they do not tend to improve already existing adaptations nor do they produce new adaptive changes). Yet phylogeny is characterized by trends toward higher aggregates and organization as well as improved adaptation.

Darwin was already basically aware of this. He dealt (theoretically) only with inherited variations (i.e., mutations); he eliminated the teleological factors in his theory of the survival of the fittest. The constant overproduction of progeny (as postulated by Malthus in 1798) and the average constancy of the population size (man's exception to this is only apparent) provide the necessary elements of the fight for survival, inasmuch as statistically the most fitted individual for any given environmental situation will have the best chance of survival. Selection thus takes place among aimless and random mutations. Out of its original structure comes a slow shifting of the characteristics of a race or species, or, speaking more generally, new types will occur as a consequence of these underlying causes. This shift increases the adaptational differential. It occurs gradually as viable mutations become available (i.e., micro-mutative), although the rates will vary with the situation. It requires from 200,000 to 500,000 years to transform one species into another one. This is true also of the hominids, from *Homo erectus* to *Homo sapiens* (see The History of Races). The obvious direction, however, in the evolution of organisms in general, and also of single groups, is by and large induced and governed by selection. Selection can often become effective for a longer period in one distinct direction, statistically favoring certain of the randomly occurring mutations. Thus the appearance of an orthogenetic course is produced. Paleontology was in a position to document this phenomenon for quite some time through a wealth of examples, and new material is constantly being gathered. But earlier the reason for the mechanism of orthoselection was not understood. We realize from this short presentation of evolutionary causes that Darwin was right in his mutation-selection theory. The author of the theory of evolution can today be considered fully verified; the objections repeatedly raised against him have in no way become more significant but rather are continually being contradicted by an ever-increasing amount of positive concrete research data.

The most recent branch of phylogenetics, population genetics (see page 203), developed much of this data, and it now occupies a central position within the over-all field of phylogenetics. Its approach is quantitative, statistical, and experimental, and with a mathematical methodology it probes deeply into the causalities of evolutionary changes and their genetic implementation: mutability, mutation pressure, allele formation, selection value, selection pressure, gene combination through hybridization, accidental gene exclusion, and so forth. At the same time it quantitatively measures the effects of these phenomena upon gene and allele ratios in the various populations, shifts in phenotype frequencies, and the mutant distributions. Even the trilobites—or, for that matter, any other organisms of the past— lived in populations. These have now been recognized as the true evolutionary units. The size of these populations is related to, among other things, the evolutionary rate. The evolution of small populations may be more accelerated than that of large populations. The populations of earlier hominids may have been very small. One, therefore, should not underestimate their evolutionary rate. In general, the evolutive processes in former populations are strictly comparable to what population genetics, through exact analysis, is now establishing for present populations.

Ultimately, any sizable changes in forms have been subjected to this same system of interacting causalities. They were produced through a slow, selectively harmonized synthesis of complex gene aggregates; one might call this additive typogenesis. The synthesis of such gene aggregates cannot be directly observed because of the long-term historical nature of such a process. This also explains the uniqueness of any such aggregate. Elementary processes can be repeated, but not the complex ones. The uniqueness of historical events in general is based upon this. It applies not only to the paleontological history of plants and animals, thus making history irreversible in time; it applies equally to man's history. Organisms are forms of the highest complexity, the highest order of interaction— they will never repeat themselves—and if there are organisms on another planet with processes comparable to ours, it is still highly improbable that their phylogeny would have run anywhere near the same course as ours; in other words, we will not—structurally speaking—ever find duplicates of man in the universe.

The History of the Descent of Man

In our discussion of phylogenetics in general, we gave some of the reasons for establishing a phylogenetics of man. We can continue where we left off. First it should be stressed that again Darwin was right: the phylogeny of man, his detachment from the animal kingdom in the course of history, the further differentiation of a branch of the primates ultimately leading to modern man—all this (as Ernst Haeckel expressed it some sixty years ago) is no longer mere hypothesis; it is now a fact.

To start out it is necessary to present a scheme of the evolutionary course of the human branch from the time it was isolated from an "ancient member" of the family of great apes.

APPROXIMATE CHRONOLOGY OF THE TERTIARY IN MILLIONS OF YEARS		
Era	Ended x Millions of years ago	Duration
Pleistocene	1	1
Pliocene	12	11
Miocene	25	13
Oligocene	34	8
Eocene	55	21
Paleocene	78	23

(After Carleton S. Coon)

Ever since their separation from their non-hominid ancestors, the hominids have formed a separate, distinct family, in the sense of zoological systematics, and a separate historic line. Both the hominids and the non-hominids, of course, are placental mammals: the structural type of their chromosomes corresponds clearly to that of the placental mammals. A great deal of data and circumstantial evidence links the hominids with the primates (see Taxonomy of the Primates) and within these with the catarrhines and with the Old World monkeys and apes (Pithecoidea).

Although there is no doubt about the catarrhine nature of the hominids or their historical descent from a catarrhine root, it is more difficult to pinpoint the phylogenetic locus from which the hominian genealogical line starts. What the first representative of the hominids looked like is, of course, a very precarious question. The formal and causal study of any changes since then is the subject of the theory of human descent.

Darwin spoke of an ancient member which he placed among the anthropoid apes (Pongidae—see Taxonomy of the Primates). Most anthropologists familiar with the phylogenetic course of the hominids agree that the ancestor of the hominids can only have been such an ancient member. Even outspoken advocates of the theory that man descended from the chimpanzee have pointed out that the pongids went through a long history of evolutionary change before reaching the modern specialized pongid type. So far there is quite general agreement among the experts. The difficulty arises when one attempts to visualize the structure of the ancestral starting point itself. The picture of that ancestor is anything but uniform.

A geochronological scheme of the Tertiary provides the basis for the phylogeny of all the Hominoidea (Pongidae and Hominidae—see Taxonomy of the Primates); any earlier era must be ruled out as the period during which the two branches of the hominids separated, and even more so, of course, the Pleistocene (Ice Age), as had at times been suggested.

The critical era includes the Oligocene and Miocene, some twenty million years. Figure 26 shows just how the phylogeny of the Hominoidea can, at first approximation, be fitted into this frame of time. The hominid line

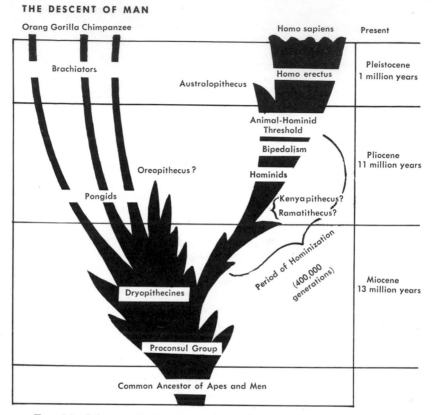

FIG. 26 Scheme of the temporal relationships between the Hominidae (Australopithecines and men) and the Pongidae (Anthropoid Apes) (after Heberer, modified).

extends all the way back into the pongid radiation of the Miocene. This line can be subdivided into three phases:

1. The subhuman
2. The animal-hominid threshold (AHT)
3. The human

In the first phase the hominids still are in a subhuman status; they are physically and consequently also psychically animal. But there are significant changes: the hominids acquire an erect walk (bipedalism) and thus the capacity of locomotion by means of the lower extremities alone and at sufficient speed (running).

In the second phase (AHT) the subhuman hominids achieve a level comparable to the starting point of the human hominids. It is extremely difficult, as will be shown later, to place any fossil discovery in this sub-human-human transition phase, because its upper and lower limits are not sharply defined, although we are quite sure of its geochronological position: it belongs in the Upper Pliocene, not later and scarcely any earlier.

The human phase is characterized by physical changes which also manifest themselves psychically. Two phenomena are especially to be considered: great adaptive radiation, and progressive cerebralization (increasing brain size) in the radiating genealogical lines. This is a complex, rhythmic event. The psychic manifestations consist of the progressive creation of culture. In the first and second phase the psychophysical hominization, or humanization, takes place within a span of 400,000 generations. After that the evolution of the genus *Homo* begins.

Figure 26, a diagram of the general structure of the hominid phylogeny, poses some problematical issues, which can be isolated with the aid of a second diagram, Figure 27; we shall also be able to compare some still debatable hypotheses. We can see, to the right of the time scale (on the left-hand side of Figure 27), the evolutionary steps which the pongids had to go through in their phylogeny. The anthropoid apes developed in the Pliocene into specialized hanging-and-swinging climbers of the kind that are still represented by pongids and gibbons (Hylobatids). Since locomotion in the trees is accomplished mostly by means of the arms, the designation "brachiator" has become popular. Groups showing a typical development of this adaptation are referred to as structural or specialized brachiators. Whereas the modern pongids are such structural brachiators, the extensive and complex group of the pongid subfamily of the dryopithecines, between the Lower Miocene and the Lower Pliocene, were hardly specialized brachiators. They were more likely prebrachiating types not unlike the more primitive proconsulines. We can describe this group as optional or generalized "hangers." Like trapeze artists and like many platyrrhines and catarrhines, they were capable of moving hand over hand, and they already show this in their differentiations. However, they were by no means structural brachiators with correspondingly adapted and proportioned extremities; in other words, they did not possess the relatively long arms (especially forearms) and hands and the relatively short lower extremities (see Taxonomy of the Primates).

The evolutionary history of the pongids is fairly clear, but the fossil records of the primates is quite incomplete and it is thus difficult to document the history of the hominid branch. Its point of departure from the pongids is thus still open to debate, as is shown in the right-hand column of Figure 27. There are three groups of hypotheses. The pongid-hominid transition phase (PHT) might be located anywhere between the Middle (perhaps even Upper) Pliocene and the (perhaps Lower) Oligocene along the indicated semicircle, as long as all three groups of hypotheses are considered equally probable. Accordingly, the various hypotheses assume different ancestral types for the hominid branch. The three groups of hypotheses can be termed: (1) the brachiator hypothesis, (2) the prebrachiator hypothesis, (3) the protocatarrhine hypothesis. There could be added a fourth hypothesis, which states that hominids go all the way back as an independent line to a tarsioid ancestry (the tarsioid hypothesis). Beyond the PHT, the subhuman phase of the hominid phylogeny thus could begin with an optional or part-time brachiator (best characterized

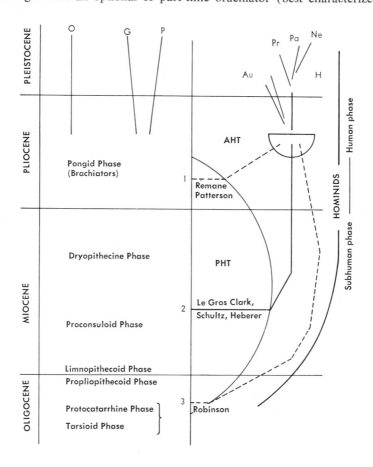

FIG. 27   The currently debatable hypotheses concerning the roots of the hominids in a non-hominid ancestral line. 1 = Brachiator hypothesis; 2 = Prebrachiator hypothesis; 3 = Protocatarrhine hypothesis; PHT = Pongid-hominid transition phase; AHT = Animal-Hominid threshold; Au = Australopithecine; H = Hominine; Pr = Protoanthropine; Pa = Paleanthropine; Ne = Neanthropine; O = Orangutan; G = gorilla; P = chimpanzee (Pan) (after Heberer)

as a grasping-and-pulling type of climber), or a protocatarrhine-like pronograde, but of course originally arboreal, ancestor.

We now have to weigh whether equal probability should be given to each of these three groups or whether one should be regarded as more probable than the others. That this is difficult to decide can be judged from the names of the experts listed in the diagram. This very complex subject cannot be satisfactorily discussed here. The reader is therefore referred to the various authors that have recently discussed the brachiator hypothesis: Gregory, Heberer, Kälin, Remane, Napier, A. H. Schultz, and others.

The prebrachiator theory appears to be the best supported and the most probable view. We can only mention a few points. The general pongid theory: the complicated structure of the tooth crown (of the lower molars) in the hominoids (pongids and hominids) is based upon polygenic inheritance, developed through additive adaptive selection from simpler systems. An identical duplication of this polyallelic system is highly improbable even under identical conditions of adaptation, analogous structures with adequate functioning can be obtained. However, we repeat: elements and simple structures can be repeated as processes, but complex structures cannot; they are unique historical events. For combinations of characteristics, the probability of a duplication decreases as the complexity of the structure increases. The pattern of the lower hominoid molars, as it occurs in classical form among the pongids of the Tertiary and as it was analyzed by Gregory (the Dryopithecus pattern—Figure 28), is basically represented in all the hominoids and has even been found in Oligocene forms such as Propliopithecus and Parapithecus. It is not probable that this so-called Y-5 pattern was arrived at several times independently in the evolution of the higher primates. Based upon this circumstantial evidence, the general pongid theory stands on rather solid ground. However, within the pongids a special type of dentition occurs. The Dryopithecines of the Miocene already show the fully developed version of it.

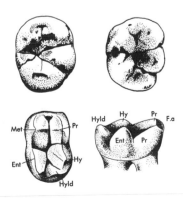

FIG. 28 The Dryopithecus pattern of lower molars in hominids. Below: Dryopithecus; above: *Homo* (schematic).
Hy = hypoconid   Pr = protoconid
Met = metaconid   Hyld = hypoconulid
Ent = entoconid

The teeth of *Sivapithecus sivalensis,* from the Siwalik Hills in India, are a beautiful example of this type of teeth (Figure 29). The most important characteristics of this dentition can also be observed among recent pongines (orangutans, gorillas, chimpanzees): relatively large, oblique incisors; dagger-shaped canines; pronounced gap (diastema) between the incisors and the canines of the upper jaw (for the locking of the lower canines); first premolar with only one (exterior) cusp and a cutting edge running forward and down from the tip of the cusp (sectorial tooth type); the cutting edge and the canine of the upper jaw forming a scissors arrangement (heteromorphous canine group); parallelism of the straight row of teeth from the tip of the canine to the third molar; simian shelf (bony bridge of the inner chin angle), etc. Compared with the jaws of pronounced hominids these characteristics represent extraordinary differences. They are so great that it is difficult to visualize this specialized and naturally adaptive dentition as a starting point for the hominid teeth.

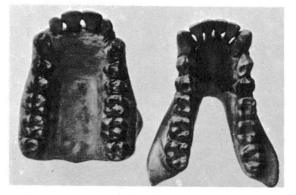

FIG. 29   Teeth of *Sivapithecus sivalensis,* Tertiary pongid of the Miocene–Pliocene era, Siwalik Hills, India (after Gregory and Hellman).

The pongid dentition is historically old and has been stable up to the present. It is known to have existed for 20 million years. It is unlikely that this phyletic stability should have been abandoned in the Upper Pliocene and replaced by a phase of considerable evolutionary changes leading in a relatively short time, still in the Pliocene, to the hominid teeth, for, in the post-Villafranchian, or Lower Pleistocene, about 800,000 years ago, we find this fully matured type among the oldest verifiable hominids, the Australopithecines. If, on the other hand, we derive the typical pongid and the typical hominid teeth from an indifferent intermediary structure, we can go back as far as the Miocene, an era in which there were generalized optional brachiators among the pongids but not yet any long-armed brachiators. Many other factors would lead one to assume that the hominids did not go through an extended brachiator and primeval-

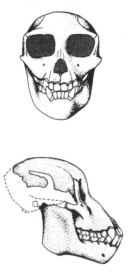

FIG. 30 Cranium of *Proconsul africanus* (reconstructed by Robinson). Newer studies will probably shorten the muzzle somewhat.

FIG. 31 Life image of *Proconsul africanus*. British Museum (Natural History) (after Oakley and Wilson).

forest stage. Before they acquire their bipedal walk, our children crawl with their fingers extended more like pronograde monkeys. They place the palm of the hand on the floor and do not use the "knuckle walk" of the great apes. The brachiator hypothesis would seem rather improbable in spite of the apparent relationship between pongines and hominines and in spite of the close serological agreement between the two groups.

The protocatarrhine hypothesis also seems weak in comparison to the prebrachiator hypothesis, for the serological relationship between pongines and hominines is too obvious. It is a forceful argument against any attempt to derive the hominids from a not yet pongid, protocatarrhine ancestor. Even the remaining hypothesis, the prebrachiator, is left considerable leeway in time, and on the segment of Figure 27, in fixing the phylogenetic point of separation for the hominid branch. For the time being, without any special reason, we will fix this point in the center of the Miocene. We do not know where, geographically, this might have happened (the problem of the native area). Only one such native area can be assumed. Is it Africa, northern India, or central Asia?

The structure of the true ancestor can likewise be reconstructed only hypothetically (something that has been tried several times since Darwin's work on descent). Today, we have fossil records which were lacking in those days and even in the first few decades of the twentieth century. Since the end of the 1940's we have been in possession of fossil discoveries from the Lower to the Middle Miocene strata of the Victoria-Nyanza Basin (in Kenya). They consist of strangely primitive hominids that appear to have been capable of further evolution, the proconsulines (the best-known form being *Proconsul africanus,* Figure 30). We have been familiar with them since the publication of Le Gros Clark and Leakey's monograph in 1951 and since the additional discoveries of fossil extremities. These extremities especially have given us a good deal of new information about this group (Figure 31 represents a reconstructed life image of this type).

The most recent study indicates that this type was endowed with a hand and arm which would have enabled it to climb very well in brachiating style without being a structural brachiator. We feel that we can use these proconsulines as a model for a hominoid evolutionary level, from which one evolutionary line would lead to the typical brachiator via the dryopithecine stage into the ecological niche of the tropical rain forest. The remainder of this line is made up of the recent pongines, whose biotope (habitat) has all the earmarks of already being a refuge area. (It should be remembered here that all the non-brachiating pongids of the past have become extinct.) Another evolutionary line may have started out from a proconsuloid form in a more open, lightly wooded savanna leading to an adaptation to life on the ground involving the acquisition of bipedalism in a strongly ortho-selective process. The hominid hand is a typical grasping organ which could have evolved only in the arboreal phase of the catarrhine phylogeny. The human foot has evolved from a grasping foot. This follows from its structure as well as from the fact that the hand is a grasping hand, since it is safe to assume that the hand was so adapted in an arboreal biotope. The grasping foot is still clearly recapitulated in human ontogenesis (Figure 32), whereas the suggested recapitulation of the limb proportions of a brachiator is quite questionable.

A constitutionally proconsuloid ancestral type without the proconsuline specializations, for instance, with respect to teeth, may have existed at the base of the decisive dichotomy of the hominoids in the Lower Miocene or slightly earlier or later. After all, there might have been adaptive radiation in the forest biotope on the one hand, or the grassland biotope on the other, with trends toward brachiation or trends toward bipedalism, the pongid line, and the hominid line, respectively. One has the impression that this second hypothesis has greater validity than the first, not to mention the third. On the grassland, the trend toward bipedalism permitted the successful group in the AHT to cross over toward the human hominids. In the course of the long journey involved in the acquisition of the erect walk, many things certainly happened. They can only be visualized by way of reconstruction, as will become apparent in the discussion of the first hominids (Australopithecines). Is there any documentary (fossil) evidence for the period between the assumed proconsuloid (loosely conceived) ancestral model and the AHT, entailing a spread of some 15 million years and perhaps a chain of 400,000 generations?

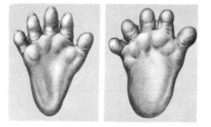

FIG. 32   Recapitulation of the grasping foot in the ontogeny of man. Left, the foot of a Rhesus (23 mm. seat height); right, the foot of a man (24 mm. seat height), adjusted for same length (after A. H. Schultz).

With this question we enter an ever-changing but much more fascinating area of research. The discoveries of Baccinello (at Grosseto, in Tuscany) originate in the Pontian (the lowest Pliocene, or, in the French scale, the uppermost Miocene). They involve a curious form designated as *Oreopithecus bambolii*, a problematical primate known since the late 1860's. Since 1949 it has again attracted a great deal of attention because of the morphological analysis and reappraisals of Hürzeler. Numerous fossil pieces consisting of craniums, jaws, extremities, and teeth are available, although in somewhat fragmentary condition. Since 1958 a full skeleton has been added. On the time scale, Oreopithecus falls between Proconsul and the Australopithecines. Oreopithecus is thought to be 10 to 12 million years old. Its structure is thought-provoking, for it possesses a complex of characteristics that are difficult to place. Experts such as Hürzeler, Heberer, Kälin, Pivetau, A. H. Schultz, etc., are of the opinion that Oreopithecus is an early hominid from the subhuman phase. Others, Königswald, Remane, Vallois, etc., consider it a cercopithecoid form, a pongid form, or a newer form between the two.

The typical two-cusped first lower premolars (Figure 33), the curved row of teeth (Figure 34), the absence of diastema (compare the straight rows of teeth with the diastema of the pongids), would characterize it as a side branch of the hominids. The skeleton shows slender extremities but without the typical brachiator's proportions. The pelvis seems to have had very large ilia; the vertebrae of the thigh region were very strong; perhaps

FIG. 33   First lower premolar of *Oreopithecus bambolii* (left) and chimpanzee (right) (after Hürzeler).

there was a beginning preference to use the lower extremities for loco-motion. All the above-mentioned characteristics in themselves would not justify a hominid designation. But, when combined, they gain in weight with each additional characteristic that is recognized as hominid (for example, the longitudinal diameters of the tooth crowns act as in hominids), and it becomes increasingly improbable that a similarly com-plex hominid group of characteristics could be found outside the hominid line.

FIG. 34   Left row of teeth in the upper jaw of *Oreopithecus bambolii* (mirror image) (after Hürzeler).

If we assume that Oreopithecus is indeed an early hominid, it would have the following significance:

1.   The independence of the hominid genealogical line would thus be documented as far back as the Miocene-Pliocene line, a time in which no structural brachiators are found. This is a new piece of circumstantial evidence against the brachiator hypothesis.

2.   Oreopithecus would be the first stratigraphically secured Tertiary hominid. Its type would correspond approximately to expectations.

3.   Oreopithecus shows a number of specializations; it is characterized as an inhabitant of the swamp-forest biotope (coal swamp of Baccinello) and is a side line the trend of which does not go in the direction of the AHT.

Aside from Oreopithecus, we have no other fossil records from the subhuman phase of the hominid phylogenesis. But this situation will change. We can expect that the present scarcity of early hominid fossil records will be overcome. Such records may in the near future provide the documentary basis for well-founded theoretical developments. The steady increase of fossil evidence, especially after the war, would seem to justify this optimism, as witnessed by Leakey's discovery, in 1961, of *Kenya-pithecus wickeri*.

All three groups of hypotheses about the phylogenetic derivation of the hominids are forced, of course, to have them enter the AHT at the end of the subhuman phase as fully bipedal forms. The problems surrounding the ancestral form with which the hominid line got started are of less significance when we are concerned with the conditions of the AHT. Two questions are especially prominent:

1.   When may we designate a hominid as human?

2.   Are there any fossil discoveries of hominids that might just fit the critical borderline subhuman/human?

With K. P. Oakley, we feel that recognition of a hominid as human in this phase depends not merely on the physical, anatomical state of the brain and brain size, but also on the functions of the brain as well as they can be judged from archaeological evidence—that is, from the shapes of tools to the extent that they can accurately be determined to be tools, namely objects created by hominids for a definite purpose. This is difficult under some conditions, and it is sometimes impossible to come to a meaningful decision. The human hominids have been defined as toolmakers. We make use of such definitions, for brain size alone in this critical phase is not the only possible evidence as to the functional possibilities of the brain.

On the time scale, the AHT falls in the Upper Pliocene (Figures 26 and 27). So far there have not been any paleontological discoveries of Pliocene hominids, if we disregard the Oreopithecus problem. In recent times Pliocene artifacts have been described, but they have not been generally accepted. Some pebble tools are believed to have originated in the Villafranchian period. Theoretically there would not be any objection to recognizing them as such. The first Pliocene datings of Australopithecines which are presumed to have already passed beyond the AHT have been proved erroneous. We therefore indeed do not have any fossil records from the Pliocene. But we will find that the anatomical type of the Australopithecines is such that they can serve as structural models of AHT hominids. At the same time they are apparently the starting point of the great radiation of the genus *Homo* which is so characteristic of the Pleistocene (see Paleoanthropology).

Australopithecines have been known to us since 1924 (from Taung, in the Transvaal). We now have also located them in East Africa and eastern and southeastern Asia. Today we have the fossil remains of well over 100 individuals.

They were beyond any doubt bipedal forms with an essentially fully differentiated erect walk. So far five pelvic fragments have been found. The shape of the ilia corresponds closely to the human form and is distinct from the ilia of semi-orthograde pongids or pronograde great apes. The vertebral column is typically human in being lordotic, and because of its width and curvature as well as the backward shift of the gluteal muscles, it has the prerequisites for facilitating the erect walk and the vertical body posture. The human structure of the pelvis has been verified; Figure 35 permits comparison of the morphological findings in pongids and orthograde hominids.

The extremities are known to us only in a fragmentary way, but they should not differ much from those of the genus *Homo*. The oldest available extremities belong to *Homo erectus* (Pithecanthropus-Sinanthropus group) of the Lower and Middle Pleistocene and they differ very little from those of today. This is indicative of the great stability of orthograde bipedalism and its anatomical basis. Even if we did not know the Australopithecines—and this was the case with respect to most of the postcranial skeleton until after World War II—the early beginnings of bipedalism would have to be placed in the Pliocene period. In the Australopithecine skeleton the cranium was carried almost at the center of gravity, balanced on top of the vertebral column; its ratio of neurocranium to visceral cranium was about the same as that of recent pongines.

The best-preserved cranium (without the lower jaw, which, however, is well known from other discoveries) originates from a form previously designated as Plesianthropus V (*Australopithecus africanus* would be preferable—see Paleoanthropology: Figure 77, Ia, b) and was found in Sterkfontein near Johannesburg. Figure 36 indicates these proportional similarities clearly. The similarity might even have been greater if the cranium of a female chimpanzee had been used, inasmuch as Plesianthropus appears to have been a female specimen. However, this outward similarity does not justify the conclusion that the Australopithecines were descended directly from typical pongine ancestors. The analysis of the morphological characteristics of the cranium and the teeth proves the Australopithecines to be typically hominid and not at all pongid.

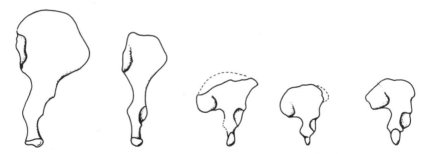

FIG. 35 Comparison of the pelvis (ilium) of pongids and hominids. Left to right: gorilla, chimpanzee, Paranthropus, Australopithecus, *Homo* (Bushman) (after Le Gros Clark).

Just the same, it is true that there are certain ties with the pongids as there are for recent hominids. Were they lacking, we would have no reason to postulate the superfamily Hominoidea. And if the Australopithecines, as older hominids, demonstrate this relationship more pointedly here and there, it is quite in line with expectations, as they are structurally a relatively old type. It is feasible to compare them with recent pongids, but one should not conclude that because of their greater similarity to them they are more closely related to them. That would be a superficial conclusion. They are only more closely related to the corresponding ancestral forms of the pongids, owing to the backward convergence of the pongid and hominid lines toward a common ancestral root, where, of course, there is identity. One can compare only commensurable factors; otherwise gross mistakes and faulty conclusions are the likely result. This is methodologically important, but is not always observed. The similarity

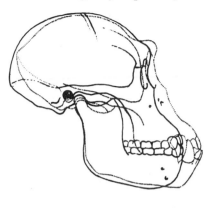

FIG. 36 Comparison of proportions of the craniums of chimpanzee (dotted line) and *Australopithecus transvaalensis* (solid line) (after Heberer, 1956).

between the Australopithecines and the hominines is visible in both their deciduous and permanent dentition. The peculiar and historically stable dental arch, which was already evident in the Miocene pongids (Figure 29, *Sivapithecus sivalensis;* Figure 37, recent pongines), coupled with parallel rows of teeth, which might even converge slightly backwards, is not present in Australopithecines. The arch corresponds there to that of the hominids. In pongids we find the heteromorphic canine group in the lower jaw. In Australopithecines, as in all known members of the genus *Homo,* and already in the Oreopithecines, the first premolar has been molarized and is bicuspid with a relatively large interior cusp. The canine is not dagger-shaped, but has the form of a spatula with the largest diameter of the crown through the middle and not at its base, as in pongids. Thus, the Australopithecines as well as the hominines have a distinctly homomorphic canine grouping. Naturally, the diastema is typically lacking. Occasionally, there are pongids that show a strong interior cusp on the first premolar, but this is not typical; it reflects a not unexpected potential for variation. Such individual variations are not taxonomically conclusive; intergeneric comparisons can be made only with statistically significant series. This also applies to the discussion on Oreopithecus.

There is general agreement that the Australopithecines are hominids. But the question remains: In what phase of hominid history did they arise? Geologically, they are relatively young. With the possible exception of one specimen from Tchad yet to be described, they are all post-Villafranchian (basal Pleistocene) and may be no more than 800,000 years old. In Java, Australopithecine specimens (Meganthropus) also go back to the late Lower Pleistocene, and the same may have been true in China.

The Australopithecines possessed a relatively small brain, though larger (just a trifle) than that of pongines and just about reaching the lower hominine values with their largest sized variants. It should be considered here that brain volume cannot be compared as such, but should be contrasted with body weight. If a gorilla's brain reaches a volume of 685 cubic centimeters, it goes along with a body weight of about 550 pounds; if an Australopithecine brain reaches 700–800 cubic centimeters, it contrasts with a body weight of at most 175 pounds. In especially large-jawed (megagnathous) Australopithecines—the Paranthropus group—the relatively small cerebral cranial surface was too small for the powerful chewing muscles. Thus a median sagittal crest (Figure 38) developed. It was not a phylogenetic reminiscence of crest-bearing ancestors, for such sagittal crests are always found—in other animals as well—if the surface of the cranium is relatively small and the chewing muscles relatively large ("Enantio-plastic," after Mollison). The morphology of the Australopithecine crests is different from that of the pongids. They are analogous functional formations which are lacking in weak and female specimens. Especially large jaws and teeth have been found in Middle Pleistocene deposits in China, and it was at first alleged that they belonged to a megasomatic type—giants (Gigantopithecus). However, it has been shown that the large-jawed paranthropines among the Australopithecines were not megasomatic, but only megagnathous, and it is possible but unlikely that the Chinese "giants" belong to the Australopithecines rather than to the pongids as currently believed.

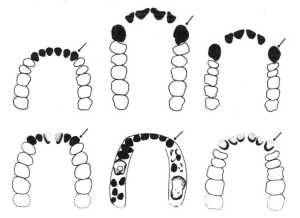

FIG. 37   Dental arches (upper jaw) of pongids and hominids. Upper left, *Homo* (Australian); middle, orangutan; right, chimpanzee. Below, three examples of Australopithecines (after Le Gros Clark).

CRANIAL CAPACITIES OF THE HOMINOIDEA (values in cm³)			
Group	Minimum	Mean	Maximum
Hylobatidae	80	95	140
Ponginae	290	450	685
Australopithecinae	450	600	750 (?)
Homo erectus	775	1000	1280
Homo sapiens	850	1300	2100

(After Keith, Oakley, and Coon)

The large jaws and molars of the Australopithecines still provide a structural model for the morphological state representing the AHT, although after the AHT they have to be eliminated from the direct genealogical line of the hominines because of their relatively young geological age as well as because of the specialized form of their teeth. The oldest of the human hominids probably looked like them in many respects. The psychic status of the Australopithecines seems to have corresponded to their morphological structure in certain interesting and characteristic ways. Their cranial capacity was sufficient to represent an early toolmaker stage, but for the time being it cannot be decided whether they produced tools or whether they only made use of naturally available objects. The latter must have been the case for quite some time during the subhuman phase; otherwise, the morphological structure of the Australopithecines could not be explained. Thus this structure also supplies proof that from a psychic viewpoint they also belonged to the human phase. They did not possess special protective or aggressive adaptations (teeth), nor adaptations for escape and had to compensate for the lack of these with brain power. Even if it should become evident that the Australopithecines did not manufacture tools intentionally in order to perform certain technical tasks, we can still regard them as models of the oldest human hominids. At the present time there is no unanimity on this question. The osteodontokeratic culture (bone-teeth-horn) as postulated by Dart at the fossil site of Makapan is controversial and the discoveries of true pebble tools and choppers of the Oldowan type in strata containing the remains of Australopithecines could indicate that they were not the hunters but rather the hunted. Yet there is no reason to deny them the capability of producing tools. Their intellectual capacity would have been adequate. But they did not yet use fire. Of course, fire is no criterion for distinguishing humans from subhumans, since it came into use rather late in the human phase. Even today the oldest evidence of the use of fire goes back to the famous discovery of Sinanthropus in Chou Kou Tien, dating back 300,000 to 400,000 years.

The course of the primate phylogeny has repeatedly been marked by adaptive radiations (Figure 26). Whenever a favorable type was reached or a new adaptive level was achieved, such radiation occurred from that base. The Miocene pongid radiation was the last one, and from it numerous fossil branches in Europe, Asia, and Africa have resulted. The hominids formed one branch. They escaped the one-sided adaptive isolation of the biotope of the tropical rain forest by moving into the grasslands during the Miocene-Pliocene era. Compared with the pongine brachiating forest specialists, the bipedal terrestrial hominids represent an open ecotype that adapts with the greatest plasticity, without any basic structural anatomical changes, to numerous special niches of its almost universal biotope. The combination of an erect walk, freedom of the hand, and cerebralization, with its functional correlations, provides the basis for the ensuing hominization. All this had been achieved in the Australopithecines. Their body, as represented in the attempt at reconstruction in Figure 39 (all the physiognomic aspects are, of course, hypothetical), was such that if there had been no compensation for their physical shortcomings through brain power, survival would have been impossible. This is the reason why the Australopithecines hitherto have been considered the most nearly original human hominids from the standpoint of structure. Since they differ from the higher hominids morphologically, they are classified as a separate subfamily (Australopithecinae), while the higher hominids are designated as Homininae.

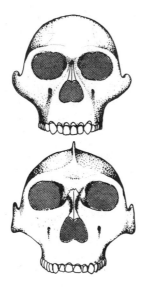

Fig. 38 Presently known types of Australopithecines. Above, Australopithecus; below, Paranthropus (freely drawn after Robinson).

The hominids had reached an extraordinarily adaptive level, from which the hominine radiation of the Pleistocene started (see Paleoanthropology). The Australopithecines thus are models for the physical

FIG. 39   Reconstruction of life image of *Australopithecus transvaalensis*. British Museum (Natural History) (after Oakley and Wilson).

image of mankind in the AHT and so to speak form the end of the hominization of the first human hominids. True human mankind is likely to have started from a basis not far removed from this model.

The physical history of the hominids has been paralleled by their psychic history. The physique and the psyche correspond; they are complementary phenomena. We expect that the functions of the brain mirroring the psychic side of life did not go through macroevolutionary saltations any more than did the physical, structural aspects. There must have been an analogously slow microevolutionary change. Both sides are expressions of a third element which in essence escapes our definitive powers.

THE FORMATION OF RACES

Racial formation is the microevolution of two or more essentially if not wholly isolated human communities into stocks which differ in gene frequencies and phenotypic characters. The how and why of the process are discussed in part in Population Genetics.

The replication of genes through generations is the predominant tendency of living organisms in reproduction. Yet, the steady trickle of spontaneous mutations, the recombination of available genes via sexual propagation, and the distributive mechanism of meiosis continuously provide a quota of novelties. Given enough time, selection and isolation will lead to evolution. Small changes in gene and chromosome are important from a genetic and evolutionary standpoint. They do not seriously challenge the tendency toward identical reproduction, and they do provide a measure of new combination possibilities, which the organism can use to make tiny adaptive steps. With population expansion these mutations, in concert with environmental changes and new living conditions, permit a slow evolution. Polymery and pleiotropy, as much as gene linkage, see to it not only that one favorable characteristic is selected, but that an entire interchangeable series can be accumulated. This may be important in distinguishing genotypes. The significant factors involved in the formation of races will now be discussed briefly.

Selection

Each genetic population, as each individual, lives in a given environment. It must adapt to the existing living conditions—climate, available food (which includes man's ability to hunt and to gather fruits), available space, the requirements of similar competing populations; general dangers to life (disease, carnivores, etc.), and social success within the community. Survival in any environment is only possible for those groups which manage to squeeze by or face all ·potential dangers and adversaries and still manage to produce sufficient offspring. The unsuited, weak, or sick individuals are either quickly eliminated or steadily reduced by a lower propagation rate. With more complex civilization and culture, man opens up ways, often because of social and political pressures, to guarantee existence to an ever-increasing proportion of partially inferior individuals, which results in increased populations regardless of the available food supply. Under the hard conditions found in nature, normally only those gene-carriers of a population remain as potential parents that manage to brave the sharp struggle for survival. The limited food supply available within walking distance normally limits the maximum size of the population, keeping it relatively small. All concrete evidence points toward the fact that, even with high birth rates, in the past only a small percentage of children actually managed to reach sexual maturity.

Whereas competition for a sex partner often adds more selective pressures within an animal population, this is not applicable to man to the same extent. On the other hand, we should not overlook the fact that a certain proportion of men managed to make available to themselves several females for the purpose of propagation. And, if we can judge from a study of living hunting peoples, the best hunter got the most women. All else equal, those parents that managed to provide the most food were able to raise the most children (see Cultural Anthropology).

Although food-gathering communities are necessarily small because of the available food supply, they are rarely completely isolated. Usually a number of such communities live side by side in a single environmental area. Trade, annual meetings held to conduct ceremonies and to initiate the young, and even warfare provide mechanisms for peripheral gene flow between them.

A community which is completely isolated faces the possibility of eventual extinction because most genetic mutations are unfavorable and the statistical chance of the appearance of a favorable mutation is small. However, complete isolation is rare. If a large number of such communities are in peripheral genetic contact with each other, there is a much greater chance of the appearance of a favorable mutation and this will eventually spread throughout the area. If the pressure imposed by the changing environment upon all the communities which comprise the regional population is severe, the mutation will spread with corresponding rapidity. This entire process is, as we have known since Darwin's time, natural selection.

In man, natural selection takes two forms, adaptation to the external environment, and adaptation to living in communities. Adaptation to the external environment has not gone as far in man as in many other animals because of his capacity to invent substitutes in the form of fire, shelter, and clothing. Nevertheless, human beings are still exposed to extremes of heat, cold, humidity, altitude, sunlight, and special diseases, and some races are better adapted to environmental extremes than are others. Such adaptations explain many of the differences in skin color, eye color, hair form, facial features, body size, and body proportions found between major human subspecies and within their component local races.

Adaptation to community living is concerned primarily with the nervous and endocrine systems. In the earliest period when *Homo* had parted company from the Australopithecines and had begun to live by hunting, hunting required group activity, a sexual division of labor, communication, leadership, and rules governing sexual behavior. These requirements favored higher intelligence and self control. Mutations favoring leadership and success at hunting must have spread rapidly as the most competent males acquired the most women.

Adaptations to climate are necessarily limited to the climatic regions concerned. The present distribution of races seems to contradict this statement, but it does not, really, because the migrations of Europeans, Negroes, and Asiatic peoples into the New World and elsewhere have only taken place during the last three or four hundred years and there has been insufficient time for selection to have taken its toll.

Adaptations to group living, on the other hand, have little to do with geography, as they benefit mankind as a whole. The mutations which produce them can spread from one major subspecies to another and undoubtedly did so in the period when the ancestors of the living subspecies were evolving from *Homo erectus* to *Homo sapiens,* and these exchanges and selections are still going on.

It has been noted by some authors that man is a slow-breeding animal, with a reproductive interval of 20 to 25 years for each generation. This fact need not, however, have slowed down the pace of human evolution. Other large animals, like the elephant family, are also slow breeders, but they evolved rapidly during the Pleistocene. In fact, the larger an animal is the more exposed he is to environmental selection, and the generation interval is thus compensated for. Human evolution was neither slow nor, as some believe, unnaturally rapid. Selection has operated in our genus and species as in other animals, and is still going on.

Selection pressure is governed by the existing environment, which is by no means static over long periods of time, but changes steadily and slowly, or periodically with the seasons. Rhythmical changes, the switch from warm to cold periods (ice ages), played an important role in the special development of man (see Paleoanthropology). Under their influence, the climatic zones, and with them the animal and plant worlds, were moved back and forth over entire continents. Man probably followed this relatively slow shift by choosing his hunting grounds and the more desirable living conditions within the limits imposed by the narrowing of the useful climate zones, and according to the availability of space under prevailing conditions of population density. The reason for the disappearance of Neanderthal man after the first period of the last Ice Age (Würm I and I-II) in Europe is an unsolved mystery. In its final phase it could have been determined by his being pushed into unfriendly environments by an expanding Upper Paleolithic population.

In the living races of man, adaptations to environment are mostly concerned with the soft parts, particularly the skin, blood vessels, hair, eyes, and the blood itself. Although we can never be sure of the skin color or hair form of any fossil man before the Upper Paleolithic, we can make certain inferences about environmental adaptation from the skeleton. In Sinanthropus and in the European Neanderthals, foramina in the facial and mandibular skeleton are large and in many cases multiple, assuring a considerable blood flow into the face to keep it from freezing. This same feature is found in modern Eskimo skulls. In the European Neanderthals a prominent nasal skeleton with a large internal chamber was probably concerned with warming inhaled air, and a combination of short lower leg segments and short, broad feet are reminiscent of modern Lapps and Fuegian Canoe Indians.

Isolation

A race is a group of individuals who belong to the same reproductive community, and are characterized by the possession of certain genes that differ from those of corresponding populations of the same species. The original gene pool of a population is steadily, but very slowly, enriched through mutations, of which only a limited number will survive selection pressures over the long term. For the accumulation of favorable (partially new) genes within a population to an extent that might become characteristic, restriction of propagative activity for a certain time is necessary, so that the gene flow between it and neighboring genetic populations is stopped. This process is called isolation. Its result depends largely on the duration and the severity of the mating restrictions—how long the gene flow in and out of the propagation circle is actually stopped. This leads us to a prerequisite for the formation of a race. It is not possible for several new races to develop sympatrically—that is, from the same original population and simultaneously in the same geographic space. The formation of a race can occur only allopatrically—that is, in separate living areas, or isolates. The original population, just before splitting into daughter populations which in turn become isolated, was essentially uniform in the racial sense, and the daughter populations have come out of the same gene pool. Differentiation starts with the actual isolation. If the differentiation continues for a certain span of time and a corresponding number of generations, the phylogenetic direction is established.

The isolation of populations is normally due to geographic barriers—seas, deserts, dry prairies, obstructive forests or tropical-rain-forest zones, edge locations (peninsulas or continental tips). Isolation effects are especially clear-cut on islands, which were only temporarily open to settlement from outside. During the Ice Age, a similar effect was produced through repeated lowering and raising of the ocean level; fluctuations of 300 feet and more occurred. This led to the drying of the shallow waters along the continental edges (for example, at times a land bridge existed from Southeast Asia to Indonesia which reduced the distance by water between the Sunda Shelf and the Sahul Shelf and thus made migration into Australia possible by crossing small bodies of water). The original settlers got to the American continent along a broad land bridge across the Bering Strait. The major geographic regions of the continents display further subdivision into river valleys and the higher-lying hills and mountain barriers, as well as into climate zones in general. The differentiation of *Homo sapiens* into the modern major races and their minor subdivisions has taken place in numerous and greatly varying niches, all opportunities for isolation.

Besides geographic isolation, there is also ecologic isolation. Its effectiveness is based upon the different biotopes (or habitats) present in the same geographic area. Biotopes are governed by differences in elevation, microclimate, and the resulting association of plants and animals, as it occurs, for instance, in an open valley, on thickly forested hillsides, or on the higher barely wooded mountain ranges. According to these biotopes, man patterns his life and, after settling down, finds greatly varying economic opportunities that easily accentuate the separation of populations living in different ecological zones. The less favorable regions tend to serve as refuges for the more primitive economic attempts.

Man has added a few more isolating barriers to the ones already existing for living beings in general; they arise from the association pattern of man (small group loyalties, marriage limitations, taboos) and tribal and language barriers. All are effective only in a limited way, but they contribute to isolation. Under primitive conditions, gene flow was certainly slowed down between the various genetic populations and the resulting ethnic units (see Social Biology).

All these isolating factors combine to make certain genes prevalent within a certain propagation circle, and selective pressures will bring about a number of prominent characteristics that will serve to distinguish neighboring populations. Not all the factors are involved in this process to the same extent (although this would be theoretically ideal). The degree and frequency of possible sexual relationships is not uniform within an isolate. Potential sex partners living at the edge of an isolate have less opportunity to mate with inhabitants of the center, because of the distances involved. Thus, under natural conditions, "pure races" with an entire offsetting combination of characteristics do not occur. Individuals only approximate the typical combination to varying degrees. We cannot compare the degree of "pureness" attained under natural conditions with that which can be obtained by conscious and careful selection in raising animals and plants. The longer the isolation, the greater will be the deviation of the daughter community from the characteristic racial combination of the parent population. The process is concluded when it results in species sterility, when physical isolation is replaced by a biological barrier. Closely related species can then live in the same geographic space, without physical barriers, and continue to remain sexually isolated. In other words, two closely related races that are mutually interfertile will develop into intersterile species if isolated for a long enough period. Human races have probably always been interfertile.

The mechanism of racial formation can be understood only if one realizes that it does not take place according to a formal plan, but by very fluid evolutionary processes, backing and filling through space and time. Different genetic populations did not suffer isolation to an equal extent, selection pressures were not equally great in all cases, and the possibilities of contact between populations were also quite variable. Unequal rates of propagation, overpopulation, and migration have led to an enormously complicated picture of populations that no longer correspond to the distribution of human races at the end of the Pleistocene (see The History of Races). Since then the Mongoloids have expanded into Southwest Asia, Indonesia, and the islands of the Pacific as well as into the Americas, which they had started to invade earlier. The Caucasoids have invaded India, north and east Africa, and, more lately, the Americas, Australia, New Zealand, South Africa, and other regions. Negroes have been carried involuntarily to the Americas and Arabia. Nevertheless, the forces of isolation and selection are still at play and it is unlikely that we will ever see a racially homogenous world.

Racial Characteristics

Among the many genetic factors and characteristics that are typical of *Homo sapiens,* there are certain combinations that, through their distribution and frequency, become characteristic for a subgroup of the species —a race. However, one can find similar mutations throughout the species regardless of race. Thus, mutants for light hair color may occur in more than one race of *Homo sapiens.* The concentration of a distinct combination of characteristics among the populations of certain major geographic areas can only be partially explained by specific selection pressures (climatic adaptations, for example). Some characteristics—varying proportions of trunk and limbs; wide or narrow, high or low face; straight, convex, or concave bridge of the nose; wide or narrow lips; protruding, neutral, or even slanting chin—possess no obvious selective advantages. This becomes especially noteworthy in extreme peculiarities—for example, in the Capoids when the females' breasts are close to the armpits, and the male penis is horizontal.

It is erroneous to believe that the frequency of certain morphological characteristics must be explainable on the basis of special selective advantage. Selection pressure generally tests the total survival value of an organism. Special features may be incidental, or they may be operative only under special circumstances. Selection may favor and accumulate apparently unessential features within an isolate, since these peculiarities are not weighed as such or independently of the survival value of the total complex of genetic factors. Aesthetic evaluations of potential mates might account for some otherwise unexplainable traits. Other usages that have nothing to do with aesthetics can become deep-seated traditions. There are many examples in ethnology. Certain Negro tribes introduce large wooden discs or pegs into the lips of women and girls, which are supposed to protect them from abduction by neighboring tribes or slave traders. These dangers no longer exist, but the disfiguring tradition continues.

The example of body odor again demonstrates subjective differences in what is considered agreeable. A European may find it difficult to endure the body odor of the primitive groups, but the opposite is also true. Natives often cannot stand the body odor of the European. They do not mind saying so and may try to avoid him for this reason. The examples above serve to stress that, within a genetic population, factors other than natural selection may account for certain increased gene frequencies. Furthermore, certain genetic factors are linked together (pleiotropic effects of genes, linkage of certain gene groups on the same chromosome). Selection for one characteristic may automatically lead to increased frequency of otherwise incidental genetic factors.

There are on the earth various zones of definite skin pigmentation, hair color, and eye color. These zones usually involve very large areas and do not have a fixed relationship to the characteristics that distinguish races. This is apparent from the fact that the selective advantage of color values (light, dark, etc.) vary with the climatic zones. Therefore, it is basically false to associate a man with dark complexion with the major race of the Congoids solely on the basis of color. Another major race, the Caucasoids, shows all the color variations from pink-white skin, blond hair, and blue or gray eyes to very dark skin, black hair, and dark eyes. The distribution and the percentage shifts of complexion can be observed in gradual clines, or transitions, without abrupt changes. Among the Caucasoids, the darkest colors are observed at the southern border—in Africa, or in southern India, carrying over to Indonesia, New Guinea, and Australia. This is a good example of directed selection. In northern, northwestern, middle, and eastern Europe, the limited ultraviolet radiation favors the skin with the greater radiation permeability—i.e., the light color mutant, depigmentation—while among the southern Caucasoid races, the selective advantage is on the side of the dark component, which is protective against radiation damage. Among the Mongoloids, the skin is probably less radiation sensitive, and therefore the color differences within this major race are considerably smaller, although there is a trend toward relatively darker colors in southern latitudes. Only the Congoids, a thoroughly tropical race, show a distinct prevalence of the dark component, but not without gradations. The simple example of skin coloring and its dependence upon changing radiation intensities points up the very complex mechanisms at work, because the skin need not respond to radiation intensity with pigmentation changes alone, but has a host of other regulatory mechanisms at its disposal.

In judging the definitiveness of racial characteristics and in applying them to racial analysis, we should never depend upon one or a few distinguishing factors, but should rely upon comprehensive combinations of characteristics. The wide distribution of the dark component of the skin between the twentieth degree of latitude north and south of the equator (Africa, southern Asia, the Pacific) and again further south in Australia, Tasmania, and New Zealand, stresses the likelihood of parallel evolutionary developments (convergence) in the accumulation of some characteristics, if we exclude their origin from a single and uniform source. This can be partially documented by the mode of inheritance of such characteristics. Thus, the epithelial fold of the eyelid of Mongoloids is dominantly inherited, whereas an apparently similar formation among the Capoids is inherited recessively—i.e., it is genetically different, based upon a special mutant gene.

The recognition of a set of characteristics as a genotypical complex is primarily the result of observations by the expert. It is not implied that all these factors have to occur as one solid genetic unit and are inherited as such. On the contrary, the set of features is a composite of largely independently inherited characteristics or groups of such, which, through isolation of the population and specific selection pressures, have been accumulated more than others. This is especially well documented by a comparison of the distribution of the blood groups among the world population and the distribution of races based on external physical characteristics. The distribution of blood groups was surely not uniform among the original genetic populations that led to our modern major races, but neither was one blood group specific to each. In the course of evolution, blood groups have been subjected, independently for each genetic population, to selective forces which did not coincide with the accumulation of external, racial traits. Thus, if we find an above-average agreement of blood-group distribution percentages in races now living far apart, it does not follow that the two genetic populations must necessarily be closely related. Historical connections can only be judged on the basis of the total complex of factors available.

The genotypical complex is composed of a whole series of characteristics—forms, shapes, colors, and qualities—which may differ from individual to individual. Single traits may be used as definitive criteria only if clinal transitions are the result of a directed selection (for instance, color distribution in Caucasoids) or if a morphological trait or complex of traits is continuously and consistently undergoing change from the population center to its periphery. Even strikingly similar single characteristics and traits can be admitted as racial characteristics only within the framework of the total complex. If it occurs at great distance from the main distribution center, only an examination of the pattern of inheritance can shed sufficient light (the manner of inheritance of the epithelial fold of the eyelid in Mongoloids and Capoids). In general, only physical traits are used for judging, since they are objectively measurable as well as statistically comparable. These procedures in themselves, however, are not conclusive either, and must be supplemented by a synopsis of the individual's entire genetic complex.

The results of constitutional research (see Constitution) show clearly that the various types occur throughout the species *Homo sapiens,* and only within limits do they appear to be more frequent in certain races than in others. Classification on the basis of constitutional types leads one to inherited and fixed character complexes, as well as to differences that can be correlated with certain modes of behavior. But as common denominators of the polytypic *Homo sapiens,* constitutional types cannot readily be used for the characterization and differentiation of major races and sub-races, because racial characteristics are associated with evolution between groups, and constitutional types are a reflection of genetic polymorphism within groups. At present, we do not yet know enough about their mutual interdependence. It is probably safe to state that constitution consists of many factor complexes which are inherited but which offer far less opportunity for selective pressures and the differentiating effects of isolation than racial characteristics. Accordingly, constitution will change much more slowly by mutation into racially identifiable traits. Race and constitution do not exclude each other, but overlap.

Mental and psychic behavior (see Racial Psychology) also is subject to inheritance, and thus cannot be excluded from a definition of race. Basically, the intellectual capacities and capabilities of the original racial populations may have been identical. Any concrete, measurable differences in the efforts of the various races toward culture and civilization, and the further differences among ethnic units, cannot be judged by universally binding and objective criteria. Even experimental tests are bound to be biased, because the starting point can never be equivalent. The style of living of communities varies. These social groups have different objectives, and their general behavior is not only the expression of their basic capacities and capabilities, but is colored by tradition. What is done, and toward what end efforts are applied in individual cases, is geared to, or determined by, environmental conditions. Genotypical behavioral traits have probably also been accumulated through selective pressures. Caucasoids can work almost as hard and energetically for short periods in a tropical environment as they would at home. But over the long term, perhaps only those lines would survive that do not overexert themselves under climatic limitations, especially since modern technology can compensate for only part of the paralyzing climatic effects.

Races

We have seen what a diversity of factors contributes to the formation of races and have recognized that a cross section made at any specific time of a genetic population is like a single picture frame on a movie film called "Race Formation—A Continuous Evolutionary Process." Races are essentially processes in the phylogenetic history of species and genera. The various elements and factors that participate in race formation—mutations of genes and individual mutation rates, selection and isolation—are constantly at work. They become apparent in the wide distribution of populations of our species in accordance with the demands of regional environmental conditions. The manifestation cannot be the same for any of the races, because the various populations that split off from the original gene pool of the still undiscovered ancestors of *Homo* were never subjected to the same conditions for the same length of time. His descendants have slowly spread out over the earth, constantly opening up new settling areas and thus exposing themselves to ever-changing selective pressures in varying isolates.

We therefore distinguish a few major races that, to provide a nomenclature, can be termed subspecies, which are themselves composed of a number of varieties. The varieties again can be subdivided into smaller subgroups (local strains). The extent of such subdivision is governed primarily by the anthropological inventory. The inner connection between major and minor subgroups is continuous, and is determined by the available isolates and the range of their effectiveness within which the selective pressures exerted their influence.

Compared with similar processes in the animal kingdom, man encounters special conditions because he is and has been relatively unspecialized. His is a broad ecotype. He can manage to survive in any climatic zone, and is adapted to animal as well as vegetable foods. His relative independence of living and eating restrictions, coupled with great mobility, permits him to cover large distances fairly quickly. These traits, in part, level out racial differences. But man has superimposed additional barriers, which had an opposite effect, even before the epoch of civilization began (see Demography, Social Biology). These barriers contributed to the maintenance of relatively small isolates and, within those, of even smaller marriage circles—special restrictions on marriage, such as endogamy, exogamy, and taboos; tribal and language barriers; class and status barriers. These internal barriers were not in force for long periods, but they prevented or slowed down the gene flow from one genetic population to another. With increasing density of population, however, the barriers became less and less formidable. In man, we have superimposed over the natural genetic populations such new major barriers as nations and peoples, which can contain several races, and more often appear united by a common language, culture, or history. Compared with the natural isolates, they are more fluid and changeable (politically motivated formation of new states, forced migrations, and so forth). They are the image of historic processes, and also the result of the continuous migratory moves of man. They show processes of superimposition as well as displacement. All this tends to complicate the analysis of races or racial mixtures present in the ethnic units, so that it is much more difficult to clarify any of the originally existing conditions. However, in studying the history of the races of man, we can rely upon archaeological finds in the soil, and various relicts in culture, language, and tradition, especially data found in writing or legend. In regions that have been particularly well studied, these findings can be supplemented by series of historic and prehistoric skeletons that inform us about race distribution and race evolution.

We can at present distinguish five major races (subspecies) in our polytypic species *Homo sapiens*—the Caucasoids, Mongoloids, Australoids, Congoids, and Capoids.

Between major races, there are more or less wide contact zones, whose population varieties are ascribed to one or the other major race depending upon the observer, who may judge the available racial characteristics differently according to the sum of major racial criteria. Furthermore, in the contact zones, the distributions of such traits may actually be rendered complicated, as expected, because of population shifts, superimposition, immigration, emigration, and the resulting mixtures and transitions. This is no contradiction of the assumed genetic fixation of racial characteristics, since selection pressures on both sides of the border within the contact zone lead to the accumulation of similar or near-identical characteristics (for example, the dark pigmentation of both Caucasoids and Congoids in Africa). Gene exchange exists because of increasing population pressure as well as the proximity of the races. Over extended periods of time, this situation leads to intermediate stages in the characteristic combinations of factors. Also, the peripheral populations of the contact zones have never intensively participated in the evolution of the factor-complex so characteristic of the nucleus of the major race. Any expansionist pressures from the center will push the peripheral segments of the population further out, so that the opposite racial elements in contact with each other are far less typical varieties to start with. This is especially applicable where so-called old forms have been pushed out into refuge areas. In concluding this subject, it should be stressed that our methodology, as a system, must of necessity be rigid, and thus can accommodate historical evolution as a living process only within limits.

GENETICS AND RACE

Racial typology in the living has been based for the most part on form and color characteristics, especially those that can be easily and accurately determined and are relatively stable with respect to environment. But even the older racial typology sometimes considered the physiological and psychological differences between races, although usually in vague and speculative terms dealing with climatic conditions. The major obstacle to progress in this field is the difficulty of demonstrating the process by which the physiological traits are inherited, and of excluding, in studying particular individuals, numerous modifying factors, such as food, fatigue, state of health, occupation, season, and climate, among others.

By far the most extensive material available concerns serological characteristics. These are, of course, chemical characteristics of the blood, which are investigated by means of biochemical techniques, rather than physiological traits or functions. The blood types are strictly inheritable (see Human Genetics), usually exactly ascertainable from blood samples, and they show considerable regional differences in their frequency distributions and thus constitute promising criteria for distinguishing racial types (see The Formation of Races).

The ABO System (see Human Genetics). The highest proportions of carriers of blood group A are found among the Australian aborigines and among certain Indian tribes of the northern plains of North America; to the east, south, and west of these plains the frequencies drop off very rapidly. Central and South America show the lowest frequencies, with less than 5 per cent of the population carrying this blood type. Frequencies in the Old World fall in between these extremes. In Europe we find the greatest frequencies among the Lapps; the lowest among the Basques, in Iceland, Ireland, and Scotland, and in parts of the Mediterranean Basin (Sicily, Sardinia, Greece).

The highest frequencies for the blood type B occur in eastern and central Asia, including India and a portion of the Malay Archipelago, as well as in the Malay settlements in Madagascar. From the Asiatic center the frequencies decrease on all sides; all of America, Australia, and Polynesia show such small values that type B had been considered non-existent in these areas. Europe shows an east-to-west drop, with the lowest values found on the western coast of the Iberian Peninsula as well as on both sides of the Pyrenees (among the Basques) and among the Lapps.

There is an especially high frequency of the blood type O among the Indians of both Americas. In Europe high percentages are observed in Iceland, Ireland, and Scotland, among the Basques, and in parts of the Mediterranean area (Sardinia).

The MN System (see Human Genetics). The largest percentages (90–95 per cent) of M are found in Central America and the adjoining parts of North and South America. Almost all of the rest of the Americas shows higher percentages than the rest of the earth. The lowest frequencies of M are found in Australia and Melanesia (less than 30 per cent). In Eurasia and Africa, the high values (65–70 per cent) are found in eastern Europe, western and southern Asia (including Arabia, India, Malaya, and Indonesia), and North Africa.

The Rh System (see Human Genetics). The *C* gene is most frequent in parts of Oceania (in New Guinea and the Philippines it is over 90 per cent), Australia (70–90 per cent), the Malay Archipelago, and eastern and southern Asia. Negro Africa is lowest in *C*. In Europe the greatest frequency is found in northern Scandinavia and in a narrow strip running southward to the Mediterranean.

The *D* gene reaches 75 per cent in northern Scandinavia and again in the eastern Mediterranean (Greece, Turkey, southern Italy, Sardinia). The frequencies in northwestern and northern Europe do not attain 60 per cent. The lowest is found among the Basques.

The *E* gene in the New World is distinctly more frequent than in the rest of the world, generally over 20 per cent, and occasionally exceeding 50 per cent. Most of Africa, Arabia, and India show low values (less than 10 per cent). In Europe, in general, the frequency increases from south to north.

Other Blood Groups. Human populations have been shown to differ in several other autosomal allelic frequencies. Among these are the P, Kell, Lutheran, Duffy, Lewis, and Diego blood groups.

At the *P* locus, *P* positive is dominant over the allele for the negative condition, so that individuals of the P positive phenotype are either *PP* or *Pp* in genotype. In general, Congoids show the highest frequency of positive phenotypes (about 84 to 98 per cent). Most Caucasoids range from 70 to 80 per cent. Most Mongoloids are lower. In the Pacific, human populations range from the lowest to the highest extremes.

The Kell locus contains at least 3 alleles, but population studies have simplified this complexity by means of a diallelic distinction: between Kell+ phenotypes who may be *KK* or *Kk,* and Kell— individuals who are homozygous recessive (*kk*). Negative individuals are in the majority of all populations studied. In some Mongoloids and Pacific peoples, everyone is Kell negative. Caucasoids range from zero to 15 per cent Kell positive. Congoids and Capoids are generally on the low side of this range.

The Lutheran locus is also diallelic, with Lu^b dominant over Lu^a. Lu^a is rare in all populations, and nonexistent in southern India, among Capoids, Australoids, and Eskimos. Among Caucasoids it ranges from about 3 to 5 per cent, and in Congoids from about 5 to 10 per cent. In American Indians it is either absent or very rare, but a Brazilian Indian sample attained 8.6 per cent.

The Duffy locus is also diallelic, with Fy^a dominant over Fy^b. High frequencies of Fy^a phenotypes, approaching 100 per cent, have been found in Mongoloids and some Australoids. Most Caucasoids range from 40 to 70 per cent, a Capoid (Bushman) sample is at 12 per cent, and most Congoids range from about 6 to 14 per cent.

The Lewis (*Le*) locus is diallelic, but the positive phenotype *Le* (*a*+) is a homozygous recessive individual. This genotype can always secrete the ABO blood group substance into saliva and other body fluids, whereas the *Le* (*a*—) individual usually cannot. In different human populations, the Lewis and secretor distributions therefore correspond. Extreme variations have been seen in the frequency of *Le* (*a*+) in Australian aborigines: one southern sample showed only 7.3 per cent of these individuals, while a central sample yielded 100 per cent positive persons. Caucasoids generally range about 20 per cent of *Le* (*a*+), American Indians are usually lower, and some Mongoloids from Asia run higher.

The Diego locus has a dominant allele, *Di* (*a*+), which is rare to nonexistent in Caucasoids, Congoids, Eskimos, and Polynesians. In East Asians it is a bit more common, ranging up to 12 per cent in Japanese. Among American Indians it is very variable, ranging from 2 to 45 per cent. Much research on this locus is currently in progress among tribal Indians in South America (Layrisse).

The geographical distribution of the various blood groups is not identical with racial distribution, and the zones often overlap. However, there are some populations that are characterized by special blood-group combinations. The Australian aborigines have very low percentages of B and M, and extremely high values for C; the Basques extremely low D values combined with lower B frequencies and higher O frequencies than those of neighboring regions. All American Indians show strikingly low B values and extremely high values for M and E; in this respect they are quite different from the population of eastern and northern Asia (very high B, low M values), areas from which, presumably, they originally emigrated. Ottenstein, Wiener, and Boyd attempted to classify races ac-

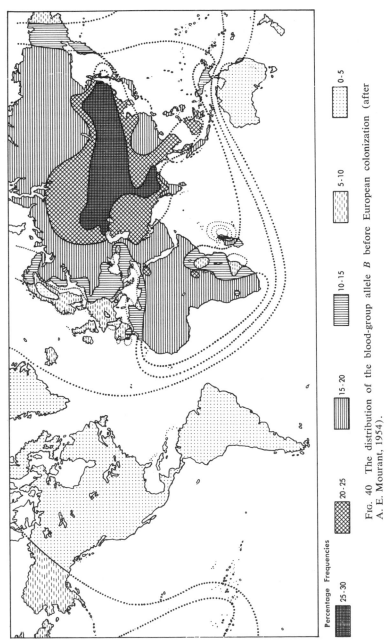

Fig. 40 The distribution of the blood-group allele *B* before European colonization (after A. E. Mourant, 1954).

Percentage Frequencies

0-5

5-10

10-15

15-20

20-25

25-30

cording to serological characteristics, and their major subdivisions were similar to those produced by the morphological-typological approach. (Boyd's groupings were: 1. Hypothetical Old European, 2. European, 3. African-Negro, 4. Asiatic-Mongoloid, 5. American, 6. Australoid.) However, attempts at further subdivisions through the use of additional serological characteristics did not lead to a plausible system.

Blood Diseases

A series of inherited pathological blood traits show great regional and racial frequency differences. The most thoroughly studied of these traits is sickle-cell anemia, a recessive and usually fatal blood disease. The heterozygotes also have the characteristic deformation in some of the red blood cells (shrinking to the shape and size of sickle cells especially if deprived of oxygen), but do not lead to crippling anemia. In America the sickle-cell allele has been found almost exclusively among Negroes, at the rate of close to 9 per cent; it is almost completely lacking among whites. In African Negroes, the frequency fluctuates from zero (among the Dinka, Shilluk, and others) to over 40 per cent (for example, among the Amba and other Bantu-speaking tribes in Uganda). As in America, the sickle-cell gene is completely lacking in the white population of Africa, as well as among the Bushmen. A further center for the gene has been found in southern India, with a frequency of 30 per cent in some tribes (the Paniyan and Irula, for example). Thus it is not exclusively a Negro characteristic, as was previously assumed. Small centers and individual cases have also been reported in Greece and Sicily.

The greatly fluctuating frequency of the sickle-cell gene among the African Negroes is related to the distribution of malaria. The gene almost certainly represents a protection against malarial infestation of the fetus when the mother is heterozygous. We find a high percentage of heterozygotes in regions with endemic malaria, and a low percentage in malaria-free areas. Thus the lower frequency of the gene among American Negroes can be explained by the fact that in non-malarial regions of the New World the heterozygote is no longer favored and the homozygous dominant genotype shows the greater fitness. Over many generations this change in natural selection probably works toward a decreasing frequency of the sickling allele. In America, an additional evolutionary process at work in the Negroids has been hybridization with whites and American Indians, which again works toward a diminished frequency of the sickling allele in the resultant hybrid population.

Thalassemia (Cooley's anemia) occurs primarily in the Mediterranean and among Italian immigrants in the United States. Heterozygotes show much milder symptoms than homozygotes. In Italy the frequencies vary from zero to 10.3 per cent. Although the disease seems to be related to the Mediterranean races, the local fluctuations that have been found appear to be independent of racial differences based on morphological-typological criteria.

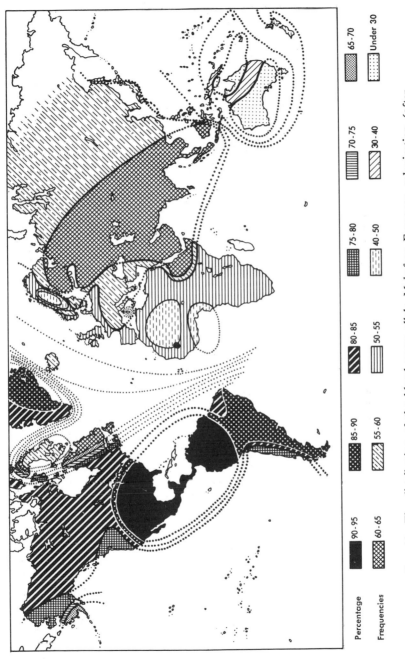

FIG. 41 The distribution of the blood-group allele *M* before European colonization (after A. E. Mourant, 1954).

PTC Tasting Ability

Next in importance are the relatively large-scale studies of tasting ability, especially the ability to recognize the bitter taste of phenylthiocarbamide (PTC). This trait, however, cannot be determined as accurately as the blood groups, for its identification depends to a great degree on a subjective evaluation on the part of the person being tested. Furthermore, the tasting ability can be modified by previously ingested food as well as the subject's state of health and even emotional factors.

In tests with aqueous solutions of varying PTC concentrations, the variation charts of tasters and non-tasters overlap. There are also sexual differences; generally there are more tasters among women (a fact which might be correlated with a lower consumption of tobacco, alcohol, and other stimuli). However, only 5 per cent of the tested persons cannot decide whether they can taste PTC, so that the observed differences in the populations are far greater than the magnitude of error in the test.

The highest percentages of tasters are found in some American Indian tribes; also, among the Chinese, Japanese, and Negroes the percentages are higher than with Europeans, among whom they vary between 58 and 75 per cent.

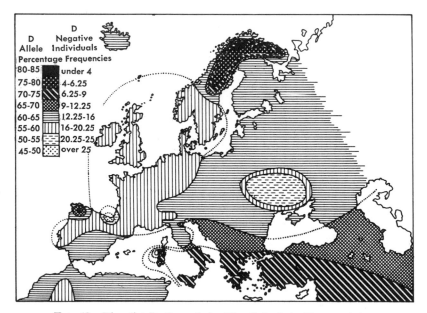

Fig. 42 The distribution of the Rh allele D in Europe (after A. E. Mourant, 1954).

Other Physiological Racial Characteristics

Research with families and twins has demonstrated that many other physiological characteristics are inherited, but it has not been possible to analyze the genes themselves. Since these traits are more subject to environmental conditions than the serological traits or the tasting abilities, it is difficult to separate racial components from mere modifications (see Constitution). Thus there are very few substantiated results. The so-called racial odor is related to the number of sebaceous and sweat glands and the chemical composition of the secretion. Some Japanese, who have fewer and smaller sweat glands in their armpits, describe the odor of Europeans as pungent and rancid, sometimes sweet, sometimes bitter. Under identical conditions Negroes secrete more sweat of higher fat content than whites. This difference may be an adaptation to a tropical climate. Racial differences for basal metabolism have best been established for the Maya, who show amazingly high values in contrast to most primitive peoples, as well as a strikingly low pulse rate. Arabs and white Americans show the same averages in the middle age groups, but a much greater variability is seen in older Arabs. We might find regionally different genetic factors in connection with other metabolic processes. Thus under identical conditions Eskimos excrete less acetone bodies (ketones) through the kidneys than whites after a few days of fasting, a fact which suggests that they would be in a better position to draw upon their own fat reserves should the need arise.

Investigation into the biochemistry of racial differences has just begun. Among other things it has been found that the potassium content of the plasma of whites in both Dakar and Paris is lower than that of Negroes. Important results are expected from research in the field of hormones. So far we know of racial differences only in the absolute and relative weights of endocrine glands; the relative weights of the thyroid glands are smaller in Malays and other Mongoloids than in Europeans. Since many constitutional racial differences (see Constitution), in addition, probably, to many other morphological characteristics, are at least possibly based on hormone metabolism, and since hormones are influenced by the environment (climate, soil, nutrition), the outlook is promising for better insights into the selective processes of race formation.

GROWTH

The fertilized human egg, which is almost spherical, has a diameter of about 0.12 mm. and a weight of around 0.0015 mg.; on the average, the adult body in American males achieves a height of about 67 inches and a weight of 158 pounds, and is a highly differentiated form consisting of a multitude of diverse tissues and organs. The interval between the stages—conception and maturity—is the period when growth takes place. Growth is (1) an increase in mass through cellular proliferation and enlargement, and (2) form differentiation through differential growth rates of the individual body parts. Most of this process occurs before birth.

Fetal Growth

The development of the fetus is directed by genes (see Human Genetics) and gene-dependent determiners and hormones. In addition to an increase in size through assimilation of nutrients, there are other developmental processes: (a) cell migrations and cell shifts, (b) separation (segregation) of the organs, and (c) specialization of the cell structure. In general, the embryo develops from the common characteristics of larger systematic groups toward the specific characteristics of the species, race, sex, and individual. Accordingly, the basic traits of the vertebral body are formed first in the human embryo. The notochord is the primordium of the axial skeleton. Dorsal to it is the primordium of the central nervous system, and the abdominal cavity and the viscera develop in the ventral region. All tissue differentiations go back to three different cellular constituents—the three germ layers. The ectoderm forms, among other things, the entire central and peripheral nervous system. The mesoderm forms the skeleton and the muscle tissues and thus the mass of the body. The entoderm forms the epithelium of the intestinal and respiratory tracts. Several classification systems of constitutional types are based upon this differentiation of the germ layers (see Constitution).

Early in the third month the specific human traits of the embryo can be recognized: the head portion (in the second month, almost as large as the rest of the body) starts to separate from the trunk, the laterally located eyes move closer together, the nose appears, and the extremities begin to look like human appendages. In relative terms, increases in length and weight are most impressive in the first months and become progressively less remarkable toward the end of the prenatal development.

Postfetal Growth

The relatively rapid fetal growth continues during the first year of life; then follows a slower increase in mass and size, followed in turn by an accelerated increase during puberty. On the average, girls remain behind boys from birth to puberty, but since in most populations their puberty starts earlier, they pass boys for 3–4 years; then they fall back again, because their growth is terminated earlier, whereas boys keep on growing for a few more years, so that the sexual differences in size in adolescence are progressive. The double overlapping of increase in length and weight in boys and girls is a usual characteristic of human growth curves based on population averages. The growth in height in girls is terminated at

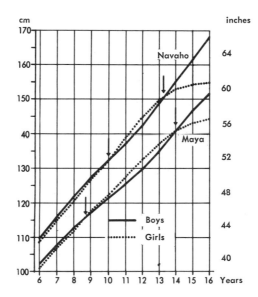

FIG. 43   Growth curves of two racially different populations
(after M. Steggerda, 1941; see also Fig. 48).

18–20 years, in boys at 20–22 years, in samples from prosperous Western
nations.

The ratio of weight to length (index of body fullness, Rohrer index,
and others) decreases from the first year to puberty and increases again
slightly after growth is terminated. As the first change in length-weight
ratio occurs, other changes in proportions are also observed. The relative
size of the head (height of head as a percentage of height of body) decreases during growth; the relative size of the legs increases. The chest
becomes flatter: the thoracic index (chest depth as a percentage of chest
width) drops more in boys than in girls. During puberty the breadth of the
hips shows a different course in boys and in girls; the relative shoulder
breadth (shoulder breadth as a percentage of height) increases in boys
and remains essentially constant in girls. On the other hand, the relative
pelvis width decreases in boys and increases in girls; the index of relative
hip breadth expressed as percentage of the shoulder breadth therefore
shows very clearly the development of sex-specific proportions (see Constitution) during puberty. The facial skeleton increases in proportion to
the rest of the head during the growth period; the face stretches and the
nose increases in height and depth more than in width. Individually, the
beginning and ending of the growth spurts, the annual growth rates, and
the magnitude of the resulting somatic changes vary considerably. From

norm tables, which have to be checked constantly because of regional and secular variations in growth, one can see how much a child differs from the average of his age class. The range of the normal is determined by the standard deviation, sigma; 67 per cent of all the variation falls within the range marked by the simple standard deviation ($M \pm 1\sigma$).

Growth does not stop in the so-called stationary phase after puberty is over, but it gradually becomes almost imperceptible. Growth continues in the longitudinal axis of the head and body until early old age—in men until about 60, in women until 50 years of age. Sitting height, face height, and head length show the greatest growth rates. The body reaches its maximum over-all height early, since the growth of the trunk is compensated for by a decrease in leg length, due presumably to relaxation of the foot structure and an altered neck angle of the upper thigh. The average weight of the adult increases faster than the height, so that the index of body fullness also increases into early old age, but decreases again at a still more advanced age because of loss in muscle volume, weight, and water content of tissues.

Allometric Growth

If the growth rate of one part (y) of the body has a constant ratio in relation to that of another part, or of the total body (x), we can calculate the relationships by means of the formula for allometric growth, letting dy/dx express the relative growth ratio of the two dimensions:

$$\frac{dy}{dx} = a \, \frac{y}{x} \tag{1}$$

integrated:
$$y = bx^a \tag{2}$$

or expressed as logarithms: $\log y = \log b + a \cdot \log x$ (3)

The symbol a stands for the constant ratio of the growth rates y and x (it assumes different values for different measurements of parts of the body); b is a scaling constant, indicating the value of y when x equals 1. In the graphic presentation, a straight line results for $\log y$ according to the allometric formula (3); its angle with the abscissa is determined by the slope constant a ($a = \tan \alpha$). If $a > 1$ (i.e., if y grows faster than x), then the straight line is steep (positive allometry). If $a < 1$ (y grows slower than x), the line is more horizontal and allometry is negative. If $a = 1$ (y and x grow at the same rate), the line is equidistant from the x and y axes, and the proportions do not change (isometry). Often the entire growth period cannot be followed with the same formula and the same line, but has to be described by a series of partial lines with changing angles; the locations where the line is broken are indicative of the influence of new developmental factors. In man, leg length shows positive allometry during the growth period and the height of the head is negatively allometric. During puberty the proportion constant a changes, so that a break occurs in the graphic presentation.

The allometric formula has also been applied to phylogenetic changes of proportions, such as the ratio of brain size to body size in mammals, including man.

Brain size is determined by:

1. the ratio of brain size to body size = constant *a,* and
2. the evolutionary stage of the brain (cephalization) = constant *b* of the allometric formula.

Within the order of the primates, the brain size of man corresponds to his body size, while the pongids—especially the chimpanzee—lag behind expectations; no linear allometric relationship is obtained, but instead there is a parabola of the form

$$\log y = \log b + a \cdot \log x - c \, (\log x)^2$$

For the brain development of man the phyletic increase in size which follows Cope's rule can be regarded as an important factor (see The Descent of Man).

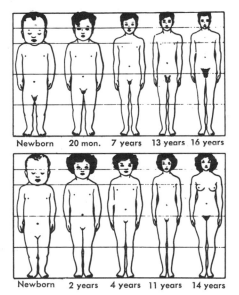

Newborn   20 mon.   7 years   13 years   16 years

Newborn   2 years   4 years   11 years   14 years

FIG. 44   Changes in proportions during growth (after R. W. B. Ellis, based on the material of W. Lenz, 1954).

Sexual Maturation

The phases of growth are determined by various hormonal regulatory systems. In early growth, the pituitary and thyroid are especially important, and perhaps the thymus. Just before puberty, other glands become increasingly active—particularly the gonads. This endocrine change first mediates an acceleration of growth in most body tissues, then a deceleration, and finally a virtual cessation of somatic enlargement. Gonadal hormones are also responsible for most of the primary and secondary sexual characteristics (see Constitution). The somatic signs of maturation in adolescence have been classified by many authors along the following lines:

Boys

Nipple and areola:	Childish—small, flat, non-pigmented
	Transition form—swelling
	Mature—offset, often pigmented nipple
Pubic hair:	Lacking
	Slight
	Downy
	Curly, with horizontal upper margin
	Mature, with pigmented hairs from pubis to umbilicus
Axillary hair:	Lacking
	Slight
	Downy
	Curly
	Fully pigmented
Penis:	Child—usually small and conical
	Lengthened
	Enlarged and thickened
	Mature, with full size and pigmentation
Scrotum:	Child—tight, round, and broad
	Longer
	Enlarged
	Mature, with rippled skin and testes the size of walnuts
Beard:	Lacking
	Abundant downy hair
	Initial terminal hairs
	Mature—fully developed
Voice:	Child—light
	Transition form—change of voice
	Mature—deep and sonorous

Girls

Breast:	Childish—small, flat, nonpigmented as in boys
	Breast bud—swelling of areola and spreading of nipple
	Mound stage—semispherical, concave areola with hemispherical nipple

Breast contd.:	Transition form—beginning of elevation of nipple
	Mature—areola even with concavity of breast, nipple clearly offset
Pubic hair:	Lacking
	Slight
	Downy
	Curly, with rounded borderline
	Mature, with horizontal upper boundary
Hips:	Childish—small
	Beginning curves
	Fullness
Menstruation:	Lacking
	Functional

The stages of sexual maturation follow a fairly regular sequence in each of the areas mentioned above, but appreciable individual variations exist in the interrelationships between areas as they develop. In boys, as a rule, the scrotum enlarges first, soon followed by a lengthening of the penis and the appearance of the first pigmented pubic hair. About a year later, axillary hair follows. The swelling of the male breast usually occurs when the penis and scrotum are close to their full mature size. Still later the pigmented hair of the beard appears.

In girls, the development of breasts and pubic hair begins about two years before menarche. Axillary hair is very variable, but usually is at least incipient at menarche.

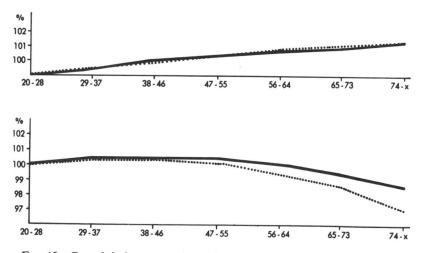

FIG. 45 Growth in later years. The changes in head circumference (above) and stature (below). 100 = average measure at 20 years. Straight line = men, dotted line = women (after Büchi, 1950).

As with stature and weight, deviations from the average timing of these events can be derived from tables of norms. Markedly accelerated or retarded maturation may be of practical importance, since degree of maturity may be highly relevant to success in school or sports, capacity for work, social behavior, interests, and occupation.

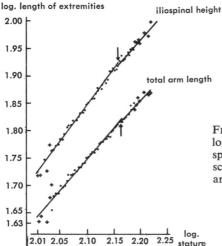

FIG. 46 Allometric growth. Growth of logarithms of arm and leg length (iliospinal height) compared to stature in schoolchildren in Barcelona (after Alcobé and Prevosti, 1951).

Psychic maturation parallels that of the body. In many investigations, low positive correlations (mainly between $+0.1$ and $+0.3$) have been found between psychic and somatic development. These findings concern length and weight measurements, signs of maturity, ossification, and total development on the somatic side, and a diversity of behavioral phenomena such as intelligence quotients, motor control, interests, friendships, ambitions, and sexual behavior. Adolescents who are early-maturing are usually more mature also in their mental and psychological development. Individuals with harmonious somatic maturation generally show a more favorable psychic condition than do those with widely dissimilar stages of development in different regions of the body. The more closely a psychological function or readiness is tied to somatic characteristics, the clearer its correlation seems to be.

Intelligence scores show an age pattern similar to that of growth stature; the maximum is attained at about 20 years. For others, more specific traits, however, maxima occur at various ages. Rote memory reaches its maximum even in childhood, but logical and systematic memory decades later.

Peak efficiency in various sports, arts, and sciences is achieved at clearly different ages. Social maturity is reached after somatic and sexual maturity, but is greatly influenced by the social environment—especially its degree of complexity and its demands upon the individual.

In modern industrialized societies, there is a marked discrepancy between sexual maturity and marriage age. In men, the greatest frequency of orgasm occurs between 15 and 20 years of age, but the marriage age is usually some years later.

The developmental processes of adulthood are largely a *terra incognita*. Since, however, the number of older people has steadily increased due to longer life spans, research in gerontology has gradually emerged— particularly detailed studies of the physical and psychological changes of older people.

Physique and Development

Several developmental changes in body build occur along with changes in proportions and sexual maturation. From infancy onward, the subcutaneous tissue is gradually reduced and the musculature increases in volume. Physiognomic changes include an increasing prominence of the nose, a development of the chin, prominence of the glabella and brow ridges, and a tightening of the cheek and mouth regions.

Zeller has characterized a number of age-specific types of physique, continuing in part where Stratz and others left off. The first change of form occurs between the pre-school and school-age types, the second between the pubescent and mature types.

The main features of the pre-school physique are: relative dominance of the head; a round, cylindrical trunk; little vertebral curvature; relatively small, round, and soft extremities with little emphasis on joints; and a large and convex forehead combined with a small, soft middle and lower face.

The school-age physique shows less dominance of the head; the trunk is more elongated with a flatter chest and broader shoulders; the limbs are longer and slenderer with a greater prominence of the joints; the face constitutes a greater proportion of the total head and looks tighter, leaner, and more sharply profiled, and more alert and objective in attitude toward the environment. Many of these changes result from a reduction of subcutaneous fat in the face, trunk, and extremities.

The pubescent physique shows features transitional between those of the school-age type and the adult (see "Sexual Maturation," above).

In the mature physique, sexual characteristics are fully developed.

The concepts of pre-school and school-age physiques have proved to be useful criteria in studies of readiness for school. On first enrollment in elementary school, children of pre-school physique are relatively retarded psychologically. If instruction is by rote, they more often suffer from difficulties in adjustment which could be prevented largely by postponing their attendance at school.

The pubescent and mature physiques are normally diagnosed by assessing the various criteria of sexual maturation.

Skeletal Age

In addition to somatic measurements and criteria of physical maturation, the teeth and skeleton are also sources of information on the developmental status of a child. In addition, the bones and teeth of children who died in prehistoric times may also be used for determining their age at death. In children, bone age is often determined in order to gain a further variable to be correlated with other findings, such as test scores, deviant patterns of behavior, and others. The first appearance and fusion of centers of ossification follows a regular pattern which is specific for each center, but wide individual variations occur in the interrelationships of the different centers. Of the more than 800 centers which appear during human growth, about half become active after birth. At this age, some of the early centers have already fused. The largest number of bones is found at puberty (around 350). Through further fusions, this number decreases to about 206.

For the diagnosis of developmental stage or age, one chooses different skeletal regions, depending on the age group. For older fetuses and infants, the fontanelles (the gaps between the bones of the cranial vault) are especially informative. The large (bregmatic) fontanelle between the frontal and parietal bones is closed between nine and sixteen months, and its diameter decreases continually after birth. The small (asterionic) fontanelles between the parietal, occipital, and temporal bones and the lambdoid fontanelle between the parietals and occipital are closed in the first few weeks after birth.

Until the second year, the foot and knee are of particular diagnostic value in assessing bone age. Until puberty, the regions most often evaluated are the hand, wrist, and elbow.

The elongation of a long bone terminates when the epiphysial centers of ossification fuse with the shaft and the intervening cartilages are obliterated. Maturity of the cranial base can be defined as the time when the cartilage between the sphenoid and occipital bones is obliterated and the two bones fuse. This gradual change occurs late in the teens.

For the assessment of skeletal maturity in older adults, teeth can be used as indicators, as well as the obliteration of the cranial sutures. This sutural union in man occurs very late, perhaps in connection with the prolonged growth of his brain and its great size. Even in advanced old age, sutural union may not be complete. The stages of this process show some regularity in man, but very wide individual variations occur in its timing. Sutural union is so poorly related to age of death that its diagnostic value in estimating this age in skulls is exceedingly poor.

According to Vallois, the sequence of sutures in which fusion can be observed is usually the following, as shown in Figure 47.

The closure of cranial sutures provides a far less precise estimate of the age of death than do a number of postcranial bones. Most valuable is probably the pubic symphysis, but the scapula and the sternum are among other bones whose detailed age-changes have been worked out.

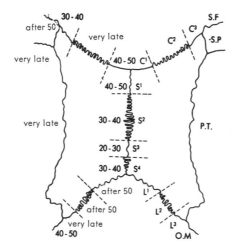

FIG. 47   The age of fusion of sectors of the cranial sutures (after Vallois, 1937). C = coronal suture; L = lambdoid suture; S = sagittal suture; P.T. = squamous (parieto-temporal) suture; S.P. = sphenoparietal suture; S.F. = sphenofrontal suture; O.M. = occipitomastoid suture.

The developmental stages of teeth are also of considerable diagnostic interest. Relevant features here include the formation or calcification of the teeth, their eruption, and the time of shedding or exfoliation of the milk teeth.

The deciduous teeth begin to form during the fourth fetal month and calcify from the cusps toward the apices of the roots. Each tooth is fully formed soon after it completes its eruptive movements, in infancy or early childhood. The first permanent tooth, the first molar, begins to calcify just after birth. Other permanent teeth form later, with some individual variations in their sequence of onset, and the latest teeth (the third molars) begin to form between the eighth and eleventh years.

The sequence of formation and emergence of the deciduous teeth is fairly regular in children. The incisors appear first, then the first milk molar (in the position of the permanent first premolar). Next come the canines, and finally the second deciduous molars.

In the permanent dentition, the first molar appears first in most children. The incisors then replace their deciduous predecessors. During the pubescent years, great individual variations occur in the sequence of loss of the remaining deciduous teeth, their replacement by the permanent canines and premolars, and the concomitant appearance of the permanent second molars. Some years later, the third molars appear, but often fail to form or, if formed, do not emerge into the mouth.

The following diagram indicates the sequence of emergence of teeth ranked according to mean age of emergence into the mouth. Actually, only a very small minority of children follow this order of dental eruption precisely.

Deciduous Dentition

Maxilla	2	3	8	5	10
	dI_1	dI_2	dC	dM_1	dM_2
	dI_1	dI_2	dC	dM_1	dM_2
Mandible	1	4	7	6	9

Permanent Dentition

Maxilla	4	6	12	7	9	3	14	16
	I_1	I_2	C	P_1	P_2	M_1	M_2	M_3
	I_1	I_2	C	P_1	P_2	M_1	M_2	M_3
Mandible	2	5	11	8	10	1	13	15

d = deciduous   P = premolar
I = incisor   M = molar
C = canine

From the skull and dentition, the following age categories may be distinguished:

I Young child (up to 7 years) — Up to eruption of the first permanent molars.

II Older child (7–14 years) — From eruption of first permanent molars to the eruption of second permanent molars.

III Adolescent (about 14–20 years) — From eruption of second permanent molars to fusion of the sphenoid and occipital bones.

IV Adult (about 20–40 years) — From spheno-occipital fusion to the onset of sutural union.

V Mature (about 40–60 years) — Sutural union partial; appreciable wear of crowns of teeth.

VI Senile (over 60 years) — Extensive sutural union, loss of teeth, and closure of alveoli where teeth have been lost.

As mentioned previously, more precise ascertainments of age are possible if details of the dentition and postcranial skeleton are noted.

There are considerable sexual differences in the ossification of the skeleton in childhood, but not in the development of the teeth. Even the fetal centers of ossification appear sooner in girls than in boys, and the same is true of the appearance and fusion of the later centers. At puberty, girls are about two or three years ahead of boys in ossification. The earlier termination of growth in girls is not due solely to an earlier onset of puberty, but is determined before birth by their more rapid skeletal development. The sexual difference in dental development in general is small. Indeed, in the eruption (but not formation) of the deciduous teeth, in some populations boys are more precocious than girls.

The Modifiability of Growth

Among the environmental conditions that can modify growth, nutrition is the most important. Protein-rich food stimulates growth. In Scottish schoolchildren, the yearly growth rate was increased from 1.9 to 2.3 inches after supplementary milk rations were given. In children in an English boarding school, the increase was from 1.9 to 2.6 inches per year. Improved nutrition affects the growth of limb bones and stature, as well as weight, some patterns of ossification, and sexual maturation.

Insofar as the differences in maturity and body size among the social classes are not inherited, they seem chiefly to reflect nutritional differences (see Social Biology). Besides the intake of calories and proteins, fats and vitamins also have important effects on developmental rates.

From experiments with animals it appears that climate—especially temperature—can influence physical growth. At low average temperatures and great fluctuations of temperature, mice will grow larger than control animals raised under higher and more even temperatures.

Other important factors affecting the physical growth of children are stresses and emotional disturbances. Landauer, Whiting, Hunt, and Mavalwala have studied a large cross-cultural sample of non-literate peoples. They note that puncturing of the skin or molding of the head in infancy are associated with tall stature in the adult. A similar phenomenon has been found in laboratory rats. Where suckling rats are rolled between the hands of an investigator, their subsequent growth is stimulated and their size is increased.

In infancy and later childhood, emotional stresses may affect caloric intake and sleep. Infants deprived of love and social contacts may fail to eat, and may even starve (anorexia nervosa). In 1948 and 1949 Binning found that where a child is deprived of a parent through divorce, death, or attempted parental suicide, its growth is retarded and may be permanently stunted. Depressed growth in a child characteristically precedes its admission into a mental hospital. Nearly all workers on progressive obesity in childhood have noted that rejection by friends and family seems to increase eating and inactivity in some children, and aggravates the problem.

Binning even claims that emotional disturbances probably affect the growth of children far more than do most of their infectious diseases. Thus, somatic growth, like many other physiological processes in the human body, intimately reflects the well-being and mental health of the individual.

In man, the extent to which there is a geographical correlation between body size and environmental temperature is uncertain, since the so-called climatic rules (see The Formation of Races) may be obscured by the selection of genetically taller individuals in cooler climates. A slight retardation of somatic development during very hot summers (and in individuals who migrate from cool to hot climates) seems to indicate that climate has a modifying effect on man as well. In northern Europe, the menarcheal age is correlated less with temperature than with the humidity of the air.

Infections and other environmentally induced diseases can hinder growth and development, as has been shown by the analysis of twins. As a rule, substantial differences between identical twins are due to illness in only one twin.

Differences in Growth between Man and Other Vertebrates

Man is characterized by a slow and retarded growth in childhood (see The Descent of Man). The growth curves of various vertebrates are analogous if brought to scale, but for man superimposition is possible only after puberty. Prior to that time, the human growth curve shows a much flatter course than other forms exhibit. The only exception is the rapid growth of the human infant, which is a continuation of the rapid late-fetal growth curve. In this respect, man differs from the pongids (gorillas, chimpanzees, and orangutans). Portman has therefore characterized man as a physiologically premature birth whose fetal growth period ends at the postnatal age of one year. He connects this premature birth with the relatively great postnatal enlargement of the human brain and cranium. Indeed, some of the developmental stages which occur before birth in pongids, such as the acquisition of species-specific locomotion and means of communication, have become parts of the endowment of learned more than instinctive behavior in man (see Cultural Anthropology). A series of other differences between man and the pongids result from quantitative differences in the growth rates of various parts of the body. For example, man lacks the *os centrale* of the wrist, which forms as a separate cartilage in the fetus and fuses with the navicular even before ossification of this region begins. In man, too, the promontory of the sacrum begins to enlarge earlier than in pongids.

Racial Differences

Within the human species, racial differences in the growth of body mass and length are especially evident. Full or mature size may be attained at different ages in different groups, but the growth curves themselves are quite similar. In all races, 75 per cent of ultimate size is reached at nine years, and 95 per cent at 15 years.

In some cases, racial differences in body size arise chiefly during adolescence. For example, in San Francisco, Japanese boys are as large as white boys of the same age until the age of 15. Thereafter, they fall increasingly behind the whites. The shape of their average growth curve is closely similar to that of Japanese boys in Japan, but at least from 6 years of age onward, the boys raised in California are consistently 1.5 inches taller. Nutrition seems to be the major reason for this difference.

Many of the racial peculiarities of body proportions and traits arise through differential growth rates before birth. At the same time, the formation of other generally human somatic characteristics takes place. Thus, Negro fetuses of the third month show a smaller height of the cranium, a broader nose, smaller hips, longer arms, and greater length of the forearm than do whites, in much the same way as the adults differ. Negro babies show earlier ossification than do whites, and are also more precocious in motor development. Negroes are not precocious in all respects, however. They tend toward lower body weight at birth and in early infancy, but the interpretation of later growth in most Negro populations is not simple because these children so often suffer from malnutrition.

Most of the older data on rates of maturation in different populations should be rechecked—particularly the alleged early maturity of tropical peoples. In the regional differences in menarcheal age, the level of civilization is more relevant than race, although race also plays a role.

In Maya girls, the menarche occurs very early (12.9 years) in spite of a lack of protein; the growth curves indicate a very early overlapping of boys' and girls' curves for stature (Maya 9 years, Navaho 10 years, whites

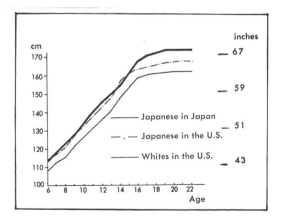

FIG. 48 Racial differences in growth (after Ishiwara, 1956).

from Michigan 10½ years). In Africa, when twenty-three populations were examined, the rank correlation between latitude and menarcheal age is positive (+0.34). In Europe, in twelve populations it is +0.25.

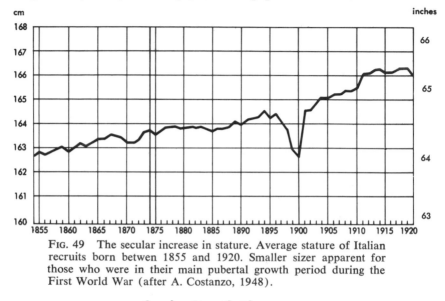

FIG. 49   The secular increase in stature. Average stature of Italian recruits born betwen 1855 and 1920. Smaller sizer apparent for those who were in their main pubertal growth period during the First World War (after A. Costanzo, 1948).

Secular Growth Changes

Among the many differences in growth due to environmental conditions, such as geography, ethnic culture, and social class, the effects on body size and early maturation are the most important and best documented. In all of the civilized countries, the pubertal growth spurt and the age of attaining full stature have been accelerating for at least the past 100 years. The most comprehensive evidence on this subject is based on military recruits. Data as early as 1741 are available from Norway, and begin in 1840 from Sweden. Italian statistics date from 1791, and those from the Netherlands begin in 1863. The magnitude of this secular increase in stature differs in the various countries, probably because of differing environmental circumstances. The increases fluctuate around Hultcrantz's figure for Sweden, which is 0.9 mm. per year. Argentina (1801–1924) shows 0.8 mm., and Estonia (1878–1933) 1.2 mm.

The secular increase in size applies to all of the other age groups as well. Even the newborn today are larger and heavier than in earlier decades, and the same applies for small children, those entering school, and students of older ages. At puberty, the differences in size between modern children and those of earlier generations are particularly striking, since the general increase in size and the acceleration of the pubertal spurt are additive. Along with the acceleration in growth, other age-dependent characteristics are also occurring earlier. The shedding and eruption of teeth occur at younger ages. Age-specific diseases such as Huntington's chorea now have their highest frequencies during the younger years. Finally, the age of menarche has been lowered by two to three years in this century.

Explanations for these striking trends are still not wholly satisfactory, but nutrition seems to be prominently involved. The consumption of meat and fats has increased greatly in the fast few decades; the protein content of the diet is practically a measure of the living standards of a population. Chronological, regional, and social differences in the magnitude of these changes point in this direction. For example, the trend toward a reduced age of menarche was reversed temporarily in Germany during the two world wars and the economic crisis around 1930. In Sweden, the curve of increased stature of military recruits flattened out during years of hardship, such as during the two world wars and the five years of poor crops from 1865 to 1870. City children usually mature faster than rural ones, except that these relationships were partly reversed after the Second World War. Besides nutritional changes, other factors may also have favored growth. Childhood diseases have become less frequent and less injurious; indeed, at present, American children usually show little or no retardation of growth during their routine episodes of illness. It is possible that relief from hard physical labor in childhood and the decreasing emotional pressures of schooling favor rapid growth.

Along with these trends in body growth, psychological development has also been accelerated. Phase-specific developmental phenomena, such as the child's low point in his relations with those who are rearing him, and peaks of spite and eruptions of anger, occur one to two years earlier than as reported in corresponding older studies. Furthermore, the average scores on intelligence tests have not decreased, as might have been expected on the basis of the greater fertility of families of lower intelligence (see Social Biology). It seems probable that accelerated somatic development is not related to the increasing prevalence of behavioral disturbances in the young today, especially in the metropolitan areas. These trends seem to be products primarily of the social situation.

THE HISTORY OF ANTHROPOLOGY

Though its roots may be traced back some time, the history of anthropology as a science seeking to comprehend the whole of man in all his various aspects is brief compared with that of other sciences. As is true of almost all the sciences, allusions to anthropology may be found in the writings of the ancients (Aristotle, Galen). The term "anthropology" goes back to Aristotle, but is not used again in antiquity. During the Middle Ages, no real progress could be made in the search for the place of man in nature. The first scientific development of basic significance in this sphere was the classification of man in the system of animals by Linnaeus (1735), who classed man alongside the anthropoid apes, calling the chimpanzee *Homo sylvestris* or *Homo troglodytes* and man *Homo sapiens*. This was the first purely scientific conception of man. Johann Friedrich Blumenbach (1752–1842) is regarded as the actual father of anthropology. His most important work, *De generis humani varietate nativa,* was the foundation for racial morphology. His grouping of mankind into five races found widespread adoption. According to Blumenbach, all the races of man evolved through environmental influences from a single ancestral form. Another landmark was the assembling of an extensive collection of skulls representing various races (now at Göttingen). Immanuel Kant (1724–1804) also occupies an important place in this earlier epoch in the history of anthropology. In his treatise *Of the Various Races of Man* (1775), Kant developed a taxonomy and a theory of race. According to his thesis, all the races of mankind go back to one polygenetic ancestral form and developed, for the most part, as the result of climatic influences. In the formulation of Kant's anthropological concepts, philosophical considerations of course played an important part.

Anthropology shared in the general growth of natural sciences in the first half of the nineteenth century. This development intensified after Charles Darwin (1809–82) logically demonstrated the evolutionary origin of all living matter, explaining it in terms of cause and effect in his theory of natural selection (see The Descent of Man). From then on, anthropology had an abundance of auxiliary sciences to draw upon—geology, paleontology, prehistory, and general evolutionary biology. In Darwin's scheme, man, though *primus inter pares,* was only one member. In many instances, this led to overestimation of the importance of the scientific approach in the reconstruction of a coherent picture of man, and sometimes scientists took no note at all of "the other aspect" of man. It is impossible to overestimate the extraordinary significance for anthropology of the change initiated by Darwin, from the old concept of a static structure of organic matter to that of a dynamic one. Even as other natural sciences —particularly biology and related subjects—were furthered tremendously by Darwinism, so anthropology thrived in this atmosphere. The fund of empirical knowledge concerning man grew enormously; a reliable foundation was laid upon which to build an accurate, scientific anthropology. One historic event of this period which should be mentioned is the founding, in 1859, of the Paris Society of Anthropology, by Paul Broca (1824–80). The achievements of the scientific societies that have arisen in large numbers since then mark the course that the development of anthropology has taken in the past century.

(The founding dates of some important anthropological societies are milestones: 1863—Anthropological Society of London; 1869—Berlin

Society for Anthropology, Ethnology, and Prehistory; 1870—Anthropological Society of Vienna; 1879—Anthropological Society of Washington; 1900—Frankfort Society for Anthropology, Ethnology, and Prehistory; 1902—American Anthropological Association; 1910—French Institute of Anthropology; 1911—Paris Institute for Human Paleontology; 1921—American Association of Physical Anthropologists; 1920—Swiss Society for Anthropology and Ethnology; 1925—German Society for Physical Anthropology. This is only a fragmentary list, but it impressively demonstrates the development of the science.)

Anthropology then proceeded at a relatively rapid pace, abetted by the increase in quantity and extent of specimen collections. The discoveries of larger numbers and complete series of skull fragments (of recently living peoples, from all over the world and especially from excavations in Western Europe) led to the new science of craniology and the development of a precise technique of anthropometry. After the introduction of the method of "indices" into anthropology, by A. O. Retzius (1796–1860), craniology (along with osteometry of the post-cranial skeleton) rapidly gained in significance. However, craniology almost became an end in itself. The reliability of its findings was vastly exaggerated and in many instances the voluminous tables of figures seemed to pretend a scientific accuracy they did not actually have. Measurements were made on living subjects also. In Germany, these investigations were furthered especially by Rudolf Virchow (1821–1902). An unrivaled interpretation of the anthropometric technique, which is still in use internationally today (see Methods of Anthropology), is given in Rudolf Martin's classic text. The "epoch of anthropometry" yielded abundant results, particularly in the field of anthropology and, by no means least, in the evaluation of the ever-growing number of fossil hominid finds. Of course, Eugen Fischer rightly points out that, in those days, biological insight into the significance of the anthropometric values was still lacking. After all, the Mendelian laws were not rediscovered until 1900, and it is only with the formulation of an accurate theory of heredity (experimental study of heredity and variations) that the true significance of data obtained by quantitative and qualitative analysis has become more and more discernible. Nor is the "age of anthropometry" over by any means. Of course, additional measurements must be and are being made. If we are to comprehend anthropological groups, and the quantitative relationships that distinguish one fossil skull from another, we cannot dispense with these measurements. We have known that ever since Schwalbe's classic studies of the Neanderthal cranium. But, even today, care must be taken not to overrate purely quantitative values (even when they have been arrived at by modern statistical methods). It should be made clear that, in addition to the quantitative relationships—indeed, often with priority over them—there is the morphological aspect, which cannot be measured by the instruments of the anthropometrist.

The science of paleoanthropology began in the second half of the nineteenth century. Its father was J. C. Fuhlrott, who in 1856 uncovered the skull fragment of "Neanderthal man" in the Neander Valley near Düsseldorf and correctly identified it as a fragment of a human form from the Ice Age. This was the beginning of the scientific investigation of fossil man. The founders of the systematic study were Marcellin Boule (1861–1942) of France and Gustav Schwalbe (1844–1916) of Germany, just to mention the two outstanding scientists in the field. Today, the scope of scientific research in paleoanthropology covers almost all the regions of the world. The number of finds continues to grow. In addition, the constantly growing fund of data available on the multiplicity of recent hominid forms has provided a further basis for the development of a scientifically sound knowledge of human races. In 1900, Deniker proposed the initial system of racial taxonomy, but without a knowledge of its genetic basis. The concept of race remained vague for a time, and systems of classification continued to be more or less arbitrary. Even at a relatively early date, an attempt was made to interpret the history of mankind from the viewpoint of the distribution of living races, although still without an adequate knowledge of the genetic basis of the concept of race. These attempts were made by scientists such as J. A. Gobineau and L. Woltmann. Without adequate genetic information, they were guided in part by romantic sentimentality and emotion, and worked with subjective criteria. The political racism of a later day was built on these irrational foundations and hence was impervious to the refutations offered by scientific data. What should be done, as von Eickstedt, one of the leading biologists of race in our own day, puts it, is to pit "the findings of the scientific study of race against the mania of racism."

As early as 1869, Francis Galton (1822–1911), a cousin of Charles Darwin, originated the science of eugenics, but an accurate genetic basis, eventually achieved through the development of Mendel's work, was still missing.

The modern epoch in the history of physical anthropology may be said to have begun with the first accurate, scientific investigation of the Mendelian laws, for this was the foundation of the structure of modern anthropology. The mighty stimuli emanating from the rapidly developing science of genetics were applied extensively to the problems of anthropology. Eugen Fischer, in his study of a population of Boer-Hottentot half-castes (the Rehoboth Bastards) in 1908, was the first to prove that, in the interbreeding of human races, the mode of inheritance of the characteristics of the races involved follows the Mendelian laws. Even before that, the Mendelian mode of inheritance for normal and pathological human characteristics had been confirmed, but it was Fischer who made the first attempt to analyze the mode of inheritance in crosses of human races. These studies represent a classic landmark in the development of anthropology. Today, "genetic analysis" of man has already made considerable advances. The science of population genetics has studied the quantitative relationships of certain genes in populations, the variations in gene concentrations, and the geographical variations in certain factors (blood groups are particularly well suited for this purpose), and is continuing these studies intensively (Boyd, Birdsell, and others). Thus the founda-tions were laid for what seems almost self-evident to us today; namely, that races are groups of individuals with similar gene compositions, which were built from mutant alleles that combined in various ways and became differentiated in their geographic regions, but which may be disinte-grated in the process of cross-breeding. Difference in race does not con-stitute a barrier to the production of offspring. It became possible to make the process of race formation increasingly understandable in terms of cause and effect. Genes go through mutation; then, through the mecha-nism of natural selection, they are either increased in frequency, becoming part of combinations in characteristic concentrations, or else they fail to perpetuate themselves.

At present, scientists are intensively engaged in analysis of the intricate interplay of the factors that make up this process. Through the use of suit-able laboratory models (*Drosophila*), experimental population genetics is demonstrating this process to us. Darwin first propounded his theory of natural selection a century ago. Today, advanced by the findings of ex-perimental genetics (the genetics of evolution), supported by the "New Taxonomy" of Sir Julian Huxley, and by paleontology (G. G. Simpson), which increasingly develops in the direction of evolutionary genetics, the reconstruction of Darwin's theory has led to an impressive confirmation of his basic ideas. Today, we speak of the "synthetic theory" of evolution (see The Descent of Man). The time has come to assess the validity of earlier attempts at a taxonomy of the races of man. Because the total fund of specialized information is still rather meager, we should begin by limit-ing our own attempts at racial taxonomy to a basis of genetics, which was possible, formerly, in theory only.

Advances made in ethnological research and in racial psychology pro-vide us with an increasing amount of material for a comprehensive syn-thesis, for a collective picture of recent mankind and present-day man. The historical processes that led to the rise of recent mankind have proven accessible to analysis (though reservedly so for the time being) (see The History of Races, The Formation of Races). Also, the extra-ordinary impetus of paleoanthropology within recent decades has gradually revealed the formal process of phylogenetic change, and the science of genetics has afforded tenable insights into the causal occurrences that take place during these processes. The picture of the phylogenetic develop-ment of the hominid family is gradually growing clearer. No little credit for this should go to the significant progress made in the study of non-hominid primates. In addition, studies (morphological and physiological) of the human soma—though at first glance somewhat scanty and, at times, appearing even quaint in the shadow of genetics—provide building blocks for the collective synthesis that is now under way. In the course of time, human genetics has been formed, from its early beginnings in the classic Mendelian epoch, into an imposing structure. One need only refer to the modern texts by Stern (1949, 1960) and von Verschuer (1959). But then, too, the classics showed the right path. The aims of anthropological research—to assist in making available the material needed for obtaining a comprehensive picture of man, to shed light on his make-up and on the structure of mankind in general, and to understand, in terms of cause and effect, the origins of that structure—are being pursued unremittingly by anthropologists the world over.

Modern anthropology, anchored in the science of genetics, is now gaining the sound foundations it needs in order to dedicate itself to the tasks that derive from its relationship to medicine and to become effective as "applied anthropology" (see Social Biology).

THE HISTORY OF RACES

This article will attempt to reconstruct the racial history of man through an application of modern taxonomy and evolutionary dynamics. At each step in this analysis, choices of conceptual models will be made, and reasons expressed for these choices. In general, we will deliberately seek resemblances in the evolutionary mechanics of man and lower animals, and emphasize the genealogical continuity of some geographical races of man, even back to ancestral forms which are quite outside the broad range of variation seen in mankind today.

In 1863, Thomas Henry Huxley rallied his contemporaries to consider "man's place in nature." By this happy phrase, he meant the study of man's evolutionary kinship with other organisms, past and present. To anthropologists ever since, evolution has been the leitmotiv of their biological studies, much as the concept of culture has dominated their work in archaeology and ethnology. The biological anthropologist not only investigates fossils which can define our own ancestry, but may search for parallelisms in the differentiation of races or subspecies in man and in other widespread organisms.

Most experts today consider modern man as a single "polytypic" species (see The Concept of Race). Such a species can be divided into geographical subspecies, each composed of at least one, and usually many, local breeding populations or isolates. Ideally, one might define isolates, subspecies, and species as being bounded by increasing barriers to gene flow outside the membership of each. The isolate, which may be the central concern of the student of microevolution, is often ephemeral and small in size, and is therefore not usually given a Linnaean taxonomic designation, but rather a vernacular name. Subspecies, on the other hand, are usually given full scientific names—to include genus, species, and sub-species. This is justified in the case of man so long as one thinks of sub-species as occupying large parts of the earth's surface, having a long history of living in these habitats, and being genetically differentiated from other subspecies except in zones near neighboring subspecies, where intermediate populations exist now and may have existed far into the prehistoric past. This concept of the geographical subspecies of man is clearly expressed even by such eighteenth-century naturalists as Blumenbach and Buffon.

When we come to apply the concept of subspecies to living men, we are faced with many difficulties, because many groups are thousands of miles from their racial homelands, and because of the extreme complexity of human hybridization, particularly in the last few thousand years. We shall therefore postpone a full exposition of human subspecies until we have completed a brief catalogue of the great regional diversity and complexity of mankind today. For this purpose, the term "stock" is employed to cover a motley of regional genetic groupings of man. In some cases, one or a few breeding isolates can be recognized. In others, fusion is still going on between originally separate populations. The anatomical features which are used to define each stock will usually be strongly prevalent in the group, but in the case of some groups it is rare for all such features to be found in an individual member of the stock, so great is the genetic diversity of men all over the world. A stock may in some cases be an emergent sub-species, and it is usually less ephemeral than a breeding isolate; at the same time its remote historical background may often be quite obscure.

The somatic differentiation of modern European stocks will be considered first, so that we may proceed from the familiar to the unfamiliar. The number of recognized stocks is arbitrary, and in the present instance is taken mainly from a brief account in Coon, Garn, and Birdsell (1950). Much more detail on the European story may be found in C. S. Coon's monograph *The Races of Europe*.

1. *Northwest European* (Figure 50, a, b). Individuals from this stock are in the great majority in the United States, Australia, New Zealand, Scandinavia, the British Isles, northwestern Germany, the Low Countries, northern France, and among the whites of South Africa. Most people derived from this ancestral region are medium to tall in stature, usually with fair skins, blue or hazel eyes, straight or wavy brown hair, and facial features fine to coarse. Rare to common morphological variants include blond, fine-featured "Nordics," similar but dark "Mediterraneans," and more squat and coarse-featured "Alpines." Most Northwest Europeans, however, do not run to such extremes, and it is inadvisable to treat such combinations of traits in northern Europe as "races" in any evolutionary sense.

2. *Northeast European* (Figures 50, c; 51, b). The major stock from the Baltic to Siberia, the Carpathians, the Black Sea, and the arctic tundra is composed of a large number of isolates of smaller people with

medium to stocky build, fair skin, brown to blond hair, rather broad faces, and often with snub noses and long upper lips. Individual variants are often "Nordic," "Alpine," and sometimes "Mongoloid."

3. *Lapp* (not illustrated). A small-sized variant of the Northeast European, living in the far north of Scandinavia as herdsmen and fishermen. Pigmentation is darker than in most Northeast Europeans, and jaws, teeth, and chins are disproportionately small and frail.

4. *Alpine* (Figure 50, e). The major stock of Central Europe from France to the Bosporus, and in Asia from Anatolia to Tadjikistan. Pigmentation is medium to dark brunet, head rounded and features usually coarse. Body hair is medium to abundant.

5. *Mediterranean* (Figure 50, d). Most of the peoples ranging from Portugal and Morocco to northern India are included in this stock. Size is usually medium, build lean, pigmentation brunet to medium brown, eyes sporadically blue, usually hazel or brown; facial skeleton rather fragile and nose often prominent, especially from Palestine to Afghanistan. Unmixed Europeans throughout Latin America are usually Mediterraneans, especially in Argentina and Chile.

6. *Nordic* (Figures 50, a; 51, a). Similar to the Mediterranean except for blondism and often larger body size. Somewhat concentrated among the Northwest Europeans as a morphological variant, and sporadically appears in some of the Mediterranean regions, especially North Africa.

7. *Hindu* (Figures 51, b; 53, c). Similar to the Mediterranean except that pigmentation is light brown to very dark. Found as populations in northern India and as isolates or individual variants elsewhere in India. Build lean.

8. *Hamite* (Figure 51, c, d). Skeletally Mediterranean, skin dark, some kinky hair and thick lips, build lean. Found in the Sudan and East Africa.

9. *Sudanese* (Figure 51, e, f). Very dark, lean Negroes, in the Sudan and adjoining parts of eastern sub-Saharan Africa.

10. *Forest Negro* (Figure 52, a, b). Peoples of West African forests and much of the Congo. Skin dark brown, hair spiral, build medium to muscular. Tissues bulge greatly around some apertures, especially nipples, buttocks, jaws, lips, and alae of the nose.

11. *African Negrito* (Figure 52, f). Central African dwarfs from the Cameroons to Rwanda and Urundi, in forested areas. Probably evolved from taller, otherwise similar peoples in Africa.

12. *Bantu* (Figure 52, c). Negroes of East and South Africa, probably recent mixtures of Strains 8, 9, 10, and Capoids.

13. *Capoid* (Figure 52, d, e). Yellow-brown people, now found marginally in southern Africa. Pastoralists (Hottentots) among them approach medium stature; hunters and gatherers (Bushmen) are nearly dwarfs. Hottentots probably hybridized with Stock 12. Hair extremely spiraled, fatty buttocks (steatopygia) (Figure 60), breasts of females close to armpits; female labia minora elongated; male penis horizontal.

a) Northwest European

b) Northwest European

c) Northeast European

d) Mediterranean

e) Alpine

f) "Dinaric"

FIG. 50   Recent Europeans.

a) Berber

b) Eastern Mediterranean

c) Ethiopian

d) Ethiopian

e) Nilote

f) Sudanese

FIG. 51   Modern Africans.

a) Archaic Congoid

b) Archaic Congoid

c) Archaic Congoid

d) Capoid (Hottentot)

e) Capoid (Bushman)

f) Congoid (Bambuti Pygmy)

FIG. 52   Modern Africans, continued.

a) Mediterranean

b) "Armenoid"

c) Mediterranean (India)

d) South Indian

e) Vedda

f) Ainu

FIG. 53   Recent Asians.

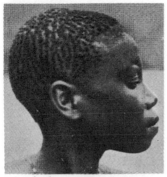

a) Andamanese

b) Tungus

c) North Chinese

d) Central Chinese

e) South Chinese

f) Archaic Mongoloid

FIG. 54   Recent· Asians, continued.

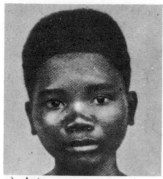

a) Aeta

b) Proto-Malay

c) Eastern Veddoid

d) New Guinea Highlander

e) Australian aborigine

f) Polynesian

FIG. 55 Indonesia and Oceania.

a) Eskimo

b) Northwest Coast

c) Boreal Forest

d) Central America

e) Brazil

f) Fuegian

FIG. 56   Recent Aborigines of the Americas.

14. *Melanesian* (Figure 55, d). Spiral-haired, dark peoples extending from New Guinea to Fiji. Build usually medium to lean, teeth large, often large brow ridges.

15. *Pacific Negrito* (Figure 55, a). Dwarf populations in the Andaman Islands, the Philippines, and New Guinea. Probably evolved from Stock 14.

16. *Carpentarian* (Figure 55, e). Lean, dark-skinned Australian aborigines, mainly in northern and central parts of the country. Hair straight or wavy, skin dark brown, teeth, jaws, and brow ridges large.

17. *Dravidian* (Figures 53, e; 55, c). Tribal and caste groups of southern India and Ceylon. Like Stock 16 but with smaller teeth. Greatly hybridized with Stock 7.

18. *Murrayian* (not illustrated). Burly, medium-brown aborigines of southeastern Australia. Abundant beard and body hair, large teeth and brow ridges. Extinct Tasmanian aborigines may have been hybrids of Stocks 15 and 18.

19. *Ainu* (Figure 53, f). Similar to Stock 18, but skin color lighter. Once widespread in Japan, now only in Hokkaido and one of the Kuriles. May be Caucasoids displaced eastward, or northerly Australoids. Now partly Mongoloid.

20. *Classic Mongoloid* (Figures 54, b; 56, a). Build stocky, skin yellowish-brown, hands and feet small, face very flat and padded with fat, eyefolds conspicuous, head hair coarse and straight, sparse body hair. Found in area of the drainage of the Amur River (Tungus); includes the Buryats of Lake Baikal, Siberian aborigines, Eskimos, and many Koreans and Japanese.

21. *North Chinese* (Figure 54, c). Taller than Classic Mongoloids, fewer eyefolds, build medium and sometimes lean. A few individuals look Mediterranean.

22. *Southeast Asian* (Figure 54, d, e). Build short, medium to stocky, Mongoloid facial specializations moderate. Includes the southern Chinese, Thais, some Burmese, Indonesians, and Filipinos.

23. *Tibeto-Indonesian* (Figures 54, f; 55, b). Tribal peoples of Szechuan, eastern Tibet, and northern Burma, Indonesia, Lesser Sundas, northern Luzon. May be hybridized in part with non-Mongoloids. Skin darker than in most Mongoloids, noses sometimes prominent, often resemble American Indians.

24. *Turkic* (not illustrated). Pastoralists and farmers of Central Asia, hybrids of Mongoloids, Mediterraneans, and probably other Caucasoids. They form a cline between Caucasoids and Mongoloids.

25. *American Indian, Marginal* (Figure 56, b, c, d, f). These are tribal peoples beyond the range of sedentary agriculture in both the Americas. Build medium to stocky, teeth large, and skulls thick. Mongoloid traits seldom extreme.

26. *American Indian, Central* (Figure 56, d). Intensive agriculturalists from the southwestern United States to Bolivia, and shifting cultivators in the tropical forests of South America. Usually smaller and more lightly built

than Marginal American Indians, with smaller teeth and more refined features. Associated with the aboriginal high civilizations of the New World, analogous with Mediterraneans in the Old.

27. *Ladino* (not illustrated). Recent hybrids of Mediterraneans and American Indians in Latin America, with varying additions of Negroid, especially in Brazil.

28. *Cape Colored* (not illustrated). Recent hybrids of South African Bantu, Hottentot, Hindu, and diverse Caucasoids.

29. *North American Colored* (not illustrated). Recent hybrids of Forest Negro and other African strains, with mainly Northwest European and minor American Indian contributions. The Negroes of the United States and Canada.

30. *Polynesian-Micronesian* (not illustrated). An intricate mixture, probably including Tibeto-Indonesian Mongoloids, Melanesians, and perhaps Dravidians as well. Polynesians are tall and stocky; Micronesians smaller and leaner, with slightly more obvious Mongoloid and Melanesian characteristics.

31. *Neo-Hawaiian* (not illustrated). Basically Stock 30, with large increments of Mongoloids and Caucasoids from both northwestern and southern Europe.

Methodologies of Racial Prehistorians

The preceding list of human stocks is designed to acquaint the reader with man as he is today. It is much too confounded with recent hybridizations and migrations to serve as a basis for studying prehistoric man. For this purpose it is better to work with a simpler taxonomic framework, and to rely mostly on skulls and teeth, which are the principal fossil remains of early man. The geographical area of this account is mainly Africa, Eurasia, and the northerly islands of Indonesia. The time span is chiefly from the end of the Lower to the Upper Pleistocene, for in this period the evidence of both bones and cultures can be reconstructed most clearly into a historical account of human races.

The hypothesis to be presented here was suggested by Franz Weidenreich in 1947, and has been much elaborated since by C. S. Coon in *The Origin of Races* (1962). Their thesis is that through much, if not most, of the Pleistocene, man was a single polytypic species, inhabiting most if not all of the temperate and tropical continental regions of the Old World. As will be shown presently, this habitat can be divided into three broad zoogeographic regions in terms of fauna. One or two human subspecies lived in each region. In the Middle Pleistocene, all or nearly all of mankind was classifiable as *Homo erectus;* i.e., a form of man with a brain about two thirds the size found in living races, and with larger brow ridges and a more projecting muzzle than can be found in man now. Since that time, the men in each region have undergone substantial independent evolution, so that some racial differences seen today can be traced all the way back to *Homo erectus.* Coon predicts that future fossil finds will make possible even more such local reconstructions. Along with this parochial evolution there was considerable gene flow between regions, so that some of the more advantageous genetic traits of adaptability and intelligence have spread from each subspecies to its neighbors. This dispersion of genes did not occur solely through the extermination of archaic populations, but often through hybridizations over hundreds of millennia.

Weidenreich visualized this process as a lattice, with verticals representing the continuity of local genes over time. These we can call *lines*. A few horizontals can be superimposed over all the lines and given the names of Linnaean species. Different lines may evolve at different rates, but the horizontals represent stages in the evolutionary process which we can call *grades*. Coon recognizes two in the evolution of the genus *Homo:* an extinct and very archaic grade (*Homo erectus*), and a more advanced one with brains as large as those in living subspecies (*Homo sapiens*). In Weidenreich's lattice model, diagonal lozenges are superimposed on the lines and grades to illustrate gene flow between lines.

Since the early nineteenth century, evolutionists have repeatedly constructed such models as knowledge of particular fossil lineages increases. The earlier geologists were mainly "catastrophists." They viewed the separations between the periods of geologic history as cataclysms during which most or even all organisms were exterminated, so that few could leave descendants. The Biblical flood was taken to be such an event. Some catastrophists even envisioned a series of special creations to repopulate the earth after each disaster. Catastrophism was bound to appeal to Christian geologists who hoped to reconcile the history of the earth with evidence from the Bible, and whose collections of fossils were so meager that few could perceive later forms as possible descendants of earlier ones.

Even today, the Pleistocene can be regarded as a series of glacial "catastrophes," so that mild varieties of catastrophism still persist among workers who study skimpy fossil records from the Pleistocene, such as the bones and teeth of early man. Thus, a modern catastrophist is tempted to emphasize both the discontinuities of culture before and after the glacial advances in cooler parts of Eurasia, and the possibility that archaic groups such as Neanderthal man may have died without issue in the glaciated fastnesses of western Europe.

In the nineteenth century, the gradual triumph of Darwinism among paleontologists and the great accumulation of fossils of many species led to the first family trees which crossed from one geological period to another. Nonetheless, seemingly aberrant organisms were often singled out as evolutionary "blind alleys," and often marginal groups were thought to have been exterminated when invaded by their more "progressive" relatives. To this day, many students think that in western Europe, Neanderthal man may have been killed off in this manner by men like ourselves.

This theory is beginning to lose plausibility today because some supposed discontinuities in the history of human tool-making are being filled in, and even physical "intermediates" between some fossil men turn up from time to time. Thus, it is the richness, parochialism, and continuity of the evidence which are now beginning to impress some anthropologists as to the plausibility of a polyphyletic scheme of human race formation, so that most of the available fossils are being welcomed into the ecumenical assemblage of human ancestry, without regard for race, creed, or color.

Zoogeographers have long divided man's evolutionary homeland into three enormous faunal regions: Palearctic, Ethiopian, and Oriental. The Palearctic region includes Africa north of the mid-Sahara, Europe, and all of Asia except southern Arabia, India, Southeast Asia, and southern China. The colder and wetter parts of this spacious realm were intermittently covered with ice during the Pleistocene, and southerly animals ordinarily migrated north between the glacial advances. As a result, its faunas typically differ more from east to west than from north to south. As we shall see, the same is true of its human subspecies.

The Palearctic region is cut off from tropical Africa by the Sahara, and from India by the Himalayas. The only area that affords easy travel to or from other regions of the Old World is the land between China and Southeast Asia. This portal seems to have been especially important for genetic interchanges between Palearctic and more southerly subspecies of man.

The Ethiopian region includes Africa south of the mid-Sahara and the southern third of Arabia. At one time migration north and south here was easy, but deserts now inhibit exchanges between the Ethiopian and Palearctic regions. During most of the Pleistocene, however, this region extended to the Mediterranean. Only with the desiccation of the Sahara have Palearctic animals and human subspecies moved significantly toward the fringes of the desert.

The Oriental region includes India, southern China, Southeast Asia, and the larger, more northerly islands of Indonesia. As stated above, its frontier is open into China, but few organisms have moved from Indonesia south toward Australia, which is a separate zoogeographic realm. Until the end of the Pleistocene, man, like other animals, was probably inhibited by these natural barriers.

There are five human subspecies identified with these zoogeographic realms. At this point we shall outline their main skeletal and dental characteristics as well as their probable habitats some 10,000 or more years ago, in the Pleistocene. Today this reconstruction seems best authenticated for East Asia and the Oriental region outside of India, less so for the western part of the Palearctic region, and least for the Ethiopian region. The eastern Palearctic subspecies, which inhabited central and northern China, is called Mongoloid. The Australoids occupied most or all of the Oriental region. The Caucasoids were to be found throughout Eurasia, from Great Britain to India, while the Congoids occupied the Ethiopian regions. The habitat of the Capoids is uncertain; it may have been either north of the Sahara or east and south of the Congoids. The early racial movements and original homelands in tropical and southern Africa are still highly conjectural. Not all workers are willing to separate the Congoids and Capoids at a subspecific level, and many prefer to regard them as variants of a single subspecies, for their blood groups are similar. We need not doubt, however, that both are ancient inhabitants of Africa. An important later development in North Africa has been the desiccation of the Sahara and the invasion of Palearctic animals, including the western Palearctic (Caucasoid) subspecies of man.

Racial History of the Australoids and Mongoloids

Anthropologists generally agree that the Australoid subspecies (*Homo sapiens australoideus*) is anatomically the most archaic of human stocks today. Members of this subspecies today include the Pacific Negritos (Stock 15), Melanesians (14), Carpentarians (16), Dravidians (17), and Murrayians (18). The Ainu (19), although at present inhabiting Japan, may be either Caucasoids displaced eastward or Australoids displaced northward.

Today, many Australoids live in the Australian zoogeographic realm, and extend eastward from Australia and New Guinea into the Pacific as far as Fiji. All are dark-skinned, and most have large teeth, massive jaws, and conspicuous brow ridges. Those in dry climates outside of Asia generally have wavy or ringleted hair, and those in regions of high rainfall usually have curly or spiral hair. The reasons for this difference are not clear, and fossil bones and teeth are not helpful in deciphering its history. As in other living human subspecies, the Australoids today are more alike in skulls and teeth than in their hair and soft parts. Most Australoids have narrow, gabled, ill-filled brain cases, small brains relative to body size, and rather long limbs.

The fossil evidence, to be reviewed presently, indicates that few Australoids today are living in or near their evolutionary homeland, which probably included most or all of the Oriental zoogeographic realm. Perhaps there was a gradual transition far back into the Pleistocene between Australoids and Caucasoids from India and southern Arabia to the Middle East, for resemblances to Caucasoids appear sporadically among the Australoids. A gene flow from Africa, which might account for the occurrence of black, spiral-haired peoples in Africa and the Pacific, is impossible to prove at present.

Toward the end of the Pleistocene, Australoids gradually infiltrated southward into the Australian zoogeographic region and, much later, moved out into the Pacific islands with advanced agricultural techniques, pottery, and a few domestic animals. While these migrations were taking place, more and more of the Australoid homeland was occupied by Mongoloids moving southward from China. A few reached India too, but most of the displacement of Australoids in India was carried out by dark-skinned Caucasoids, and is still going on today.

China itself seems to have been the homeland of much of the Mongoloid subspecies (*H. sapiens mongoloideus*), an eastern Palearctic form of man. These men have expanded far and wide since the Pleistocene, so that they are now the most numerous of all the living races. In our classification of living mankind, strains which are at least partially Mongoloid include Stocks 2 (Northeast European), 19 (Ainu), 20 (Classic Mongoloid), 21 (North Chinese), 22 (Southeast Asian), 23 (Tibeto-Indonesian), 24 (Turkic), 25 (American Indian, Marginal), 26 (American Indian, Central), 27 (Ladino), 30 (Polynesian-Micronesian), and 31 (Neo-Hawaiian).

The Mongoloids show a large number of anatomical specializations which are particularly to be contrasted with the Australoids. Mongoloids are generally lighter in skin color, with smaller and very specialized teeth, smaller brow ridges, straight, coarse hair, large brains relative to body size, well-filled crania, and rather short extremities.

The dental and facial specializations of the Mongoloids are numerous, and probably very ancient indeed. Except for the nose, the upper face is pushed forward and is flat across the front. The nasal root is usually flat, the malars broad and flat, and the incisor region broad, principally because the lateral incisors are wide in relation to the centrals. The upper incisors usually have a strongly shovel-shaped lingual surface, produced by vertical marginal pillars. Close to the gum, nodules of enamel are seen at the base of the shoveling. Rarer peculiarities include teatlike cones on the occlusal surfaces of some newly erupted premolars, nodules or "pearls" of enamel extending onto the roots of the labial sides of some molar teeth, and collars or swellings of the crowns of canines, premolars, and molars. (This kind of swelling is called a cingulum.) Occasionally the enamel of molars is wrinkled. A number of Mongoloid populations show very high frequencies of missing third molars. Many molars show fusion of roots and enlarged pulp chambers (taurodontism). In sum, Mongoloids have very robust front teeth and markedly reduced third molars.

The muscles of mastication are set far forward. The masseters seem to be especially important in the chewing of Mongoloids, and are strongly attached on the zygomatic arches and the prominent cheekbones; the gonial region of the mandible is turned outward in many individuals to form the insertions of these powerful muscles. Especially in arctic Mongoloids, a frequent feature is a bony swelling below the gumline of the mandible in the premolar region (*torus mandibularis*). This torus is found occasionally in other arctic peoples as well, being frequent in the medieval Caucasoid population of Iceland.

In the area where the Palearctic and Oriental regions meet in southern China, Mongoloids and Australoids have probably exchanged genes for hundreds of millennia. Weidenreich has shown that some of the regional gradients of morphological differences between Mongoloids and Australoids can be traced back to the Middle Pleistocene populations of *Homo erectus*. His analysis is based on skeletal and dental differences between *Homo erectus* found in Java ("Pithecanthropus") and Peking man—the subspecies found in the upper cave of Chou Kou Tien near Peiping ("Sinanthropus"). (See The Descent of Man.)

133

The Pithecanthropus finds (*Homo erectus erectus*) extend from the late Lower Pleistocene into the Middle Pleistocene. These were long-legged, upright men with gabled cranial vaults, large brow ridges, large teeth, and a cranial capacity of perhaps 775–900 cc. (Figures 73; 74; 77, I, c).

The Middle Pleistocene men of China (Sinanthropus," or *Homo erectus pekinensis*), of whom fragments of some forty individuals are known, were short-legged men with more globular brain cases, small brow ridges and teeth, and cranial capacities of some 1,015–1,225 cc. (Figures 73; 77, I, e). The face is smaller and less robust than in the Javan populations. The cheekbones and muscles of mastication are set further forward, and the gonial angles of the mandible are everted. The lower jaws show the *torus mandibularis*. Bony knobs (exostoses) occur in peculiar spots where they are often found in Mongoloids: on the buccal aspect of the mandible and in the external auditory meatus.

Mongoloid dental features are especially numerous. They include shovel incisors and even canines, the cingulum on canines and all posterior teeth, wrinkles on the occlusal surfaces of the molars, taurodontism, and some reduction of third molars.

The persistence of this subspecific difference between men of the eastern Palearctic and Oriental regions can be traced in a few intermediate fossils over a time span of from over 300,000 years ago to the present.

In Java, a set of eleven skull caps and two tibiae are referred to as Solo man (*H. erectus soloensis*) (Figures 74; I, d). As Weidenreich has shown, these specimens are transitional between the Middle Pleistocene *H. erectus erectus* from Java and the modern Australoids. The Solo cranial capacities range from about 1,035 to 1,350 cc. These sizes are almost exactly in between the estimates for the earlier specimens and the averages for modern Australian aborigines (males, 1,350 cc.; females, 1,150 cc.). The Solo crania are angular, gabled, and ill-filled. Both tibiae indicate that Solo man was long-legged, like most modern Australoids. The Solo population probably lived in Java in the late Pleistocene.

Two skulls from Wadjak, in central Java, represent still younger specimens. These individuals are very much like living Australian aborigines, although their brains are rather large for Australians.

A skull of late Pleistocene age from Aitape, in northeastern New Guinea, suggests that man may have reached this region late in the Pleistocene, and that peoples somewhat more archaic than the living Australoids, but more modern than Solo man, may have been the first arrivals.

In Australia itself, three putatively old skulls (Keilor, Talgai, and Cohuna) are of uncertain age, but very likely post-Pleistocene. All can be matched in large collections of modern Australian aboriginal skulls.

This evolutionary lineage is the most satisfactory history of a single human subspecies which has so far been reconstructed, and most of this outline was worked out by Weidenreich. In the past few years, stages of Mongoloid evolution have been filled in by the discovery of three finds in China and one in Japan, all from the later part of the Middle Pleistocene.

Shifts of Human Subspecies
from *PLEISTOCENE* to *POST-PLEISTOCENE*

PLEISTOCENE

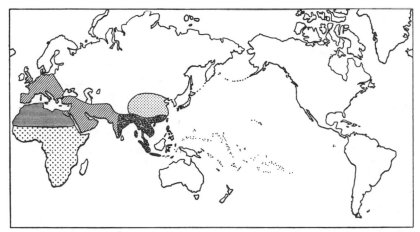

EARLY POST-PLEISTOCENE

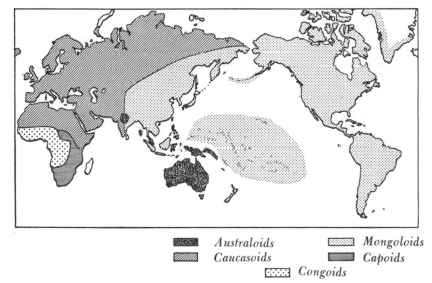

Australoids   Mongoloids

Caucasoids   Capoids

Congoids

In 1954, three human teeth were found in Ting-Tsun, Shansi, northern China, in a series of excavations of sites whose artifacts were related to, but later than, those associated with Peking man. The two upper incisors were shoveled and the lower second molar was very much like those of *H. erectus pekinensis.*

In 1957, southwest of Changyang in Hupei Province, a piece of maxilla and three human teeth were found in association with a late Middle Pleistocene fauna. These teeth have wrinkled crowns, like the premolars and molars of Peking man, but are slightly smaller and more modern in form.

In 1958, at Mapa, in Kwangtung Province, southern China, part of the cranial vault and upper face of a man were found in a late Middle or early Upper Pleistocene deposit. This specimen may be a good intermediate between *Homo erectus* and either the Australoid or Mongoloid subspecies.

In 1957, a humerus was found in east-central Honshu, Japan, in Ushikawa Quarry, in a late Middle Pleistocene deposit. It has thick walls and a thin marrow. In this respect, it recalls Peking man more closely than the modern Japanese.

All of the Upper Pleistocene finds from the Far East are remains of anatomically modern man, but with specific Mongoloid affinities.

In 1958, in Liu-Kiang, Kwangsi Province, southern China, a nearly complete cranium and some limb bones, and two femora which may be from another individual, were found in a site that seems to have been Upper Pleistocene. As to be expected in a skull found near the putative Australoid-Mongoloid frontier, this specimen may well be a racial intermediate. Cranially, it looks more Australoid, but the teeth are Mongoloid and the face is somewhat flat. The limb bones are suggestive of an individual so small that it may be a prototype of the dwarf Australoids or eastern Negritos.

In 1922, a shovel incisor not unlike the Sinanthropus series was found in the Ordos country in the bed of the desert river Sjara-Osso-Gol. The fauna found with it was Upper Pleistocene, and its cultural associations were apparently Upper Paleolithic. Two more Ordos specimens were discovered in 1957 from similar deposits—part of a femur and a broken parietal bone. The bones are a little thicker than those of modern man.

In central Honshu, Japan, five fragments of skull cap and one pelvic fragment were located among an Upper Pleistocene fauna. So far, the evidence indicates only that these fragments were from an archaic form of modern man.

Remains of at least seven individuals were found at Chou Kou Tien in a cave higher on the hillside than those where Peking man was discovered. Three skulls from this deposit were described by Weidenreich. The male seems to have been a primitive Mongoloid with taurodont molars and a mandibular torus, Mongoloid malars, and a guttered nasal sill. This skull is similar to that of a large-faced American Indian. One of the two females could readily pass for a modern Eskimo, and the other for a somewhat less extreme Mongoloid. The date for these individuals may be final Upper Pleistocene, or slightly later.

In 1956, a cave called Kait'o-Tung in Lcipin, Kwangsi Province, was excavated, and a cranial base and some facial parts were found along with three Upper Paleolithic tools. This skull is insufficiently preserved to reveal its racial identity.

The archaeological evidence on early man in the Americas indicates that archaic Mongoloids were probably the first migrants from Asia in the Upper Pleistocene. Even today, the average American Indian is more likely to show archaic features than the average Mongoloid from eastern Asia. Both local evolution in the New World and gene flow from Asia have wrought minor genetic changes in the American Indians, but have by no means obscured their very numerous Mongoloid features, such as skin color, hair color and form, dentition, prominent malars, and even the patterning of their finger and palm prints. Archaic features have persisted, especially among the marginal hunting and gathering peoples of both continents, such as large brow ridges, prominence of the lower (but not upper) nose, and a rather long, narrow head. The Eskimos apparently represent one of the later migrations into the New World, and are therefore assigned to the Classic Mongoloids (Stock 20).

Racial History of Africa

For a long time, Africa has been the home of members of three human subspecies—Caucasoid, Congoid, and Capoid—and a multitude of intermediate populations and individuals. In this section we are concerned with the more southerly Caucasoids, especially Stock 5 (Mediterranean), the sporadic occurrence of depigmented individuals in North Africa (6, Nordics), and Hamites (8).

In the African context, skeletally Caucasoid individuals have small teeth, narrow and prominent noses, and faces with little or no anterior projection of the forehead or of the jaws. These individuals may vary in skin color from the paleness of a northern European to the darkest of browns. In general, the darker groups are admixed with Congoids.

The Congoids range from pygmies to giants, and the living stocks include 9 (Sudanese), 10 (Forest Negro), 11 (African Negrito), and 12 (Bantu). These groupings are somewhat dissimilar in size and shape, but most Congoids have broad, rather flat noses, prominent foreheads and occiputs, sometimes palpable brow ridges, and usually prognathism of both jaws and rather retreating chins.

Congoid teeth are usually large. Shoveling of the incisors is usually absent, but nodules often occur on the upper lingual aspect of the maxillary incisors, and often one or two vertical ridges occur away from the mesial and distal aspects, and extend up the lingual face of the upper incisors. Occasionally molars are wrinkled. The molar row is generally large and unreduced in complexity of cusps. Congenital absence of the third molars is notably rare.

The Capoids (Stock 13) exhibit a great disproportion of size between the large cranial skeleton and the small face, especially in the small-sized groups. The brain case is swollen and globular, with a prominent forehead and a markedly bent cranial base (nasion-sella-basion angle). The face is short, flat, puny, and infantile. From the front, the face looks triangular, with moderate breadth across the zygomatic arches, and a tiny chin.

The teeth often show moderate shoveling of the maxillary incisors and some enamel pearls of the upper molars. Third molars are seldom missing, but the maxillary third molars are a bit more reduced in complexity than in most Congoids. Taurodontism is sporadic. Although the teeth in general seem closest to those of the Congoids, Coon thinks that their tenuous resemblances to those of Mongoloids indicates a common ancestry of the two subspecies, perhaps in the Lower or Middle Pleistocene, at or even below the *Homo erectus* grade.

Ancient Capoids were middle-sized, with large brains. Modern representatives are sometimes nearly as large (Hottentots and some northern Bushmen), or somewhat dwarfed (most of the living Bushmen). The fossil evidence suggests that this dwarfism may be recent.

Turning now to the remote history of the Africans, it is important to note that in the Lower and Middle Pleistocene, the Ethiopian fauna extended to the Mediterranean. Africa was a major homeland of Australopithecus, whose subspecies are now known or suspected from southern, eastern, and western Africa, Palestine, and Java (see The Descent of Man).

By the Middle Pleistocene, *Homo erectus* lived in northern and eastern Africa as well as in the Far East of Asia. Our major uncertainty is whether Africa was the only region where *Homo erectus* evolved from subspecies of Australopithecus, or whether this transition also occurred separately in Eurasia. In East Africa we have Leakey's "Zinjanthropus" finds from Olduvai Gorge, and the Kanam mandible from the Gulf of Kavirondo, Lake Victoria, which may be a female of this same type. These finds indicate the presence of a tool-using, meat-scavenging Australopithecine of probable Lower Pleistocene age.

In North Africa, the remains of *Homo erectus mauritanicus* consist of a parietal fragment and three mandibles from Ternefine, in the Department of Oran, Algeria. The fauna was Ethiopian and dates from the early Middle Pleistocene. Stone tools here include handaxes (recalling both western Eurasia and Africa) and choppers, chopping tools and flakes—tools contemporaneous with *Homo erectus* in both Java and China.

The parietal is primitive in the simplicity of its pattern of grooves for the middle meningeal artery. The mandibles all indicate hominids with a broad cranial base—a diagnostic feature of *Homo erectus*. The teeth look slightly Mongoloid: with taurodontism, wrinkled molars, and a basal cingulum. Some details are also like those of African Australopithecines. The incisors are too worn to permit a diagnosis of possible shoveling.

Coon thinks that the Ternefine remains are an advanced sort of *Homo erectus* with both cultural and dental affiliations with Peking man. One possibility is that an incipient Mongoloid dentition first appeared in Africa. It became exaggerated in the ancestry of the Mongoloids, and lost in the earliest Javanese ancestors of the Australoids. In support of this possibility is the prevalence of slight shoveling and basal nodules on the lingual aspects of the upper incisors in some African Australopithecines, and a few wrinkled molars.

In 1953, a mandibular fragment and four teeth were found in Casablanca, Morocco. These pieces show clear genetic continuity with the Ternefine specimens, although they are perhaps 200,000 years younger and date from the Third Glacial advance.

At Smugglers' Cave, Tamara, Morocco, a nearly complete mandible was found, again with dental resemblances to the Ternefine and Casablanca specimens. A still later collection, probably from early in the last glaciation—some shattered pieces of skull and teeth—was found at Rabat, on the northwest coast of Morocco. The teeth show slight shoveling of the incisors, cingulums on the upper canines, and some features of the premolars recalling Peking man. Roughly contemporaneous is an immature maxillary fragment called Tangier man, again with this kind of dentition. A nearly complete cranium of an adult, primitive ancestral Bushman and the left half of a similar, adolescent second skull were found in 1961 and 1962, respectively, at Jebel Ighoud, Morocco.

Although all but the last two of these specimens are meager, they add up to perhaps a quarter of a million years of local evolution, always with suggestive resemblances to *Homo erectus* as seen in the Middle Pleistocene of China. The materials do not prove that all of the later finds were already *Homo sapiens,* but their Aterian stone industry showed hafted, pressure-flaked implements and other tools exemplifying considerable technical skill. As we shall see in discussing the European Neanderthal forms of man, these North Africans may have contributed to their ancestry. Their possible contribution to the ancestry of the more southerly living races of Africa is not certain. Coon thinks that they are ancestral to the Capoids because to this day tenuous similarities can be found between this subspecies and the Mongoloids in facial flattening, skin color, slight shoveling of the upper incisors, and enamel pearls on some upper molars.

The living peoples of North Africa are overwhelmingly Caucasoid. They apparently reached their present homeland before the end of the Pleistocene, with the incursion of a Palearctic fauna. One of their two cultures, both of which included blades and microliths, is called Mouillian. The second (Capsian) may be a little later. The Mouillian population was more rugged in physique, and the Capsians more linear. Their place of origin may have been the Middle East or, perhaps less likely, western Europe.

In 1958, south of the Sahara, at Olduvai Gorge, Tanganyika, Leakey found a few deciduous teeth, associated with an early handax cultural layer and probably dated early in the Middle Pleistocene. These teeth are large enough to have been Australopithecine. In a similar bed was a faceless and broken brain case, called the Chellian-3 skull. It is as old as the Peking specimens of *Homo erectus*. Its brow ridges are very large and robust, and its cranial capacity about 1,100 to 1,200 cc. It is certainly an important East African form of *Homo erectus*. A fragmentary skull from Lake Eyasi, Tanganyika ("Africanthropus"), perhaps later in age, may be a related form. So is a scrap of mandible from Diré Dawa, Ethiopia.

At least in the refuge areas of southern Africa, this subspecies persisted very late. The famous Broken Hill skull (Figure 77, I, f) from Northern Rhodesia is very much like it, and postcranial fragments associated with it indicate a long-legged physique. Broken Hill man had a cranial capacity of 1,280 cc., and comes from an Upper Pleistocene horizon as recent as 25,000 years ago.

In the Cave of Hearths at Makapansgat, Transvaal, a major Australopithecine site, Dart discovered a mandible of a child about twelve years old, associated with a late type of handax. It has rather small, plain teeth, a stout body, and probably no chin. Like Broken Hill man, it is probably Upper Pleistocene, and perhaps a member of the same race.

From still further south, on a farm east of Saldanha Bay, some ninety miles north of Capetown, have come slightly older remains—a skull cap and a mandibular fragment. The skull cap is much like that of Broken Hill man.

The preceding evidence indicates a very conservative, long-lasting evolutionary line of *Homo erectus* with enormous brow ridges. The major unsolved problem in the racial history of southern Africa is the degree to which this very archaic form of man contributed to the ancestry of the living Congoids and Capoids.

Incontestable remains of *Homo sapiens* in Africa are very difficult to sort into evolutionary lines, and even harder to relate to local forms of *Homo erectus*. One obstacle is the scarcity of known archaeological sites in or near the tropical forests, and another is man's way of life in such an environment. In the wet tropics, the soils leach with great speed, corpses are quickly destroyed through decay and predation, and many forest dwellers may be remote from sources of good stone for implements. Thus, in a rain forest, we may have no bones for the diagnosis of the subspecies of early man, no tools, and not even ashes from whatever fires he may have made. These factors may lead us to underestimate grossly the antiquity of *Homo sapiens* in equatorial Africa, to say nothing of his earliest use of fire and other evidences of high intelligence. With these formidable obstacles in mind, we shall review some of the fossil remains of *Homo sapiens* in Africa south of the Sahara.

In 1932, Leakey found four skulls and a few postcranial fragments associated with handaxes in a deposit at Kanjera, on the south shore of the Gulf of Kavirondo, Lake Victoria. The dating of these finds is much disputed, and may be as early as the Third Glacial or as late as the end of the Pleistocene. In the three better-preserved skulls, one had appreciable brow ridges and two none. Two showed, at the root of the nose, evidences of nasal bones which narrow at the top. The cranial form was long, narrow, and low in the two best specimens. Brain size was some 1,350 to 1,400 cc. The parietal region was ill-filled, as in the Peking and Javan forms of *Homo erectus* and in some Australian aborigines. Associated with one specimen was a full-sized femoral shaft.

These remains of Kanjera man indicate that *Homo sapiens* in East Africa was probably contemporaneous with *Homo erectus* further south. Both may be ancient forms of Congoids. If Kanjera man is early, the Congoids may have evolved about as early as some other subspecies of *Homo sapiens*. If he is recent, the Congoids, as Coon suggests, may have evolved at the end of the Pleistocene from very late forms of *Homo erectus*.

At Cape Flats, near Capetown, three skulls were found in a deposit with a Stillbay culture reminiscent of that of Broken Hill man. One has been described. It has a cranial capacity of 1,250 cc. and has large brow ridges and a rugged face. The teeth are like those of Congoids. Another Stillbay site on the border of Swaziland and Zululand (Border Cave) has yielded a similar skull. They are early post-Pleistocene inhabitants of South Africa, but not Capoid. Coon thinks that they are descendants of the local strain of *Homo erectus,* and are actually the southernmost of the Congoids.

In the highlands of Kenya and Tanganyika, four sites have been found which are clearly those of Capsian migrants from North Africa. They are later than the North African Capsian, and the skulls are indistinguishable from those in the north: i.e., they are Mediterranean Caucasoids with Caucasoid teeth, but their stature is somewhat taller than is usual in North African Capsians. At that time, crossing from North Africa to Kenya by way of the Sahara would not have been difficult, since the climate was not as dry as it is now. Skeletally Caucasoid peoples persisted through the Neolithic in Kenya, and presumably became hybridized extensively with the Bantu Congoids, who moved into the highlands in the Iron Age.

The theory of a northern origin of the Capoids dates back to 1905, when Biasutti thought that Bushman-like traits could be seen in the earliest pre-Dynastic Egyptian skulls. In 1924, a skull some 5,000–10,000 years old was found on the bank of the Blue Nile, 200 miles south of Khartoum, at Singa. The Singa specimen coexisted with extinct species of antelope, porcupine, and giraffe. The skull has a narrow, bulging forehead and parietals, moderately large brow ridges, rectangular orbits, a flat face, and a large jaw. It is apparently a Capoid of large body size.

At Homa, Lake Victoria, Kenya, two skulls have been found in a Mesolithic shell mound with Early Wilton (Bushman) artifacts. These, too, are the remains of large-bodied Capoids. At Boskop, on the east bank of the Mooi River in the southwestern Transvaal, a third such skull has been located. From Florisbad, a mineral spring twenty-five miles north of Bloemfontein in the Transvaal, has come what seems to be a fourth. All are presumably post-Pleistocene.

Some 8,000–9,000 years ago, Capoids were the main, if not the only, inhabitants of southern Africa. The fairly abundant skeletal remains indicate that some populations became small and others did not. Dwarfism and fetalization of the face were most extreme in the marginal, desert-dwelling Bushmen. The Hottentots were larger and less fetalized, and were also probably more hybridized with Congoids.

Less than 1,000 years ago, large Capoids built hilltop forts or shrines at Mapungwe and Bambandyanolo, near the Limpopo River in the northern Transvaal. These forts were in use until less than 200 years before the Dutch settled in Capetown. The abundant skeletal remains of these people were unequivocally Capoid, and clay figurines of the women show the steatopygia and elongated labia minora which can still be found in living Bush and Hottentot women.

Another large Capoid people (the Duwwud) still live by three salt lakes in the Fezzan, Libya. The Sandawe, a tribe speaking a language related to Bush and Hottentot, still live in central Tanganyika.

The sum of this evidence suggests that the Capoids are a northern people who have moved south since the Pleistocene. Perhaps they were displaced by Mouillians and Capsians along the Mediterranean coast. They may be the descendants of the Ternefine subspecies of *Homo erectus*. They are a sizable ingredient in the racial ancestry of the present-day Bantu (12) and Cape Colored (28) peoples of tropical and southern Africa.

Most of the Africans south of the Sahara today are Congoids. We have encountered them so far at the extremes of their ancient, more restricted homeland, in the Kanjera, Cape Flats, and Border Cave specimens previously described.

The oldest modern-looking Congoid skeleton which has yet appeared is Asselar man. This specimen was found in the dry bed of a former river about 250 miles north of Timbuktu in the Sahara. While he was alive, the river flowed copiously and contained mollusks and crocodiles, and the countryside was alive with game. Asselar man probably dates from the early post-Pleistocene. His postcranial skeleton is much like that of a slim, long-limbed Sudanese Negro of today. His brain was large (1,520 cc.), and his face short, like many West African and also Bantu men of today. His teeth were large and typically Congoid.

At least ten other Congoids have been found in association with Neolithic, and possibly Mesolithic, artifacts, in a rock shelter at Kourounkorokalé, in Mali, twenty-three miles southwest of Bamako. Some are short in stature. Other Mesolithic skeletons, perhaps no more than 5,000 years old, come from Khartoum. One, which has been described, is much like a living Sudanese: Congoid with Caucasoid admixture.

One of the most important Congoid stocks is the pygmy, or African Negrito (11). These very small people often have sizable brow ridges, bulbous foreheads, and pop eyes. They are hairier than most other Congoids, and not so dark in skin color. Today, about 168,500 pygmies live in isolated tracts of forest from Gabun and the Cameroons in Central

Africa to Uganda and Rwanda and Urundi. Their former habitat may have been more continuous and more extensive.

Coon believes that the modern large Congoids represent crossings of pygmies with all the other African varieties of man, especially archaic large Congoids in eastern and western Africa. Other mixtures have probably included Caucasoids in northeastern Africa and the highlands of eastern Africa, and Capoids in both eastern and southern Africa. Large Congoids have also invaded pygmy territory, especially since the Neolithic, occupying tracts of forest land and practicing slash-and-burn agriculture. These movements even today involve considerable hybridization, especially between larger men and pygmy women.

In recent millennia, speakers of Bantu languages have pushed vigorously out of the Congo into eastern and southern Africa. Bantu were still moving toward the Cape of Good Hope when the Dutch arrived there in the seventeenth century. In each new migration, Bantu probably hybridized with indigenous pygmies, Caucasoids, and Capoids, so that in South Africa particularly, the Bantu are highly composite genetically.

This reconstruction of Congoid history is based heavily on the present-day distribution of this subspecies in Africa. Of all the racial histories now being reconstructed, this one is probably the most in need of revision and clarification in the light of future discoveries. In the meantime, Congoids are increasing rapidly in the new nations of Africa. The slave trade brought millions of them to the New World; Brazil has the largest number of them, with the United States second. Gene flow between Congoids and other races have produced hybrids such as Stocks 27 (Ladino), 28 (Cape Colored), and 29 (North American Colored).

In the United States, gene flow between Caucasoids and Congoids has gone on for over 300 years. It is estimated that most North American Colored people have some non-African ancestry, and Stuckert claims that about one-fifth of the Caucasoids in the United States are part African. Although the United States can be expected to preserve a considerable separation of the two groups, in a few centuries all of America's colored population will be part European, and a minor African strain will pervade the whites. These trends will not necessarily make perceptible changes in the average phenotypes of the two unless the magnitude of gene flow between them undergoes great changes.

Racial History of the Caucasoids

Historically, the Caucasoids are the western Palearctic subspecies of man. The stocks of modern man which are mainly Caucasoid are 1 (Northwest European), 2 (Northeast European), 3 (Lapp), 4 (Alpine), 5 (Mediterranean), 6 (Nordic), 7 (Hindu), 8 (Hamite), and perhaps 19 (Ainu).

The fossil remains of Caucasoids are more numerous than those of all the rest of mankind put together. This abundance is probably a result of the following factors: prolonged archaeological searching in Caucasoid territory, burials of bones in sheltered places such as caves, and conditions

143

of soil and climate which did not lead to the leaching and disappearance of skeletal materials in all cases.

The hallmarks of the Caucasoid skeleton have already been mentioned under the racial history of Africa, but need further elaboration here. In general, the brain is large, even in very ancient Caucasoids. Except for a few early fossils, the teeth are small to medium in size and rather plain. A frequent feature is Carabelli's cusp, an accessory flange or ledge on the anterior, lingual aspect of upper molars. As the tooth wears down after many years, this ledge comes into function as an extension of the chewing surface. It can therefore help to extend the life span of the tooth. In subspecies other than Caucasoids, this feature is rare.

Caucasoid molars are relatively reduced and simple in form, and the frequency of congenital absence of the third molar is high, but generally not at the Mongoloid extreme.

Accompanying these plain and simple teeth is a vertical profile of the jaws below the nose, even in many ancient Caucasoids. The nose is rather narrow and prominent, with a high root. The degree of facial flattening is the lowest of all the subspecies of man. The muscles of mastication are set well back, and the malars are rather feeble and retreating. Compared with those of Mongoloids, the masseters are weak, but the temporals and their bony attachments (especially the coronoid process) are often strong, especially in ancient Caucasoids.

In the fossil history of man in Caucasoid territory, no indubitable remains of *Homo erectus* have yet been found. Instead, a great deal is known about more advanced grades of *Homo sapiens,* some of which preserved archaic facial features along with their large brains. The western Palearctic region seems to have been a central location in the formation of human races, and peripheral Caucasoids have probably exchanged genes with their neighbors of other subspecies since the Middle Pleistocene. In India, they met Australoids. In southern Arabia, they met people who may have been Australoid or, less likely, Congoid. Toward North and East Africa they apparently encountered Capoids and Congoids. At least after the Pleistocene, if not earlier, they met Mongoloids in Assam, Bengal, eastern Europe, and central and western Asia. This extensive hybridization may have been an important reason why most Caucasoid populations have shown advanced skeletal features at least as early as the other human subspecies, and sometimes even earlier. Because of their eventful history, Caucasoids today have poorer reasons than any other human subspecies for considering themselves a "pure" race.

The earliest human tools from Caucasoid territory are from early Middle Pleistocene deposits. Throughout the Middle Pleistocene, Europe and western Asia were inhabited by makers of handaxes, and this implement is widely distributed from the Atlantic coast of Europe and northern Africa to India. Thus, except for Africa, these tools seem to demarcate the very extensive territory in which Caucasoid evolution took place. In Eurasia, all the modern inhabitants of handax territory are Caucasoids except where Huns, Mongols, Turks, or African slaves have left appreciable numbers of mixed descendants.

In the Caucasoid realm, the earliest evidence of human bones and teeth is from Europe, in one corner of handax territory. These remains were found in 1907 in a sandpit in Mauer, six miles southeast of Heidelberg. Their date may be the beginning of the second, or Mindel, glaciation, about 350,000 years ago—thus apparently contemporaneous with the Peking and Ternefine forms of *Homo erectus.*

The ascending ramus of the Mauer jaw is remarkably broad, a feature which is due chiefly to a prodigious development of the coronoid process and may indicate powerful temporal muscles. The gonial region, however, is rounded. Thus, the masseter and medial pterygoid muscles were not so far forward or as powerful as in Peking man. In these respects the Mauer jaw was already differentiated in a Caucasoid direction.

The intercondylar breadth is narrower than in a typical *Homo erectus,* so that the cranial base may have been reduced in breadth. Narrowness of the cranial base in hominids generally is evidence of an inflated brain case and perhaps a large brain.

The teeth are about as large as in living Australian aborigines, and completely lack Mongoloid specializations. This large but plain dentition could have evolved into that of modern Caucasoids through a simple reduction in size.

With teeth of rather moderate size and a somewhat narrowed cranial base, the Mauer jaw may have belonged to a form of *Homo erectus* as advanced as the Broken Hill man of Rhodesia (Figure 75). It is even possible that his brain was large enough to qualify him as *Homo sapiens.*

At Steinheim, twelve miles north of Stuttgart, a woman's skull was found in deposits dating from the great (Mindel-Riss) interglacial, perhaps 250,000 years old (Figure 77, II, e). This specimen differs radically from *Homo erectus* in several features—a modern-looking, rounded occiput, narrow cranial base, and fairly small brow ridges. Prognathism of the lower face was minimal. All the teeth are smaller than the average for Australian aborigines, and are plain Caucasoid teeth except for moderate taurodontism. The third molar is very reduced in size. The cranial capacity was about 1,150–1,175 cc.

A similar but more fragmentary specimen, consisting of a thick occipital and two parietal bones, comes from Swanscombe in a terrace of the Thames River (Figure 75, II, f). Tools from a Middle Acheulian flake-and-handax culture are associated with the remains. As the frontal region is lacking, nothing can be said about brow ridges, but the brain was probably larger than the Steinheim specimen (about 1,275–1,325 cc.).

During the Riss glaciation, the colder parts of Europe seem to have been abandoned by man. The Riss-Würm interglacial, however, ushered in the early Upper Pleistocene, and human skeletal remains of this interglacial are known from France, Italy, Germany, Czechoslovakia, Yugoslavia, and, outside Europe, from Israel.

Two skull caps from Fontéchevade, in Charente, France, are associated with a Tayacian flake industry and a warm climate. These skulls are thick-walled, long, and broad. One has a capacity of 1,460–1,470 cc. (Figure 76). The brow ridges of both are probably even smaller than those of most modern Europeans. Aside from this progressive feature, they seem to resemble the Swanscombe and Steinheim specimens of the previous (Mindel-Riss) interglacial.

Two skulls from Saccopastore (Figure 77, II, c), just outside the walls of Rome, show an odd combination of archaic and modern features. The cranial capacity is about 1,200–1,300 cc., the cranial bases narrow, and the brow ridges fairly small. The faces are long, and the upper face projects forward to resemble a muzzle. These specimens are associated with Mousterian implements.

At Ehringsdorf, near Weimar in eastern Germany, along with a very diversified Mousterian industry, a large skull was found with fairly large brow ridges, but otherwise much like the Steinheim and Swanscombe specimens in form. A stone brain case from Gánovce, near Poprad, Slovakia, is probably contemporary and has a capacity of 1,320 cc.

From 1895 to 1906, at Krapina, in Croatia, Yugoslavia, along with a poorly described group of implements, were found five identifiable skulls, over 600 scraps of bone, and over 270 teeth. Brow ridges are large, noses salient, and the vault low; the brain sizes in the two best skulls are in the range of about 1,200–1,450 cc., at the least. Of great interest is the fact that many of these people were brachycranial (roundheaded), like most living Croats. This trait has become increasingly prevalent in modern man, but not wholly from genetic causes (see Constitution).

Two mandibles from France, as well as those from Ehringsdorf and Krapina, should be mentioned. Of the French finds, one is from a cave in Montmaurin (Haut-Garonne), and the other from Monsempron (Lot-et-Garonne).

The jaw from Montmaurin is robust, chinless, and small, with a convex lower border. It is slightly similar in form to the Mauer jaw, but far less massive and a little broader in the bicondylar dimension. The specimen from Monsempron is noteworthy in having a *torus mandibularis,* a feature mentioned in connection with Mongoloids and with some present-day Arctic Caucasoids.

One adult mandible from Ehringsdorf is rather like that from Heidelberg, but with more of a suggestion of a chin and a less massive body.

Eleven scraps of mandible found at Krapina are thick, prognathous, mostly chinless, and with rounded, blunted gonial regions.

The dental particulars of these early Upper Pleistocene Europeans show variations which could occur within a single human stock. All are within the size range of living *Homo sapiens,* but some are larger than in modern Europeans. The teeth of both the Heidelberg and Swanscombe finds could also be included in this collection. It would appear that the crowns of European teeth today are not much smaller than those of these early fossils, but some evolution seems to have taken place in the molar region, and perhaps in the incisors. In Heidelberg man, on one side the second molar is probably the largest, and the first and third equal. Perhaps on the other side the third is smaller than the first. The Montmaurin mandible shows the very primitive order 3>2>1. An immature jaw from Ehrings- dorf shows 2>1, whereas in an adult female from Ehringsdorf we find 2>1>3 on one side and 1>2>3 on the other. At Krapina we find 1>2=3. On the whole, the teeth of central Europe are more advanced in size-order than those of France, and the later teeth are more progressive than the earlier. Modern Caucasoids usually show the order 1>2>3.

Not all of the molars have been adequately studied, but taurodontism was certainly more prevalent than in living Caucasoids. At Ehringsdorf, the permanent teeth of a child's jaw were taurodont but those of the adult were not. The Krapina population runs to extremes in taurodontism, and one tooth has an enamel pearl. At least one upper first molar has a Cara- belli's cusp.

The incisors show more shoveling in these early people than in modern Caucasoids. An upper central incisor from Monsempron is moderately shoveled and has a lingual tubercle. Moderate shoveling is seen in many of the Krapina specimens, along with some basal tubercles. Except for the "Caucasoid" Carabelli's cusp, these dental traits seem to show genetic connections with the North African peoples descended from Ternefine man.

At Krapina, where postcranial remains are most abundant, the people were rather small in size, with definitely Caucasoid traits of the carpus and scapula. Perhaps they were built like the slender tribal peoples of India today at the Caucasoid-Australoid frontier, such as some of the primitive Dravidians and Veddas.

The oldest fragments from the rich and long-occupied Tabun cave at Mount Carmel, Palestine, are a straight femoral shaft and a worn molar tooth. Both resemble those of the Ehringsdorf and Krapina people.

We now turn to the early part of the Würm glaciation, from about 75,000 to 40,000 years ago. In the Caucasoid homeland, the major culture was the Mousterian, a composite of many earlier traditions of flake and core techniques. In some places this culture dates back into the previous interglacial (Riss-Würm). It is found all the way from Shansi in China to Europe. Its broad distribution suggests that Caucasoids probably ex- changed genes with early Mongoloids in China, Australoids or Congoids in southern Arabia, and Capoids presumably in North Africa.

Over this huge area, thus far the eastern region shows the clearest con- tinuity of evolution from archaic to modern Caucasoids. Our major prob- lem is to decide how much of the Caucasoid homeland was involved in this fairly rapid "modernization" of human populations. In the Middle East, for example, cultures of broadly Mousterian affiliation are associated with the bones and teeth of Caucasoids of Neanderthal, intermediate, and modern types. Furthermore, the transition from Middle to Upper Paleo-

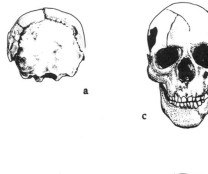

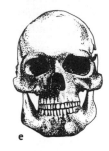

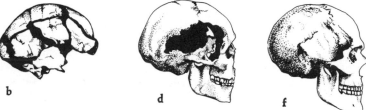

FIG. 57

FIG. 57   Europeans of the Third Interglacial (a) Swanscombe (England). (b) Ehringsdorf, near Weimar. Europeans of the Fourth Glacial (c, d) Combe Capelle, male. (e, f) Male from Oberkassel.

FIG. 58   Europeans of the Upper Paleolithic and Mesolithic (a, b) Oberkassel, female. (c, d) Bottendorf, male. (e, f) Gramat, male.

FIG. 59   Central European Neolithic skulls (a, b) Bell Beaker male, flat occiput. (c, d) Bell Beaker female, convex occiput. (e, f) Danubian I male, gracile and longheaded.

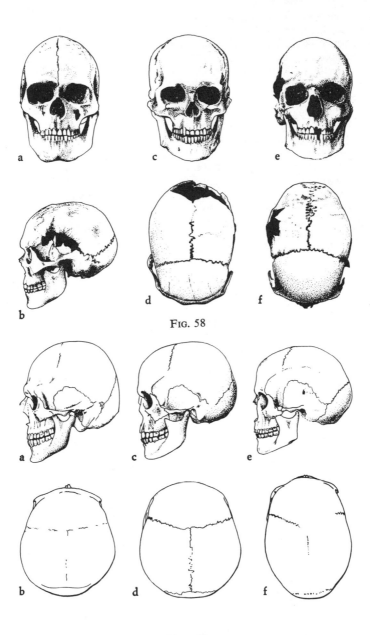

a   c   e

b   d   f

FIG. 58

a   c   e

b   d   f

FIG. 59

lithic cultures is rather gradual. In Europe, on the other hand, fewer physical intermediates are found, although two Mousterian sites are known in association with skeletally modern Caucasoids. Perhaps modern western Caucasoids were immigrants who did not entirely evolve from western Neanderthaloids, but nevertheless may have still been culturally Mousterian when they reached Europe.

In discussing the archaic Caucasoids of the early Würm glaciation, we use the term "Neanderthal man" in a more restricted sense than do many other writers. Here we employ the term to refer to archaic Caucasoids with peculiarities of head, face, and body. These features were most extreme in western Europe, but even in Uzbekistan only slightly more advanced strains of Neanderthal man have been found.

In western and southern Europe, the remains of about fifty-five Neanderthal skeletons are known, but most are fragmentary. They are remarkably homogeneous morphologically, and apparently constitute three partially isolated groups: one in France, Belgium, and western Germany; a second in Spain and Portugal; and a third in Italy.

The Italian group in particular forms a clear evolutionary and cultural line of descent from the early Mousterian people of Saccopastore, who are the most Neanderthaloid of the Europeans of the preceding interglacial.

The cranial features of these western Neanderthal men are characteristic (see Paleoanthropology). The occiput is abruptly rounded and projecting, and the lambdoid region has a characteristic "sagging" look (see Figure 77, II, a, b). The brain case is broad, overlying a narrow cranial base. The brow ridges are fairly large, the nose very projecting, and the interior passages of the nose exceedingly capacious. The malars slope sharply back, the zygomatic arches are rather slender, and the gonial region is rounded. All of these features add up to rather feeble masseter muscles. The maxillae have a swollen appearance, but little or no prognathism below the nose. The size of the brain is as large or larger than that of tall modern Caucasoids: some 1,525–1,640 cc. in males and 1,300–1,425 cc. in females. The chin is not as prominent as in most living Caucasoids, but is usually clearly present. As in some arctic Caucasoids and in Mongoloids in much of their range, three of the ten best-preserved western Neanderthal mandibles have the *torus mandibularis*.

Aside from the brow ridges, deep, round orbits, and rather large teeth, these features are ultra-Caucasoid, but with clear reminiscences still of *Homo erectus* in the facial region.

About half of the well-studied western Neanderthal molar teeth are taurodont. Some moderate shoveling and basal tubercles of the upper central incisors have been seen, some posterior teeth show a cingulum, and a few teeth are wrinkled. These features recall the North African descendants of Ternefine man, but may also indicate exchanges of genes with Asian Mongoloids. In general, these features are less extreme than in the Krapina people, so that perhaps they were gradually being lost in the dentition of Neanderthal man as time went on.

From seven fairly adequate skeletons, and from footprints in some caves where they lived, we can reconstruct the physique of western Neanderthal men. These people were short to medium in stature and very powerful and burly, with large and massive rib cages, very powerful shoulder and forearm muscles, and large, broad feet. They were just as erect in posture as modern man. It is possible that this burly, squat physique, and the enormous nasal air chambers for the warming of breathed-in air, may have been physiological adaptations to living in the cold and desolate tundras of periglacial Europe.

From Piñar, near Granada in Spain, comes evidence of genetic and cultural mingling of Neanderthals and modern Caucasoids during the Gottweig Interstadial (Würm I-II). Here, a cave with a Mousterian culture was found with slight traces of Upper Paleolithic influence, and a modern Caucasoid mandible. Either modern man arrived in western Europe from elsewhere with a culture which was still Mousterian, or the local Neanderthal peoples abruptly evolved into modern Caucasoids.

In central and eastern Europe, the climate was so severe that Mousterian sites are rare. Three mandibles are known from Hungary and Czechoslovakia, and they resemble the western Neanderthals except for a greater degree of alveolar prognathism. From the Subalyuk cave in the Bükk Mountains in Hungary, the mandible and some of the postcranial bones of a very small woman have been discovered, as well as the bones of a child.

A very important find is a skull from a Mousterian level in a cave called Veternica near Zagreb, Yugoslavia. Above it is a culture transitional from Mousterian to Upper Paleolithic. One skull from the lower level and three from the upper are all modern Caucasoids. They date from the Gottweig (Würm I-II) Interstadial, like the remains from Piñar in Spain. Here is evidence of cultural continuity from the Middle to Upper Paleolithic in Yugoslavia. Again we are faced with the possibility that Mousterian Neanderthal populations evolved into modern Caucasoids in Yugoslavia, or else modern men at a culturally Mousterian level had already arrived there from elsewhere.

The Crimea contains several Mousterian sites, and in two of them skeletal remains are known: Kiik-Koba and Starosel'e. At Kiik-Koba a hand, foot, tibia, and tooth were found, and in Starosel'e a battered infant skeleton. The former is much like a western European Neanderthal man. The infant is from a late Mousterian site. It has a rather thick vault for its age and somewhat large molars. Perhaps it is an intermediate between a Neanderthal and a modern Caucasoid.

In southwestern Uzbekistan, some seventy-eight miles south of Samarkand, a Mousterian cave site called Teshik-Tash yielded the remains of a nine-year-old Neanderthal boy. Its date is disputed. Some of the Soviet workers think it is from the Riss-Würm Interglacial, but the American Movius favors assigning it to the Würm I-II Interstadial. If the latter date is correct, this Teshik-Tash boy may have been contemporaneous with an Upper Paleolithic culture 150 miles to the south, in Afghanistan. The

151

brain is large, and the face lacks the puffy maxillae and sagging lambdoid contour of typical western European Neanderthaloids. Cranially, it is a less archaic form of Caucasoid than its western relatives, and from the neck down, it is wholly modern.

In Anatolia and Iran, Mousterian industries are associated with a few small skeletal fragments, but seven Neanderthal skeletons have been recovered from an immense cave called Shanidar in the western Zagros Mountains of northern Iraq. Dates from over 60,000 years ago to 46,000 are calculated from Carbon-14 for the Mousterian at Shanidar. Like the find at Teshik-Tash, the largest adult male from Shanidar has a less "sagging" lambdoid region than the western Neanderthals and smaller brow ridges. His cranial capacity was very large: over 1,700 cc. The superior ramus of the pubic bone is peculiarly flattened. The form of the pubic bone is unknown in the European Neanderthals, but a similar peculiarity was found in a Palestinian Neanderthal woman from Tabun, to be mentioned presently. Reports on the other six skeletons are not yet available.

For the period of Würm I in Palestine, skeletal remains are known from six caves, and range from Neanderthals like those at Shanidar and Teshik-Tash to modern Caucasoids. One of the "intermediate" specimens, Skhul 5, could pass for an Australian aborigine (Figure 77, II, d).

From Zuttiya in Galilee and Tabun at Mount Carmel, evidences of fairly archaic Neanderthals are found for Würm I. The best-preserved woman of Tabun has the short stature, bowed forearm bones, and burly build of a western Neanderthal, but her cranial vault shows the eastern trait of a more elevated lambdoid region. Her pubic ramus resembles that of Shanidar's largest male.

Also on Mount Carmel, near the Tabun cave, is the Skhul cave. Its inhabitants lived perhaps 10,000 years later, and the remains of ten individuals are known from this cave. They are decidedly transitional from Neanderthal to modern man, and suggest that Palestine at this time may have been a zone of hybridization of Caucasoids, Capoids, and perhaps even Australoids. The Skhul people had variable but usually beaky noses, strong zygomatic arches, large brains, and prognathism of the jaws in some cases.

The Tabun teeth show slight shoveling, and in one canine, a slight cingulum. Shoveling and ridging are less prominent in the Skhul people, indicating that in this line of evolution, as in Europe, Caucasoids were losing these archaic traits. Mongoloids, as we have mentioned, have retained and even exaggerated them.

The Skhul pelves had lost the Tabun-Shanidar flattening of the superior ramus of the pubis. Most of the Skhul people were medium to tall, with few Neanderthal postcranial features except for a burly rib cage in one man (Skhul 4).

Contemporaneous and similar in culture to the Skhul people were the inhabitants of Ksar Akil, outside of Beirut in Lebanon. From this site has come an excellent skull of a modern Caucasoid child.

In describing the postcranial materials from Tabun and Skhul, Sir Arthur Keith and T. D. McCown noted the many detailed resemblances between these remains and those of South African Bushmen. These similarities appear in the vertebrae, ischial portions of the pelvis, the sciatic notch, hands, wrists, feet, and ankles.

These discoveries indicate that in the early Würm period, southwestern Asia may have been a zone of race mixture between Caucasoids, Capoids, and perhaps Australoids. Here, in all probability, modern Caucasoids evolved out of Neanderthal ancestors. With less certainty, this zone of Caucasoid evolution may have included the Crimea, the Balkans, and perhaps even Spain.

During and after the Gottweig Interstadial (Würm I-II), or from about 40,000 to 29,000 B.C., Neanderthal populations gave way to modern Caucasoids. At this time, a clear continuity from Mousterian to Upper Paleolithic cultures is seen in Palestine, Lebanon, Syria, and possibly western Iran. To most workers, this continuity is not yet convincing in Yugoslavia and Spain, which we have already mentioned, nor in Hungary. Future research may well extend this zone of continuity into Turkey, Iran, Afghanistan, Central Asia, and Europe.

The sites where Upper Paleolithic skeletal remains have been found include forty-three in France, twelve in Germany, and eight or less in Czechoslovakia, the Low Countries, Spain, Italy, Britain, Austria, Switzerland, Hungary, Rumania, and the Soviet Union. This concentration in the west and south is similar to the antecedent Mousterian distribution. Modern Caucasoids persisted through bitter glacial climates until the end of the Pleistocene, around 8000 B.C., but the places which were too cold for Neanderthal man may have been too much for the later Caucasoids as well.

Europeans of the Upper Paleolithic often lived and buried their dead in caves, and adorned the walls of these shelters with extraordinary works of art. These art styles show continuity in some places for 20,000 years. Although representations of the human form are rare, a few of the cave drawings and paintings, and sculptured figurines and bas-reliefs, allow us to reconstruct external features of the people in addition to internal details ascertainable from their bones and teeth.

Important differences between Upper Paleolithic and modern Europeans can be found in the jaws and teeth. These early peoples chewed vigorously on tough foods and probably skins, wore their teeth down rapidly, and experienced little or no dental decay. In childhood, these habits modify the growth of the face in the direction of low, broad dental arches and evenly spaced teeth, short faces, rugged zygomatic arches, and perhaps even low orbits. Trends away from such features in modern Europeans are not necessarily evidences of genetic or evolutionary changes in the face, but probably result from feeble mastication, slow wearing down of the teeth, and often the effects of dental caries and extracted teeth on the growth of the dental arches, according to Hunt.

European men of the Upper Paleolithic were usually of medium rather than tall stature, and the women were rather short. The physique was fine-boned, and in warmer regions the shins and forearms were elongated. The hands and feet were like those of slender living Europeans. The brains of the men were rather large (mean about 1,580 cc.), and in the women were small to medium (about 1,370 cc.). The brain cases were generally narrow and the zygomatic arches broad and strong, but not jutting forward.

The cave art and the statuettes reveal skin colors much as in modern Europeans. Men may show beards and baldness, and most have prominent noses. Female statuettes, sometimes pregnant, are typically very obese, with subcutaneous fat distributions all too familiar to us in fat Caucasoid women today. It is possible, however, that steatopygia, now a Capoid specialty, was commoner in Europe then than now (Figure 60).

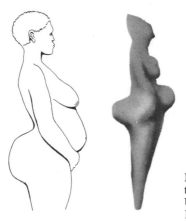

FIG. 60 Left: steatopygia in a female Hottentot. Right: stylized steatopygia in an Upper Paleolithic female statuette from the Riviera (about 6–8 cm. tall).

Space permits only a very short account of the subsequent racial history of the Caucasoids. In brief, some of the physical differences between eastern and western Neanderthal man still persist today. In the west, brow ridges are still larger than in the Middle East, and a crude gradient of increasing frequency of archaic Caucasoid features can be traced from the Middle East to maxima in southern Norway, Iceland, and Ireland.

Some 10,000 years ago, at the end of the Pleistocene, the climate gradually became milder and the ice melted in northern Germany and finally Scandinavia. Many of the arctic animals, such as reindeer, mammoth, and musk ox, retreated northward near the ice or became extinct. Man moved northward, too, so that the Upper Paleolithic people of Europe eventually became Mesolithic fishermen, shellfish diggers, and hunters of smaller game. A clear continuity of both culture and physical type can be traced in Europe between Paleolithic and Mesolithic peoples. Indeed, much of the ancestry of the present-day peoples of Europe, particularly in the North, seems to be basically western Neanderthals, much hybridized with modern Caucasoid migrants from the Middle East and, perhaps later on, North Africa.

As the ice melted and people moved northward, perhaps their pigmentation became less dark, but bones and teeth do not allow us to do more than guess how or when this blondism became prominent in Caucasoids, particularly in the North. As populations moved toward Scandinavia in Europe, the Caucasoid Mouillian and Capsian peoples, who were mentioned in the racial history of Africa, may have spread from east to west. Later, some of the Capsians pushed as far south as the highlands of Kenya.

In the Middle East since the end of the Pleistocene, there has been a trend toward slenderness of build and smallness of teeth. This region was at least the western portion of the homeland of the Mediterraneans (Stock 5). From the Middle East to India, our knowledge of Mediterranean and Australoid evolution is negligible.

The Middle East seems to have been the center from which most of man's basic knowledge of agriculture and animal husbandry originated. This so-called "Neolithic revolution" began about 8,000 years ago. These technological changes permitted far greater numbers of people to occupy fertile lands than had ever before been possible. The earliest Neolithic peoples were Mediterraneans. Once their new way of life had prevailed in their homeland, they moved vigorously across North Africa into western Europe, and also into the Balkans and eastern and central Europe. Gradually the Neolithic way of life spread throughout the Old World except to such isolated groups as Australian aborigines and African pygmies and Bushmen. The high cultures of the New World seem to have evolved largely or wholly in isolation from these developments in Eurasia and Africa.

When metals began to be exploited and towns sprang up in the Middle East, the Mediterranean peoples became still more slender and their teeth smaller. Similar changes can be traced in the bones and teeth of man's domesticated animals. Certainly these animals were selected for tractableness, but there may also have been incidental selection for toleration of crowding, infections, and squalor, as well as diets deficient in protein in youth. Similar selective processes very likely work on crowded human populations in towns and cities. In man at least, some of these tendencies are non-genetic and can be reversed in a single generation of excellent health and nutrition, so that present-day Americans look more like Upper Paleolithic peoples than did their immediate ancestors, according to Hunt.

Brachycephalization

One of the outstanding historical changes in modern man is the rounding of the head. (For data on this subject in historic times, see Constitution.) At birth, in all living human subspecies, the breadth of the head averages about 80 per cent of the length. Most of the postnatal

155

growth of these dimensions is completed in the first year of life. If the head grows mainly in length, the individual will have a medium or long-headed cranial form. If breadth grows more actively, he will be round-headed. (For the most widely used subdivisions of the breadth-length index, see Methods of Anthropology.)

By no means all of these postnatal changes in head form are genetic in origin. As Walcher first showed, the head of an infant is heavy and plastic enough so that if he habitually lies on his back, the final shape of his head will be somewhat rounded. Bayley showed that relatively inactive infants, who voluntarily spend much of their time on their backs, also develop somewhat rounded heads.

This plasticity of the infant head can be far more drastically altered by hard cradleboards, head binding, or tight swaddling. The occiput alone, or both the forehead and occiput, can be deformed, either obliquely or transversely. Two of the photographs in this volume (Figure 50, f—"Dinaric"; and Figure 53, b—"Armenoid") illustrate examples of Balkan and Middle Eastern peoples who often use cradleboards which compress the infant occiput. The terms "Dinaric" and "Armenoid" have long been used by anthropologists to refer to alleged racial types whose brachycephaly was considered fixed and hereditary. Modern work on cranial deformation in the Middle East, especially studies by Ewing, have shown that so many alleged Dinarics and Armenoids spent their infancy on cradle-boards that the cephalic index is a most unreliable hallmark of taxonomic status in many parts of the Balkans and southwestern Asia.

Even with little or no deliberate deformation of the infant head, this index can change in a single generation when peoples migrate to the United States (Boas). In fact, some modern European populations lately have been becoming more longheaded (see Constitution).

Brachycephaly, in fact, is neither uniquely human nor wholly modern. The orangutan is brachycephalic, and so are a majority of chimpanzees. At least one of the Australopithecines (Paranthropus) is also brachyce-phalic. All three of the best-preserved Middle Paleolithic skulls from Krapina are roundheads, and the most complete specimen from Fonté-chevade is nearly so (cranial index about 79).

Among the Upper Paleolithic Caucasoids of Europe, two of the three adult skulls from Solutré, Saône-et-Loire, France, are brachycrane, as well as some of the sample of over thirty skeletons from the Mouillian site of Afalou-bou-Rhummel, in Constantine, Algeria. Three out of eleven Mesolithic skulls from Ofnet and Kaufertsberg in Bavaria are brachycrane.

From the Neolithic on, a sizable number of archaeological sites show impressive increases in the cranial index. Krogman showed that the Meso-potamians of Aliçar Hüyük from 3500 B.C. to A.D. 1500 showed an aver-age increase from 72.9 to 88.4. In Switzerland and southern Germany, Hug found increases from 76.1 to 84.4, from the Neolithic to the Renais-sance.

Among Caucasoids, the regions of greatest brachycephaly are generally at high altitudes, such as in or near the Alps in Europe, in the Caucasus, and among the Lapps. More moderate brachycephaly prevails in much of central and eastern Europe, the Balkans, Italy, Germany, and parts of France. In Europe, even mesocephalic averages are confined to Norway, Sweden, Iceland, Great Britain, Portugal, and Spain. In all European countries where the phenomenon has been studied, the indices have at least slightly increased since the Neolithic.

Among Mongoloids, the great majority of living groups are brachycephalic. The main exceptions are Marginal American Indians. Nonetheless, much of this distribution is recent, as though there have been independent evolutionary trends toward roundheadedness in widely separated regions of the earth.

The subspecies least affected by this trend have been the Capoids, the tall Congoids, and the Australoids. Even in these subspecies, however, a few roundheaded groups appear, especially among pygmies. Among these are the pygmy Aeta of the Philippines, the Mincopies of the Andamans, and the Baining of New Britain. Among Congoids, groups in the central Congo basin and the Cameroons are roundheaded.

Weidenreich believed that brachycephalization is a real evolutionary trend, independently expressed in different subspecies, toward withdrawal of the face under the brain case and foreshortening of the cranial base. He considers it one of the final adaptations toward an erect posture. It is not related to an increase in brain size or to any obvious differences in behavior or intelligence between longheads and roundheads.

Even in these world-wide evolutionary trends, it is remotely possible that responses of the infant head to pressure have contributed to it. If recent mankind has been gradually acquiring a less massive and less mineralized skeleton, perhaps a given amount of occipital pressure on a modern-day infant's head may make it more globular than such pressure might have done to the skull of an earlier child.

Bielicki has carried out family studies in Poland which indicate that the more brachycephalic soldiers in the Polish army have more surviving siblings than Poles with longer heads. Even if this finding is substantiated by further work on the selective advantage of being round-headed, the possible biochemical reasons for this situation are still unknown.

Pigmentation

In classical antiquity, Poseidonius believed that the colder parts of Europe predisposed men to barbarity and were related to their fair coloration. With the advent of scientific anthropology in the eighteenth century, practically all writers remarked on the climatic differentiation of human skin, hair, and eye color. Buffon was especially explicit on this point.

In 1833, Gloger carried out a pioneering study of climate and pigmentation in birds and mammals. Most of his data apply to European birds, but he also mentions weasels, hares, bears, and men. His cases for the most part apply to differences between species, but within genera; however, some are variations between subspecies of a single species. Modern workers have found that in general these rules fit polytypic species better than the extensive, very ancient adaptive radiations encompassed in the higher taxonomic units.

In modern terms, Rensch formulated Gloger's main generalization as follows: Within a polytypic species of warm-blooded vertebrates, members in warm, dry regions tend toward intense melanin deposition in exposed parts of the body. Individuals in cool, moist regions show less. In warm, arid regions, dark-brown melanin (in birds, eumelanin) is deficient, but yellowish or reddish-brown melanin (in birds, phaeomelanin or desert coloration) is abundant. In cool regions, reddish-brown melanin is deficient, and in the Arctic, dark-brown melanin is reduced (polar coloration).

Rensch tested this rule in 156 comparisons of subspecies of birds in three families, and found that exceptions ran to 12 per cent. In thirty-four pairings of mammalian subspecies in Europe, he also found that 12 per cent were exceptions to the rule.

Rensch says that natural or experimental hybridization of subspecies with different patterns of pigmentation show that these differences are hereditary. Furthermore, if populations have recently migrated from one extreme climate to another, Gloger's rule applies poorly or not at all to them. In general, such recent migrants still retain their ancestral pigmentation.

Rensch and many other workers feel that intense dark melanization may protect against the tropical sun. Reduced colors in the Arctic may aid in the utilization of the feeble winter sunlight, or as protective coloration in the snow. Desert yellowish colors, too, may serve as a means of concealment.

In man, the climatic differentiation of skin color seems clearest in the Caucasoids from subarctic Europe to the Sahara, and in the Congoids and Capoids down to the Cape of Good Hope. It can also be traced from Scandinavia along a line down to southeastern Australia. This trend is much slighter from the Pacific coast of Siberia to Indonesia, which is Mongoloid territory, and among the Mongoloids of the New World as well.

Perhaps this monochrome quality of Mongoloid skin color is a result of the fact that their movements into warm climates have been recent. If so, they seem to exemplify what Rensch noted in subspecies of birds which have changed climates too recently to have altered their pigmentation. In Mongoloids and Caucasoids, however, the palest aboriginal skin colors seem to be established along the damp northwestern coast of Europe among Caucasoids and in North America among Mongoloids.

The mechanisms that underlie these patterns in man are not clear. Statistics on skin cancer indicate that dark coloration may partially protect against sunlight. Dorn and Cutler noted that age-adjusted incidences of this disease in ten metropolitan districts of the United States were twelve times as high in white males as in non-whites, and seven times higher in white women than in non-whites. Allison and Wong found that in Hawaii, the whites again had the greatest incidence, and rates declined with increasing pigmentation in various non-white and hybrid groups. Since skin cancer is ordinarily a disease of the post-reproductive years, however, it is difficult to see how susceptible individuals might be less able to procreate in their most fertile years. Equally uncertain is the possible reduction in reproductive fitness of persons with pale skin due to sunburn in the tropics.

Under primitive conditions, hunting or combat may be more efficient with certain skin colors. Cowles notes how well Negroes with scanty clothing can conceal themselves in the jungle. Similar arguments may apply to the "desert" coloration of the Capoids.

Trends in the color of hair and eyes are clearest from subarctic Europe and adjacent parts of Asia into Africa and India. Nothing as yet can be said about possible adaptive advantages of blond, red, or brown hair in the more northerly Caucasoids, or of blue eyes.

Body Shape and Size

In addition to Gloger's rule on pigmentation, zoologists and anthropologists for over a century have studied the possible relationships between body shape, size, and climate. In warm-blooded vertebrates, the two rules most often applied have been those of Bergmann and Allen.

Bergmann (1847) was a physiologist whose interest lay in the body mass, surface area, and heat production of animals. He pointed out, for example, the fact that large, but not minute, organisms are warm-blooded. He produced extensive evidence from Eurasian birds and domestic and wild mammals that, in general, the smaller-sized geographic subspecies of a species are found in the warmer parts of its range, while the larger-sized subspecies are more often localized in the cooler districts. He extended this rule to variations between species in a genus, but later workers have found that these comparisons are seldom valid.

Allen (1877) was a taxonomist who worked mainly on the extensive collections of North American birds and mammals in the Smithsonian Institution. He independently rediscovered the Bergmann generalization, but thought that exceptions to it might occur where the largest-sized subspecies lived near the center of their range or original habitat. In addition, he observed that protruding body parts, such as tails, ears, bills, extremities, and so forth, are relatively shorter in the cooler parts of the range of a species than in the warmer parts. This pattern today is known as Allen's rule. Finally, he noted an aggregation of mammalian subspecies of maximal size in the north-central states of the United States, with trends toward decreasing size in all directions from this point. Actually, the stature of American Indians also exhibits this tendency.

The rules of Bergmann and Allen are supposedly related to the conservation of body heat. Bergmann himself noted that in many mammalian species, large body size in cold regions is found along with thick subcutaneous fat and abundant fur. Because mass increases as the cube of linear body measurements, and surface area as the square, Bergmann pointed out that larger individuals tend to have a smaller body surface relative to mass than do smaller members of a species. Allen's rule, too, may be relevant to heat conservation, since the more globular the shape of an animal, the less heat it may lose through exposure of its small limbs, ears, tail, or even skull and snout.

In 1908, Ridgeway, in an address to the British Association for the Advancement of Science, applied these rules to man. He noted that in the New World, large and sturdy American Indians were found in the pampas of South America and in northern North America. In most of Europe and Asia, comparable reductions in size can be found from north to south. Ridgeway noted, too, the climatic variations in pigmentation which we have already discussed.

In the past several years, numerous workers have tested the applicability of these thermal rules to man, notably Coon, Garn, Birdsell, Roberts, M. T. Newman, R. W. Newman, Munro, and Schreider. In general, it can be said that great body weight, short limbs, and relatively small surface areas in man are found in conditions of extreme cold, but not excessive subcutaneous adipose thicknesses. Conversely, in a number of tropical desert localities (northern Australia and the Sudan), tall lean peoples with attenuated limbs are found.

Although these extremes of physique must be considerably conditioned by heredity, some of the differentiation of physique with climate in a single human stock may have some environmental basis. In even climates such as Hawaii, seasonal periodicity in human growth is very slight, but in temperate zones, the rate of appearance of centers of ossification and statural growth are greatest in the spring, and the increase of muscular strength behaves similarly. Ponderal growth, presumably largely fattening, is most obviously seen in the fall.

In tropical regions, this seasonal weight gain with chilling weather is probably not evident, and the epiphyses of the long bones are apparently more continuously active. This hypothetical mechanism could produce people whose physique is relatively linear, with elongated extremities, in warm climates. Quite similar effects have been seen in experiments on the growth of mice in warm and cold rooms.

It would seem, then, that in analyzing the formation of human races, care must be taken to differentiate between fixed, hereditary features of the body, teeth, jaws, and face, and those modifications which are reversible in one generation when environmental conditions are altered. In general, where the evolutionist fails to appreciate these plastic responses of the human organism, he will exaggerate the degree to which man today differs from his ancestors in the Upper Paleolithic.

HUMAN GENETICS

The experiments of Johann Gregor Mendel constitute the starting point for both general and experimental genetics. In 1865, Mendel's *Research Upon Plant Hybridization* appeared. That same year saw the publication of the essay "Hereditary Talent and Character," by Francis Galton, the founder of the scientific study of twins and families. Immediately following their rediscovery by Carl Erich Correns, Hugo de Vries, and Erich von Tschermak-Seysenegg in 1900, the Mendelian laws were proven valid for heredity in humans as well; in 1902 their validity was confirmed for alkaptonuria, a disturbance of protein metabolism; in 1905 for brachydactyly; and soon thereafter for normal racial characteristics (researches by Eugen Fischer with the Rehoboth Bastards, 1908). As early as 1775, Immanuel Kant had postulated that in the study of the races of man, consideration should be given only to those traits that can be transmitted by inheritance; now this theoretical requirement could be complied with in scientific practice. Along with anatomy, physiology, and psychology, human genetics became a basic science of anthropology as well as of medicine.

First and foremost came the question of the hereditary nature of normal human characteristics and their modes of inheritance, which had significance particularly for the interpretation of racial relationships and racial origins (see The Formation of Races). In the course of these studies it was discovered that a number of anthropological characteristics were subject to the influence of environmental factors; this discovery gave rise to new questions involving constitutional biology (see Constitution). In addition, the hereditary structure of populations and changes therein were noted (see Social Biology) and also given practical consideration in population policies (see Demography) and in eugenics (the cultivation of inherited traits, the hygiene of heredity). Recently the general conditions affecting heredity and the effect of natural selection and the assortative process on inheritance have been expressed more clearly by mathematical methods in the study of population genetics (see Population Genetics). More recently still, the search for the active mechanisms of the genes (phenogenetics) has come to play an important part in general genetics; it has yielded fruitful results for anthropology as well (see Genetics and Race, The Formation of Races, Constitution); it may well introduce a new phase in ethnological research and lead to a more profound understanding of the psycho-physical differentiation of the species *Homo sapiens*. The hereditary nature of talent and character and its significance for pedagogy and social policies had been recognized as early as Galton. Lately, the study of behavior has also raised the question of hereditary modes of behavior and of the survivals of instinct in man (see Cultural Anthropology).

Chromosomes and Genes

Human cytogenetics (the genetic study of cells) involves considerable difficulty. For a long time there was uncertainty even as to the number of chromosomes responsible for transmitting human genes. By now it has been fixed at 46, arranged in 23 pairs; namely, one pair of sex chromosomes—two X chromosomes in the female, and one X and one (smaller) Y chromosome in the male—and 22 pairs of autosomes. The detailed structure of the chromosomes, particularly the linear arrangement of the chromomeres, in which the individual genes are probably located, and the mechanisms of chromosome division and distribution in cell division are exactly the same in *Homo* as they are in all other organisms. The number and shape of chromosomes depend on the species and, along with other characteristics, serve as an indication of points of relationship. In this respect *Homo* bears a striking resemblance to other members of the Primate order.

As a result of specific cell division processes, egg and sperm cells each show only a single (haploid) set of 23 chromosomes, which, at the time of fertilization, joins with the chromosomes of the other cell to form double (diploid) sets. It is in this process that sex is determined; if a sperm cell with an X chromosome fertilizes an egg cell also bearing an X chromosome, the child will be a female (XX); sperm cells bearing a Y chromosome will produce a male child (XY). With 23 chromosomes there are 2^{23} possible combinations for the parental chromosomes. This estimate is based on the unlikely possibility that crossing over of genes did not occur in these cases. Since most sperms and eggs transmit chromosomes which are mosaics of maternal and paternal genes, the actual probability of identity in two siblings is almost infinitesimally small, being about 8.3×10^{29}. Hence, every human individual who does not have an identical twin is probably genetically unique.

The number of genes in man may be estimated by comparing the total length of human chromosomes with that of the chromosomes in the fruit fly (*Drosophila*), the most popular laboratory animal in experimental genetics; estimates range from 24,000 to 42,000 for the single chromosome set. The influence of individual genes can be determined only if different alleles of them are present (for example, a dominant allele *D* for pigmentation and a recessive allele *d* for lack of pigmentation), which, in mating, can combine to form various genotypes or inherited patterns (dominant homozygote *DD*, heterozygote *Dd*, recessive homozygote *dd*) and can cause various phenotypes or external forms (for instance, strong or weak pigmentation).

At least 336 individual genes are known in man thus far, divided as follows: 51 for normal characteristics and 285 for hereditary defects. The heavy preponderance of pathological genes is explained by the fact that the majority of normal traits depend on the interaction of numerous genes (polygeny, polymery), which renders genetic analysis difficult or entirely impossible. Hereditary defects, on the other hand, frequently originate through one single defective gene (monogeny, monomery). In related types there is agreement in the number and shape of chromosomes, as well as in single genes, depending on how close the relationship is. Hence the study of comparative inheritance permits analogous conclusions with regard to human genes and gene effects wherever the same hereditary traits occur in related genera (chondrodystrophy, pigmentation marks, and so forth).

Methods of Human Genetics—the Study of Twins and Families

Human genetics has at its disposal an invaluable method of determining whether the formation of any one given characteristic was influenced by hereditary predispositions; namely, the "twin method." There are two

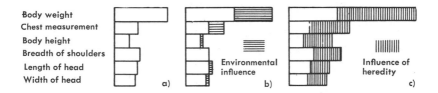

FIG. 61 Influence of hereditary and environmental factors on variability of measurement characteristics. Mean difference in twins: a) monozygotic twins reared in same environment; b) monozygotic twins reared apart; c) dizygotic twins reared in same environment. The increase in difference in b) is attributable to environmental factors; that in c) to hereditary factors. Weight and chest measurements are more highly susceptible to environmental factors than body height, breadth of shoulders, and head measurements (after von Verschurer, 1934).

kinds of twins: (1) Monozygotic, or identical, twins (derived from one ovum), which originated in an early phase of embryonic development from the division of a germ cell produced from one fertilized ovum, and which therefore closely resemble each other genetically and phenotypically. (2) Dizygotic, or fraternal, twins (derived from two separate ova). Originating from two ova which were separately fertilized either simultaneously or nearly so, these are no more similar to each other genetically and in appearance than any other offspring from the same pair of parents.

These two types of twins may be quite easily distinguished one from the other by a polysymptomatic similarity analysis; i.e., by the comparative study of similarities with regard to numerous characteristics, including blood groups, head and body measurements, color of hair and eyes, fingerprint ridging, ear patterns, and physiognomic features. In testing any one trait to determine whether or not it is hereditary in origin, the frequency of concordance (similarity) and discordance (dissimilarity) between two in a pair of twins is determined with respect to that particular trait.

If the proportion of concordance is clearly larger in the monozygotic than in the dizygotic twins, this is an indication that hereditary predispositions had a part in the formation of the trait. Differences between monozygotic twins may be based either on errors in measurement or on environmental factors (modification). The magnitude of average differences between pairs of monozygotic twins may be an indication of the extent to which these traits are or are not affected by environmental factors. Blood groups, for example, are absolutely unaffected by environment; on the other hand, traits such as body measurements, and body weight in particular, are relatively susceptible to environmental influences. However, the twin method does not reveal the full extent to which any one trait is modifiable, for even when monozygotic twins are reared apart, the environments are never totally different in every respect. Thus the increase in stature during the past century (see Growth) has shown that body height is more modifiable than the tests made with twins might have indicated.

Also the testing of twins can furnish no evidence concerning the mode of inheritance for a trait, and thus no evidence in regard to the genes involved. This can be achieved only through studies of families. Because of the small number of descendants in human families, children from a larger number of families must be taken as a test group when Mendelian relationships are to be studied. In humans, tests with racial hybrids replace the cross-breeding experiments conducted by observation. The most extensive studies of this kind, which tested the mode of inheritance for a number of racial characteristics, are those conducted with the Rehoboth Bastards, the progeny of interbreeding between Dutchmen and Hottentots in South Africa, the half-castes of Kisar, and mulattoes (crosses between whites and Negroes) in Jamaica.

Heredity of Morphological Traits

Studies made with twins and families show a preponderance of hereditary components for the measurements and proportions of the body as a whole and of its parts. Numerous single genes influence growth, partly as superimposed controlling mechanisms acting through hormonal or neural regulatory systems. From hereditary pathology we know also of single genes which cause characteristic disturbances during growth and thus also in body stature and proportions, and whose normal alleles therefore are obviously essential for undisturbed growth (for example, chondrodystrophy—stunted growth with shortening and thickening of the extremities due to disturbances in cartilage formation; Hanhart's dwarf-

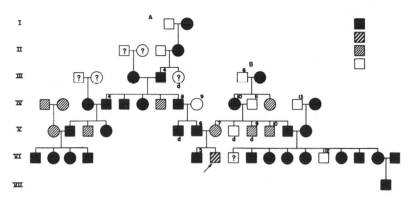

Fig. 62 Heredity of hair textures in a tribe of Negro hybrids (after Gates, 1949).

ism—inhibition of growth beginning during the third year; and so forth). It is possible that extreme growth phenomena in a race, particularly dwarfism, are attributable to genes that have a relationship with such anomalous mutants.

The physiognomic features which are important factors in racial taxonomy (forehead formation; position of eyeball; form and position of palpebral fissure; shape of lid fold, epicanthic fold; shape of eyebrows; nasal profile; shape of nostrils and septum; position of cheekbones; height and profile of integumental lips; width and form of membranous lips; shape of chin; and so forth) are not affected by environmental influences and, in their adult formation, are dependent only to a small extent on growth modifications. The same is true for hair texture, which characterizes the main racial strains (for example, frizzy hair in Congoids; straight hair in Mongoloids; straight, wavy, or curly hair in Caucasoids), for cutaneous ridging (which reveals extensive regional and racial differences), for ear formation, and for iris structure. Hence all these characteristics are significant as well both for the determination of whether twins are identical or fraternal and the determination of ancestry (see Paternity Diagnosis).

To a great extent, the pigmentation of skin, eyes, and hair, another main factor in racial taxonomy, is also unaffected by environmental influences, but it does show certain changes with advancing age (darkening of hair and eye color in populations of mixed color; in Negroes the skin color of the newborn is lighter than that of adults). Studies of families, and particularly those of half-breeds, show that there is a distinct tendency for the pigmentation grade that happens to be the stronger to dominate. However, this is not a matter of simple dominant-recessive relationships. Involved here are several genes which should be extensively homologous to those of other mammals. There are also hereditary disturbances in pigmentation (albinism; i.e., partial or complete lack of pigmentation; and melanism; i.e., local overproduction of pigment). It is possible that these are connected with pigmentation variants whose frequency is determined by race; particularly, albinism may be related to the depigmentation occurring in northern Europe, but this question has not yet been cleared up in detail.

Heredity in Blood Groups

While most of the normal traits in humans are polygenically caused, it has been possible to find the genes involved, and simple modes of inheritance, in a number of serological traits. These traits offer the best instances, in human genetics, for the simple Mendelian categories (dominant, recessive, combined behavior, multiple allelomorphic relationships). In the case of blood characteristics, the factors involved are probably intercellular gene influences in which the hereditary predispositions have a direct bearing on certain components of the cell. Thus far the molecular structures involved could be determined only through clumping reactions (agglutination). In the ABO System, the longest-known system, two antigens (agglutinable substances) were found in the blood corpuscles and two antibodies (agglutinating substances) in the serum, from which are derived four "blood groups": (1) *Blood group O:* No serum will agglutinate the blood corpuscles of individuals in this group; the serum from this group will cause agglutination in the blood corpuscles of the

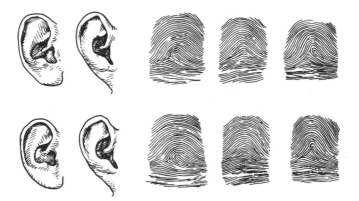

Fig. 63 Heredity of morphological characteristics. Ear pattern and cutaneous ridging of the fingers (1–3) in monozygotic twins. Above, first twin in pair; below, second twin (after Abel, 1940, and Lotze, 1937).

HEREDITY OF EYE COLOR						
Parents	No. of Parents	Eye Color of Children in %				No. of Children
		Without Pigment	Weak Pigmentation	Medium Pigmentation	Strong Pigmentation	
Without pigment × without pigment	189	85.2	14.8	—	—	440
Without pigment × weak pigmentation	283	51.6	32.6	12.3	3.6	585
Without pigment × medium pigmentation	153	37.2	21.5	26.3	15.0	274
Without pigment × strong pigmentation	108	20.5	16.3	27.4	35.8	215
Weak pigmentation × weak pigmentation	91	25.9	42.0	23.0	9.2	174
Weak pigmentation × medium pigmentation	43	17.3	29.3	36.0	17.3	75
Weak pigmentation × strong pigmentation	21	12.1	30.3	3.0	54.6	33
Medium pigmentation × medium pigmentation	129	17.0	20.16	30.4	32.0	253
Medium pigmentation × strong pigmentation	84	7.0	13.2	21.7	58.1	129
Strong pigmentation × strong pigmentation	14	7.1	17.9	14.3	60.7	28
	1115					2206

(Without pigmentation = 1a − 3; weak pigmentation = 4a − 7; medium pigmentation = 8   11; strong pigmentation = 12 − 16 in the Eye Color Table of Martin-Schultz.)

(After Tillner, 1953)

three other groups. (2) *Blood group AB:* The blood corpuscles of this group will be agglutinated by serum from any of the other three groups; the serum of this group will not cause agglutination in the blood corpuscles in any of the other groups. (3) *Blood group A* and (4) *Blood group B:* Serum of these groups will cause agglutination in each other's blood corpuscles and in the corpuscles of blood group *AB.* In other serological agglutination traits the antibodies are not contained in human serum but are derived from the blood of some animal.

Up to now we know of at least 46 hereditary blood characteristics which

MODE OF INHERITANCE IN MN BLOOD GROUP				
Traits of Parents	No. of Families	Traits of Children		
		M	MN	N
M × M	24	98	—	—
N × N	6	—	—	27
M × N	30	—	43	—
M × MN	86	183	196	—
N × MN	71	—	156	167
MN × MN	69	71	141	63

(After A. S. Wiener, 1943)

are attributable to at least 16 genes (gene loci) with two or more alleles each. Thus far the most important of these for the physiology of race (see Genetics and Race) and the establishment of paternity (see Paternity Diagnosis) are: (1) *The ABO System* with at least four alleles (A_1, A_2, B, O) of one gene locus (multiple allelomorphic relationship); A and B are dominant to O; A_1 is dominant to A_2, and A and B are of equal dominance. (2) *The MN System:* One gene with two alleles M and N, without dominance; thus three traceable phenotypes M, N, and MN; only in rare instances are there other mutants; namely, "weak" $N(N_2)$ and weak $M(M_2$ and $M^c)$. (3) *The Rh System:* Three gene loci situated in the same chromosome with at least two alleles Cc, Dd, and Ee and a series of rare mutants (C^w and others). In Cc and Ee it is possible also to determine the heterozygotes (combining mode of inheritance); however, thus far, it has been possible to trace d only through the absence of D. Other hereditary blood traits are: *The P Factor:* One gene locus with at least two alleles, with P + dominant to P −. *The Lutheran Blood Group:* One gene locus with two alleles, with Lu (a+) dominant to Lu (a−). *The Kell Blood Group:* One gene locus with two alleles, with K + dominant to K −. *The Lewis Blood Group:* One gene locus with two alleles; here the absence of the antigen Le (a−) is dominant to the presence of Le (a+). *The Duffy Blood Group:* One gene locus with two alleles; with Fy (a+) dominant to Fy (a−). *The Kidd Blood Group:* One gene locus with two alleles, with Jk (a+) dominant to Jk (a−). A number of additional antigens are known thus far only from individual families, but new hereditary blood traits are constantly being discovered.

In addition, a number of hereditary diseases of the blood have become important factors in anthropology, for they show distinct racial and geographical differences. The sickling phenomenon, which causes a sickle-like deformation of the red blood corpuscles in an oxygen-poor medium (sickle-cell trait) in heterozygotes, gives rise to a serious, usually fatal blood disease (sickle-cell anemia) in homozygotes. This phenomenon, which was first discovered in American Negroes, is as good as nonexistent among whites in the United States. Subsequently, gene centers were found also in India, southern Europe, and the Near East. In African Negroes the frequency of the sickle-cell trait varies between zero and 44 per cent. The great regional differences in frequency may have some bearing on the spread of malaria, for in regions plagued with endemic malaria the sickle-cell trait occurs with greater frequency than in regions free of malaria. "Sicklers" inoculated with malarial parasites will contract milder cases of malaria than others. Obviously, then, the sickle-cell trait serves as a protective device against malaria. Thus the heterozygotes are favored by natural selection; while homozygotic "sicklers" are decimated by sickle-cell anemia and normal homozygotes are decimated by malaria. The biochemical character of the defective hemoglobin (blood pigment) S, which is at the root of the sickle-cell trait, has already been clarified to a great extent (a glutamic acid constituent of the normal hemoglobin chain is replaced by a valine. Thus sickle-cell anemia is a "molecular disease," according to Pauling). Other abnormal hemoglobin types, too, show regional differences in frequency.

Heredity of Psychological Traits

Studies made on twins and families have also shown a hereditary component for a number of psychological traits, but thus far it has not been possible to analyze single genes except in cases of certain forms of feeble-mindedness. In the psychological sphere the environmental factors are particularly complex, because here the totality of the cultural and social environment also has a part in the formation of the phenotype. The relationships between genes and environment are further complicated by the fact that both are correlated with one another; parents not only transmit their hereditary traits to their offspring but also create the environment in which these offspring grow up.

PAIRED CORRELATIONS FOR INTELLIGENCE	
Kind of relationship	r
Monozygotic twins reared in same environment	0.88
Monozygotic twins reared apart	0.77
Dizygotic twins	0.63
Siblings in same environment	0.50
Siblings reared apart	0.25
Parents–children	0.50
Grandparents–grandchildren	0.15
Foster parents–adopted children	0.15
Adopted children in same family	0.35
Adopted children and natural children	0.35

(After A. Anastasi, 1958)

Voluminous material is available particularly on the hereditary nature of intelligence, which is determined through testing or through evaluation by teachers. In all the test series, monozygotic twins show greater similarity to each other than dizygotic twins, and similarity between relatives is in proportion to the closeness of the relationship; foster children or adopted children show less similarity to their foster or adoptive parents than do the natural children of these parents; the intelligence of illegitimate children in orphanages is correlated with that of their natural fathers; and so forth. In experiments with animals, intelligent as well as dull strains can be produced. However, the environmental factor, too, shows up in such tests.

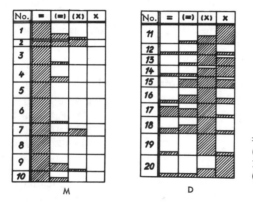

= strong concordance
(=) weak concordance
× strong discordance
(×) weak discordance

Fig. 64 Heredity of psychological traits. Character traits in 10 monozygotic and 10 dizygotic pairs of twins (after H. Lottig, 1931).

Outstanding creative ability occurs with a greater-than-random frequency in families that have also produced other outstanding personalities. We know also of a number of families showing frequencies of one special talent, such as those of musicians (Bach, Mozart, Strauss, Weber); mathematicians (Bernoulli); scientists (Darwin, Galton); artists (Cranach, Holbein, Tischbein); literary and philosophical talents (Gerok, Hauff, Hegel, Hölderlin, Kerner, Mörike, Schelling, Schiller, and Uhland were all related to one another). On the other side, among the numerous forms of feeble-mindedness the hereditary forms predominate, with a high concordance in monozygotic twins and a high probability that offspring of feeble-minded parents will be tainted. Less subject to environmental influences than the "cortical personality traits" (thinking capacity, abstractional ability) are the endothymic personality traits (basic mood, emotionality, vital impulses); this susceptibility decreases the closer they come to the autonomic response. In addition, monozygotic twins are more similar than dizygotic twins as regards expressive gestures and other movements, as regards personal tempo (measured by beats and metronome tests), as regards character structure, and as regards criminality and the type of crime. However, it is naturally all the more difficult to compile extensive series of investigations, the more intensive the character analysis is. The same is true in family studies, where, in many instances, character traits may be traced through several generations. In experiments with animals it is possible to breed not only intelligent and dull strains but also strains displaying qualities of boldness and diffidence, activity and passivity, aggressiveness and shyness.

The extent to which talent and character are hereditary sets the limits within which training is possible. In those cases where there is still no reliable evidence, or where individual differences in modifiability are very great, the educator, in principle, will have to assume amenability to training and education. In addition to such objectivity, however, prejudices have thus far been a factor too, particularly in the psychological sphere, in the evaluation of the role of hereditary and environmental factors. Thus there is a clear relationship between attitudes of optimism and pessimism regarding environment on one side, and political attitudes on the other. A high valuation of hereditary and racial factors will be found preponderantly among advocates of political conservatism; those of more liberal political thought tend to hold an optimistic view with regard to environmental factors.

METHODS OF ANTHROPOLOGY

As a discipline in the natural sciences, anthropology works basically with the methods of science. Only when it extends into related fields does it go beyond these limits and draw on findings that derive from the arts. By combining quantitative analyses with qualitative data it becomes possible to arrive at an approximation of a total picture of man in all his diversity. The primary basis for research in this field is comparative and special human anatomy and physiology. Experience gained from research in these fields also serves as a basis for the development of techniques for the study of individual and group differences. Although there had been earlier attempts to devise a system of description and classification of the physical characteristics of man and their variability (see The History of Anthropology), it was not until the second half of the nineteenth century that a scientifically accurate method of research and quantitative measurement was developed. This was true particularly in connection with the methods and specially designed instruments for measuring the human skeleton and the body of the living person and also with the uniform system of methods adopted to carry out comparisons for the purpose of determining such aspects as shapes, colors, and physiological variants. The classic work on modern anthropological technique is Rudolf Martin's *Lehrbuch der Anthropologie* (*Textbook of Anthropology*), the first edition of which appeared in 1914. It laid the basis for the development of world-wide scientific techniques in anthropology and, repeatedly revised and brought up to date, stands as the standard work to this day.

The principal method of quantitative investigation continues to be measuring, or anthropometry. Measurements are made which show the absolute metric values, and the ratio between them (indices) serves as a basis for correlation and comparison. The overemphasis on techniques—the use, that is, of anthropometry purely as a tool for measuring—has led to an exaggerated estimate of what it is able to convey about the significance of the data in question. There has frequently been a tendency to confuse extensive tabulation of figures carried to the second or even third decimal point with scientific insight. Today a more critical attitude toward method has led to more modest expectations of what can be achieved by exclusively anthropometric means. At the same time, anthropometry must not be regarded as being of no value at all. It goes without saying that to submit the material under investigation to scrupulously accurate measurements is an absolute prerequisite. Anthropometric technique is difficult, and is not a skill that can be acquired without training. The errors so frequently committed in the past were due to an inadequate command of technique. It is important to remember that all that measurement by itself can achieve is a precise quantitative assessment of the material under examination. But it is this concern for precision that underlies the development of all the other methods of research, including those of psychology. Measurement as such cannot tell us anything about the *morphe*, the organic form of the object; nor can it convey the total effect of its plastic concreteness. A person's physiognomy, for instance, cannot be expressed in terms of measurements.

Anthropometry began with the large-scale collection of skulls in the eighteenth century (Blumenbach's extensive collection of skulls of various races is the classic example), which led to the development of craniometry (the science of measuring the skull). In due course this was extended to include measurements of the post-cranial skeleton and the body of the living person, which in turn gave rise to osteometry (the science of measuring the bones) and somatometry (the science of measuring the body in the living person). Anthropometry today is used as the general term to denote the science of measuring the human body and its parts. A large number of landmarks, of varying degrees of importance, have been internationally agreed upon for measurements of the skull. The selection given below represents what are for the most part, if not in all cases,

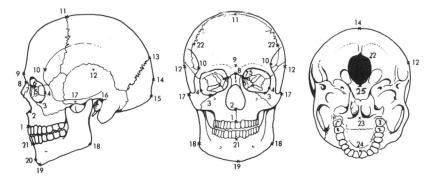

FIG. 65 The most important landmarks for measuring the skull
(after Martin). Left, norma lateralis: 1. Prosthion. 2. Nasospinale.
3. Orbitale. 4. Ectoconchion. 5. Lacrimale. 6. Dacryon. 7. Maxillo-
frontale. 8. Nasion. 9. Glabella. 10. Frontotemporale. 11. Bregma.
12. Euryon. 13. Lambda. 14. Opisthocranion. 15. Inion. 16.
Porion. 17. Zygion. 18. Gonion. 19. Gnathion. 20. Pogonion. 21.
Infradentale. Middle, norma frontalis: 22. Coronale. Right, norma
basilaris: 22. Opisthion. 23. Staphylion. 24. Orale. 25. Basion.

the generally accepted landmarks of the skull and skeleton (as defined in
Martin and Saller, 1957).

Landmarks for measuring the length of the skull (see Figure 65):

(9) *Glabella:* the most prominent point between the supraorbital
ridges. (11) *Bregma:* the point of intersection of the coronal and sagittal
sutures. (15) *Inion:* the point of intersection of the *lineae nuchae supe-
riores* (base of the external occipital protuberance) and the mid-sagittal
plane (not always easy to determine). (14) *Opisthocranion:* the most
distant posterior point on the skull. (25) *Basion:* the point of intersection
of the anterior margin of the foramen magnum and the mid-sagittal plane.
(8) *Nasion:* the point of junction between the naso-frontal suture and
mid-sagittal plane. (1) *Prosthion:* the point on the alveolar margin of the
maxilla between the upper incisor teeth. (19) *Gnathion:* the most inferior
point on the lower border of the mandible.

Landmarks for measuring the breadth of the skull:

(24) *Orale:* the mid-point between the posterior margins of the alveoli
for the two central incisor teeth. (12) *Euryon:* the most prominent lateral
point on the surface of the skull. (22) *Coronale:* the most lateral point
on the coronal suture. (10) *Frontotemporale:* the deepest point on the
incurvature of the temple (*linea obliqua*). (17) *Zygion:* the most exterior
point on the zygomatic arch. (16) *Porion:* the mid-point on the upper
margin of the external auditory meatus. (18) *Gonion:* the most lateral
external point of junction of the horizontal and ascending rami of the
lower jaw.

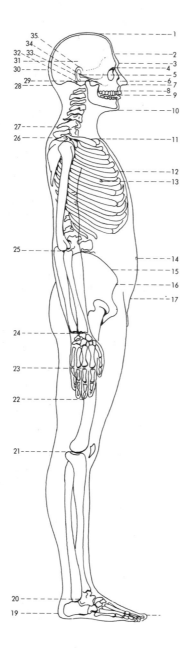

F. 66 The most important landmarks for somatometric measurements (after Martin).

1. Vertex
2. Trichion
3. Glabella
4. Nasion
5. Tragion
6. Alare
7. Subnasale
8. Prosthion
9. Stomion
10. Gnathion
11. Suprasternale
12. Mesosternale
13. Thelion
14. Omphalion
15. Iliocristale anterior
16. Iliospinale anterior
17. Symphysion
18. Acropodion
19. Pterion
20. Sphyrion
21. Tibiale
22. Dactylion
23. Phalangion
24. Stylion
25. Radiale
26. Acromion
27. Cervicale
28. Inion
29. Zygion
30. Opisthocranion
31. Euryon
32. Subaurale
33. Praeaurale
34. Postaurale
35. Superaurale

Some important cranial measurements:

Maximum cranial length: from glabella to opisthocranion. *Maximum cranial breadth:* from euryon to euryon. *Maximum frontal cranial breadth:* from coronale to coronale. *Minimum frontal cranial breadth:* from fronto-temporale to frontotemporale. *Bizygomatic diameter:* from zygion to zygion. *Length of the cranial base:* from nasion to basion. *Cranio-facial depth:* from basion to prosthion. *Total facial height:* from nasion to gnathion. *Upper facial height:* from nasion to prosthion. *Cranial arc and circumference* (measuring tape). *Horizontal circumference:* from glabella to opisthocranion. *Transverse cranial arc:* from porion to porion. *Sagittal arc:* from nasion to bregma to opisthion.

Angles which cannot be directly measured on the object itself can be determined by means of photographs and drawings. The landmarks used for measurements of the head correspond to those used for measurements of the skull (see Figure 66). For landmarks used in osteometry and somatometry, see Figure 66.

Fossil remains are frequently found in a more or less fragmentary state of preservation. The following terms are used to denote the relevant state of preservation of the skull: *cranium*—the skull with the lower jaw; *calvarium*—the skull without the lower jaw; *calvaria*—the brain case (the skull without the facial portion and lower jaw); *calotte*—the skull cap or top of the brain case. All measurements and other data concerning the person or object, such as age, sex, weight, teeth, and so forth, are

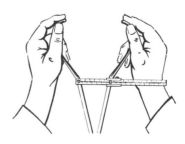

FIG. 67   Sliding calipers.   FIG. 68   Spreading calipers.

entered in specially prepared recording blanks. The absolute values of the measurements depend on the individual dimensions, which are highly variable. Therefore the general practice is to determine the ratio between two absolute measurements. This is done by expressing the smaller one as a percentage of the larger one. The result is called an *index*. Indices are easily determined by specially prepared lists of indices. There are also formulas for working out the ratio between several indices. Indices are relative coefficients that permit computations to be made independently of the absolute measurement values.

Examples of Anthropometric Indices:

$$\text{Cranial breadth-length index} = \frac{\text{Maximum cranial breadth} \times 100}{\text{Maximum cranial length}}$$

The indices are grouped as follows:

Cranial index (skull)

under 74.9	dolichocranic (long skull)
75.0 to 79.9	mesocranic (medium skull)
80.0 and over	brachycranic (broad skull)

Cephalic index (head, living)

female	*male*	
under 76.9	under 75.9	dolichocephalic (long-headed)
77.0 to 81.9	76.0 to 80.9	mesocephalic (medium-headed)
82.0 and over	81.0 and over	brachycephalic (broad-headed)

$$\text{Facial index} = \frac{\text{Facial height} \times 100}{\text{Breadth of zygomatic arch}}$$

Grouped as follows:

Facial index (skull)

under 84.9	euryprosopic (broad-faced)
85.0 to 89.9	mesoprosopic (intermediate)
90.0 and over	leptoprosopic (narrow-faced)

Facial index (head, living)

female	*male*	
under 80.9	under 83.9	broad-faced
81.0 to 84.9	84.0 to 87.9	intermediate
85.0 and over	88.0 and over	narrow-faced

Indices are, of course, also used in osteometry and somatometry.

Cranial or cephalic measurements are made with the skull or head in a definite plane in relation to the measuring instrument. This also permits comparative measurements to be made. The almost universally adopted position is that of the so-called Frankfort Plane or Horizontal (Frankfort Agreement, 1884), which is determined by the tragial notch of both ears (poria) and the lowest point on the left infra-orbital margin (orbitale, Figure 65, 3). For drawings the arcs of the Sarasin systems and other arcs, a number of extremely complex devices are available (craniophores) which hold the skull in a free-swinging position for easy adjustment in any desired plane. Special instruments are used for measuring angles and angles of torsion. All of this applies, *mutatis mutandis*, also to the measurements of the post-cranial skeleton and the body of the living person. This account must suffice as a preliminary glance at anthropometric techniques.

To meet the requirements of the different types of measurements, a series of specially designed instruments is available, the three most important of which are: (1) *The sliding caliper* (Figure 67), a calibrated rod fitted with a sliding bar capable of a high degree of accuracy, used for measuring short diameters such as teeth. (2) *Spreading calipers* (Figure 68), used for measurements between specially designated rather than anatomically fixed, obvious landmarks—for example, maximum cranial length (from glabella to opisthocranion) or maximum cranial breadth (from euryon to euryon)—whereas the sliding caliper is used for measurements between anatomically clearly fixed landmarks (such as sutural junctions). (3) *The anthropometer,* a large sliding caliper for measuring a subject's total stature; with a reduced calibration scale it can also be used as a small sliding caliper for measurements on the skull and head (for example, height of the ear) and for measuring transverse diameters of the body and segments of the limbs. The sliding caliper can be used for measuring angles by means of an attachable goniometer, which can be read like a protractor.

As already mentioned, the methods of quantitative measurement do not lend themselves to a recording of the shape, the *morphe,* of the measured skull, cranial segment, or skeleton and its parts (or of the head and body of the living person). To overcome this difficulty and to provide a means for comparative study, special schemes and formulas have been worked out which make it possible to determine such aspects as arcs (horizontal, transverse, and so forth) of the cranial vault, contour of the face, shape of the nose and of the nasal cavity in the skull (*apertura pyriformis*), development of the nasal spine and bone, and so on. The total morphological picture can then be determined by means of the resultant data in conjunction with other observations, such as the specific gravity of bones and cranial capacity, to name only the most important.

Mention must also be made of the study of physiological characteristics. Here, too, specially designed instruments are available (dynamometer, apparatus for studying respiration, and others). Chemical tests (blood-group typing) represent another special technique, along with standardized recording blanks for the tabulation of such data as color and form or texture of skin, eyes, and hair. Finally, there is the classification of

177

individuals into constitutional types (see Constitution). This extension into the areas of psychology, medicine, and ethnology marks the limit of anthropometric techniques.

It is essential that all data of a qualitative and quantitative nature be studied in relation to other observations and never in isolation; that is, their correlations must be established. In this way it is easier to see whether two or more characteristics occur in combination—for example, the so-called light complexion: light skin, blue eyes, blond hair—than it would be if individual data were listed in a purely arbitrary way.

There is no need to stress the importance that photography (and more recently color photography) holds for morphology. Here, too, anthropologically exact observation requires accurate positioning of the head, and so forth, and adjustment of the posture of the individuals or of the position of the skeleton or skeletal parts to be photographed, for otherwise comparisons would be impossible.

It must also be determined to what extent the characteristics under investigation may be genetically conditioned or may represent a phenotypical pattern. This brings us to the science of human genetics (see page 161) and—as applied to evolutionary processes and the distribution pattern of characteristics and their genetic basis—to the field of population genetics (see page 203).

Finally, the data obtained by the various methods described must be treated statistically. This will shed light on such factors as variability, diffusion, and population structure. Statistical examination of the data also makes it possible to determine whether the incidence of differences between individuals or between ethnic groups is "significant"; that is, whether such differences have a genetic basis and can thus be interpreted as a group characteristic. Important observations about the genetic situation can also be derived from the use of statistics in conjunction with a careful analysis of correlations. The statistics of correlations shows the interrelations between the individual segments of the body during growth, the difference in their proportions in the two sexes and in different races, populations, and constitutions, and the interrelations between biological groups. However, it is not possible to discuss here statistical methods in general or the methods used in working with correlations in particular. The use of statistics, like the use of anthropometry earlier, has carried the application of mathematical methods to an extreme. They are, nevertheless, precise methods for determining group differences and group similarities for both small clusters of groups and of divisions (see The Concept of Race).

The world distribution pattern of inherited characteristics, as they occur both separately and in combination, can be presented geographically; thus there are available scientifically based maps showing the distribution of ethnic groups and divisions. These maps make it possible to illustrate the spatial changes in the genetic structure and groups of mankind, which in turn mark the point where the study of population genetics and the history of races begins.

By examining all the data which modern methods have made available and by treating them as interrelated links, anthropology will be brought closer to its goal of arriving at a total picture of man in all his diversity and of perceiving the natural order inherent in this diversity as a thread in the fabric of mankind.

PALEOANTHROPOLOGY

Paleoanthropology is the study of fossil hominids. Strictly speaking, it should begin with the first appearance of the hominids as a separate family, which took place about 700,000 years ago, but the Hominidae must have come into being before that, for at that time it already included two subfamilies, the Australopithecinae and the Homininae.

Like other paleoanthropological surveys, this one will begin with the fossil record and then deal with the comparison of Hominidae with Pongidae (apes), for only by this comparison can hominid anatomy be understood.

It is almost as difficult to set an upper limit to the time span of fossil men as it is to discover when they began, because the degree of fossilization of a specimen depends to a certain extent on local soil factors. Some Pleistocene specimens are not completely fossilized, whereas some post-Pleistocene ones are. Nor can morphology be used as an infallible criterion, because in some racial lines of descent, evolution moved at a faster pace than in others. The only valid criterion is time itself, however measured.

In this article we shall not consider skeletal material from the late Pleistocene (from the Gottweig Interstadial and later—about 40,000 years ago in Europe) which is, in the opinion of all competent workers, of the modern *Homo sapiens* type.

Paleoanthropology thus begins with the threshold between other animals and men, in the broad sense. This threshold was probably first crossed in the Upper Pliocene, but we have no specimens from that period. It ends with a second threshold, at which most if not all early types of man had evolved into modern *Homo sapiens*.

Methods of Paleoanthropology

The same methods are used as with paleontology, for paleoanthropology is simply human paleontology (see Methods of Anthropology).

Stratigraphy and Chronology. The scientific study of a fossil-man specimen begins with locating it in space and time. If it was found in a stratified site, the location of the exact stratum in which it lay must be determined. This is not always easy, as many specimens are unearthed by workmen or amateurs. If the specimen was accompanied by animal bones, it can usually be placed in its proper part of the Pleistocene by counting the percentage of extinct species. Paleontology and paleobotany also tell us what the climate was like. The fluorine test tells us whether the specimen really was contemporaneous with the accompanying fauna, or whether it was intrusive in the stratum. In general, a fluorine content of 1 to 3 per cent broadly corresponds to the Lower Pleistocene, and a fluorine content of 1 per cent to the Upper Pleistocene, but owing to variations in local conditions, the fluorine test is useful only for matching bones in a single level.

The radioactive carbon test (Carbon-14) is also widely employed. An unstable isotope, C-14, is produced in the atmosphere by cosmic radiation; its ratio to regular carbon is constant, remaining at 1 atom to 13 billion. Each living organism absorbs carbon from the air, and while alive preserves the same ratio. But when the organism dies the C-14 in it is gradually lost, at a fixed rate, until eventually none is left. The half-life of C-14 is 5760 ± 30 years. By determining the residual amount of C-14 in charcoal and certain other substances found in sites (but not in human bone itself) by means of Geiger counters, physicists can date specimens to a maximum age of 70,000 years. Actually only one laboratory, at Groningen, in the Netherlands, has reached this maximum, and few laboratories go past the 50,000 mark. All the Upper Paleolithic men of Europe and some of the Neanderthals fall inside this range. Unfortunately only specimens dug up in the 1950's and 1960's can be dated by this method, which is comparatively new. Even newer is the argon-potassium method (Argon-40), which depends upon the amount of argon formed in potassium after the potassium was last heated to a temperature high enough to let out the argon trapped in it. This method depends on the fact that Potassium-40 decays into Argon-40 and Calcium-40, and that when the potassium is heated to 500° C. or more, the Argon-40 escapes, and the process recommences once the potassium has cooled. It is useful for dating volcanic materials, as at Olduvai Gorge in East Africa, and tektites from outer space, as in Indonesia and Australia. One celestial shower of tektites which fell 600,000 years ago scattered these small, glassy nodules widely. Argon-potassium dating began only in 1959.

Metrical and Morphological Analysis. When a specimen is found in a site by a professional, he uncovers but does not remove it. Then he photographs it *in situ* and applies some kind of hardening solution. Once it is out of the soil he cleans it carefully, hardens it further if necessary, and restores it by cementing the broken pieces together. Later he has casts made of each piece, and only then can he attempt to restore the missing parts on a cast. A professional will not put plaster on an original specimen.

It is a dangerous practice to restore too much. For example, an attempt was made to reconstruct the jaw of the fossil primate Gigantopithecus on the basis of a few teeth, and when three whole jaws were later discovered they bore little resemblance to the reconstruction. Also, the Florisbad skull from South Africa was reconstructed with plaster placed on the original specimen in such a way that it looked slant-browed and long-faced, like a very primitive man, but when the plaster was removed it was found that the skull was modern in type.

Most professionals frown on restorations of the soft parts, but still there is pleasure in making them and they are rewarding if they are not taken too seriously. Two workers independently restored the soft parts of Rhodesian man and both made him a Negro; he could hardly have been anything else. However, the early restorations of Neanderthal man suffered from the handicap that in the European specimens the nasal bones had been removed after death, and the European workers were convinced that Neanderthal was brute-like, as shown in Figure 69. Actually most if not all Neanderthals had prominent, high-bridged noses, as was found when the unmutilated skull of Shanidar I was unearthed in Iraq.

Divisions of the Pleistocene

The materials of paleoanthropology as defined above belong exclusively to the Pleistocene. This geological epoch is characterized by a considerable decrease in temperature in comparison with that of the preceding epoch, the Tertiary. Toward the end of the Pliocene the climate began to cool, and in the Pleistocene it reached its climax three times when ice caps formed simultaneously over both the northern and southern hemispheres. These climaxes were known as glacial advances. Between them occurred warm intervals known as interglacials. In the tropics, rainy periods (pluvials) more or less coincided with the furthest advances of the glaciations.

In each ice cap a large portion of the earth's water was immobilized. This led to a lowering of sea levels around the world by over three hundred feet, and to the emergence as dry land of portions of the continental shelves. Thus large faunal migrations took place over land that is now flooded, and many of the existing early hominid specimens must lie under water. For example, various Indonesian islands, which were important as the breeding ground of the Australoid subspecies, from Pithecanthropus onward, were, several times, only highlands in a broad extension of the Malay Peninsula.

Günz, Mindel, Riss, and Würm are the names of four Swiss river valleys which had local mountain glaciers during the Pleistocene. The last three arose at the same time as the northern European ice caps. (We use the Swiss names to designate the ice periods instead of the ice-cap names because the glacial sequence was first worked out in Switzerland.) Before Günz there were other cold periods of lesser magnitude, which

DIVISIONS OF THE PLEISTOCENE IN EUROPE AND WESTERN ASIA				
	Geology	*Began Thousands of Years Ago*	*Archaeology*	
HOLOCENE	Postglacial	3 5 9 10	Iron Age (W. Asia) Bronze Age (W. Asia) Neolithic (W. Asia) Mesolithic (Europe)	
PLEISTO-CENE	Würm 2 & 3 Gottweig Interstadial Würm 1	30 40 70	Magdalenian, etc. (Europe) Aurignacian Perigordian Levalloisio-Mousterian	Upper — PALEOLITHIC
	Riss-Würm Interglacial	150	Levalloisio-Mousterian, Mousterian, Upper Acheulian	Middle — PALEOLITHIC
	Riss 1 and 2	250		
	Mindel-Riss Interglacial	400	Middle Acheulian Lower Acheulian	Lower — PALEOLITHIC
	Mindel 1 & 2	500		
	Cromerian Interglacial	550 ca	Abbevillian	
	Günz Glacial (no ice cap)	600		
	Tiglian Glacial (no ice cap)	700		
	Villafranchian	1,000		
PLIOCENE				

(After Carleton S. Coon, see *The Origin of Races*, 1962, p. 335)

neither created ice caps nor produced river glaciers in Switzerland. One is the Tiglian, which occurred in northwestern Europe, and at roughly the same time there was another, called the Donau, in central and eastern Europe. In the Himalayas and in America four periods of glaciation matched those of Europe. The earliest part of the Pleistocene, the Villafranchian, was formerly considered part of the Pliocene, but is now attached to the Pleistocene because at its beginning some of the most characteristic Pleistocene mammals, notably horses, cattle, sheep, camels, and elephants, first appeared.

Paleolithic Cultures

Only the hominids are tool-makers and tool-users. By studying tool types archaeologists can divide the world on geographical lines, and can study the developing styles of tool-making from simple to complex, and can gain some idea of the increasing intelligence and artistry of our ancestors. The early hominids needed tools because their canine teeth, instead of serving as fangs, were ground flat by the human style of chewing, and their nails were suited for supporting grasping fingertips rather than for clawing. Once he began hunting, an erect hominid had to have weapons, and weapons are made with tools.

It is hard to tell when tool-making began, for the earliest tools are virtually indistinguishable from naturally broken stones. We have no demonstrable tools from prior to a date of about 700,000 years ago, when they turn up in Lower Pleistocene deposits in Africa, in some sites associated with Australopithecine bones and teeth and in others which have no hominid remains.

The earliest implements were pebble tools—water-rolled pebbles broken in two to produce a sharp edge at the point of fracture. After the first pebble tools came choppers and chopping tools; the former were stones retouched along one edge of the fracture, and the latter were retouched on both edges. Pebble tools, choppers, and chopping tools have been found in East and North Africa, in India, southeastern Asia, and China. After the beginning of the Middle Pleistocene a new kind of tool was first seen in Africa, Europe, the Near East, and India—the handax. A handax is a large, almond-shaped implement flaked on both sides and both bilaterally and bifacially symmetrical. It was an all-purpose cutting tool. The earliest and crudest are called Abbevillian, the later and finer Acheulian. They were never made in eastern or southeastern Asia.

The handax-makers produced flakes as by-products of their industry, and some flakes were also used as tools. In fact, in all parts of the world where tools were made, flake industries arose, either as parts of a handax complex or of a chopper-chopping tool complex or independently. In Europe the earliest independent flake culture, very crude, was the Clactonian, followed by the Tayacian, which eventually evolved into the Mousterian, the industry of Neanderthal men.

During the Middle Pleistocene a new technique of making flakes was invented, the Levalloisian. Instead of knocking off a flake more or less at random and then trimming it to the desired shape, the tool-maker shaped the core in such a fashion that he could then remove a flake of the desired shape which would require little or no trimming before use. This Levallois technique was combined with the Mousterian techniques to form a so-called Levalloisio Mousterian culture, which the later Neanderthals, among others, used. In North Africa a non-Neanderthal people created, out of Levallois flakes, beautiful bifacial points with stems for hafting; they looked like American Indian arrowheads. During the Gottweig Interstadial and later, Europeans made tools from narrow blades, which were struck off prepared cores with elastic punches. Because race is transmitted by genes and tool-making techniques by teaching, tool industries and race are not necessarily related. Yet when two kinds of people with a common border make similar tools one is forced to postulate interracial contacts and the possibility of gene flow.

The taxonomy of fossil men (see Taxonomy of the Primates) has not been worked out to the satisfaction of all. Two principal systems have been proposed. One is European (Sergi, Vallois, Heberer, *et al.*); the other is American (Coon, 1962). According to the European system, three grades are recognized: Protoanthropi, Paleanthropi, and Neanthropi. No agreement has been reached among the proponents of this classification as to which genus and species each specimen in the lower two grades belong, but they do agree that all Neanthropi are *Homo sapiens,* and that the living races of man did not branch off from a parent stock until the grade of *Homo sapiens* had been reached.

According to Coon's system, there have been but two known species, *Homo erectus* and *Homo sapiens,* each of which represents a stage in the evolution of five separate lines or geographical races—Australoid, Mongoloid, Caucasoid, Congoid (African Negroes and pygmies), and Capoid (Bushmen and Hottentots). Each race was already present in the species *Homo erectus* and each evolved, by parallel mutation, peripheral gene flow, or both, into the corresponding races of *Homo sapiens,* some earlier than others (see The History of Races).

According to most present-day European workers, and also according to Coon, who follows Mayr, Simpson, and Washburn, among others, in this respect, the generic and specific terms initially given most fossil men, such as *Pithecanthropus erectus, Sinanthropus pekinensis,* and *Atlanthropus mauretanicus,* are taxonomically invalid and of descriptive value only.

The Australopithecines constitute a sub-family (Australopithecinae) parallel to that of true men (Homininae) (see The Descent of Man). The former were erect or semi-erect bipedal primates with cranial capacities within the range of the living great apes (Ponginae)—325–685 cc. Their teeth resemble those of men morphologically but differ from the latter in that the cheek teeth (molars and premolars) are relatively large and the front teeth (canines and incisors) are relatively small.

These creatures are found in South and East Africa, in two fossil groups. The earlier and smaller ones include Taung, Sterkfontein, Makapansgat, and the Olduvai Child. The later and larger ones are Kromdraai, Swartkrans, and Zinjanthropus (a name coined by Leakey after the Arabic *Zinj* or *Zanj,* meaning Ethiopia and by extension East Africa). The first group were as large as present-day pygmies, the second as large as full-sized men.

FIG. 69 Reconstruction of the soft parts of the classic Neanderthal man (after Heberer). In contrast to many earlier attempts (see Kurth, 1958), Heberer's gay and lifelike reconstruction makes Neanderthal man look like some of the living primitive peoples. However, he probably had a more prominent nose. In the European Neanderthal skulls the greater part of the nasal bones is missing, possibly because the brain was extracted postmortem through the nasal passages. In the Shanidar skull from Iraq, whose owner was killed by rockfall, the nasal bones are intact and prominent.

Two lower jaws found in Java along with Pithecanthropus 4 and dated at about 700,000 years old and named Meganthropus, were probably, but not certainly, those of Australopithecines, and the same is true of certain teeth from China of unknown date. Thus the range of the Australopithecines may have extended from Africa to East Asia and Indonesia.

It is not known whether the larger Australopithecines in Africa evolved locally out of the smaller ones, or whether they represent successive invasions from another source. Three specimens from Swartkrans, called

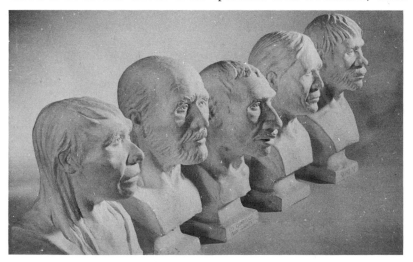

FIG. 70 Flesh reconstructions of fossil men. Left to right: Steinheim, Crô-Magnon, La Chapelle aux Saints, Upper Cave of Chou Kou Tien, Skhul 5 (after Maurice P. Coon).

Telanthropus, may not be Australopithecine at all, but human. Although the dating of the African finds is still under discussion—depending on the interpretation of a series of Argon-40 dates from Olduvai Gorge—it may be tentatively stated that they cover a period from 700,000 to 500,000 years ago, that is, the late Lower Pleistocene. One new specimen from Tchad may be older, and Swartkrans and Telanthropus, as well as the two Australopithecine teeth from the bottom of Olduvai Layer 2, may be younger.

As with the fossil human specimens, those of the Australopithecines have been given extravagant taxonomic names, now generally abandoned. Some workers hold that the African specimens belong to two genera, *Australopithecus* and *Paranthropus;* others that they constitute but two species, *Australopithecus africanus* and *Australopithecus robustus.* In any case, they cannot yet be shown to be older than their sibling subfamily, the Homininae, and their unique genus *Homo.*

I. Homo erectus (The Protoanthropines)

Returning to the Homininae, some, but not all, of the European authors recognize the following specimens and groups of specimens as Protoanthropi: the Pithecanthropus and Solo skulls of Java; the Sinanthropus remains from China; the Saldanha and Broken Hill skulls from South and East Africa. And they will undoubtedly so classify Leakey's new Chellian-3 skull from Bed 2 of Olduvai Gorge. These are exactly the same skulls called *Homo erectus* by Coon. The Heidelberg jaw from Germany and the three Ternefine mandibles from Algeria are Protoanthropine in form but cannot be definitely assigned to *Homo erectus* until corresponding crania shall have been found.

The crania listed above have in common the following features, lacking singly or as trait complexes in *Homo sapiens:* small cranial capacities ranging from 775 cc. in Pithecanthropus 2 to 1325 cc. in Broken Hill; heavy brow ridges; extensive nuchal crests in most specimens; sloping foreheads; gable-formed cranial profiles seen from front and back; relatively flat frontal and parietal arcs and a deeply curved occipital arc; simple patterns in the grooves left by the mid-meningeal arteries on the inner sides of the parietals; a flattish cranial base; and, in Broken Hill and probably in Solo 11, an enlarged pituitary fossa (only these two have the appropriate part of the cranial base intact). The crania which have teeth and palates have relatively large teeth and palates in comparison with their cranial capacities. All which have eyesockets preserved have large orbital fossae.

In addition to these points in common which distinguish the skulls listed from those of *Homo sapiens,* Coon sees a number of differences concerned not with grade but with racial line. (In this he partly follows Weidenreich.)

The Javanese skulls show an almost flat transition from brow ridge to forehead. In Sinanthropus there is a nearly horizontal slope from the glabella to the beginning of the forehead, followed by a sharp bend up-ward before curving backward. In both forms the region of the orbits and brow ridges is relatively flat from side to side. Sinanthropus, however, also has a forward stance to the malars and shallow eyesockets produced by the forward attachment of the temporal muscles on the frontal bone. Sinanthropus has relatively large front teeth and small cheek teeth, with elaborate shoveling in the incisors and canines, and a mandibular torus (bony brace) on the inside of each half of the lower jaw. The Javanese skulls lack these specializations and their cheek teeth are relatively larger. In general, as Weidenreich first pointed out, Sinanthropus foreshadowed the Mongoloids, and the Javanese skulls the living Australoids.

Except for the isolated Heidelberg jaw, there are no Caucasoid (Euro-

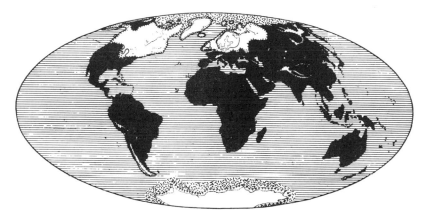

FIG. 71   The maximum of the last (Würm) glaciation in the Pleistocene (after Brinkmann).

pean and West Asian) Protoanthropines and, by definition, no Caucasoid *Homo erectus* skulls. But the Heidelberg jaw is narrow between the condyles, as in more recent Caucasoid mandibles, and its teeth, which are Caucasoid in form, are small for the jaw.

The Ternefine mandibles from Algeria are, in contrast, wide to the rear, with flaring gonial angles. These and other features, combined with tooth form, relate them closely to the Sinanthropus mandibles. Other jaws found in Casablanca, Rabat, and Temara carry the Ternefine line on, in Morocco, from the beginning of the earliest Würm period, when we find a maxilla and upper teeth from Tangier which morphologically match the earlier mandibles. Two crania from Jebel Ighoud in Morocco, not yet fully described, are of the same type. Thus North Africa possessed, during the Middle and part of the Upper Pleistocene, a local population with

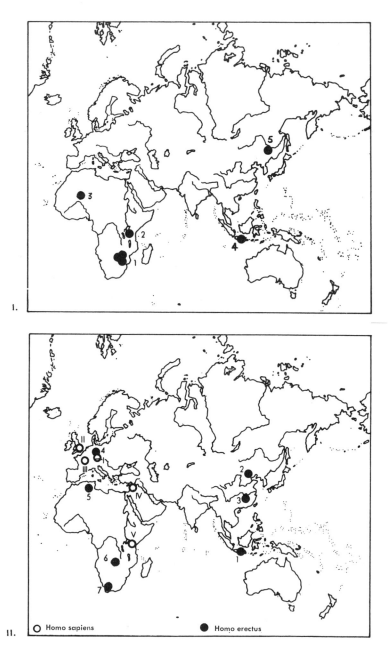

I.

II.

○ Homo sapiens   ● Homo erectus

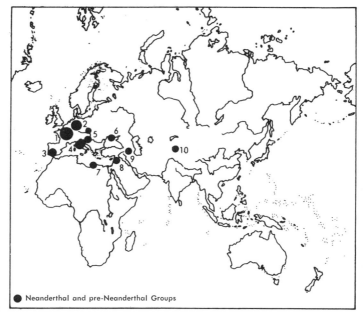

III.

FIG. 72 Regional distribution of the major groups of fossil hominids.

I. Distribution of the Australopithecines: 1. Transvaal   2. Olduvai
3. Tchad   4. Java   5. China

II. Distribution of *Homo erectus* and early *Homo sapiens:* 1. Java
2. Chou Kou Tien   3. South China   4. Heidelberg   5. Ternefine
6. Broken Hill   7. Saldanha
I. Steinheim   II. Swanscombe   III. Fontéchevade   IV. Mt. Carmel
V. Kanjera

III. Distribution of the Neanderthals and the pre-Neanderthals:
1. France   2. Belgium, western and middle Germany   3. Spain
4. Italy   5. Croatia   6. Crimea   7. North Africa   8. Palestine
9. Iraq   10. Uzbekistan

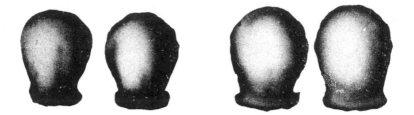

FIG. 73   Hominine skull types in top plan view. From left to right: Pithecanthropus; Sinanthropus; Neanderthal; Rhodesia.

FIG. 74   Hominine skulls, back view. From left to right: Pithecanthropus; Ngandong; Neanderthal; *Homo sapiens.*

closest known relationships to Sinanthropus. Evidence from later periods tentatively identifies it with the Capoids.

The Chellian-3 skull from Olduvai, on the other hand, is not Sinanthropus-like at all, for it has a flattish forehead like that of Pithecanthropus and brow ridges that sweep backward to either side, as in modern Negroes and Caucasoids (when they have brow ridges). The same configuration is found in the Saldanha skull cap and the virtually complete cranium of Broken Hill, and Broken Hill's face (the only complete *Homo erectus* face yet found), although very large, is morphologically Negro, as are its teeth. From Chellian 3 to Broken Hill, therefore, we may tentatively identify a slowly evolving line leading in all likelihood to the modern Negroes and their dwarfed kin, the pygmies.

II. Early Homo sapiens (The Paleanthropines)

The European designation of Paleanthropines includes a mixed group consisting of the European and western Asiatic skulls from the Third Interglacial and Würm I periods; in Europe they are called pre-Neanderthals and Neanderthals. The peoples so designated were Caucasoid in form but archaic in that they had heavy brow ridges, more or less sloping foreheads, and large, long faces, although their cranial capacities were as large as those of modern peoples. While their exact origin is unknown, their Caucasoid affinity is clear. Despite statements to the contrary, their trunk and limb bones were fully human. Most of the peculiarities attributed to them can be explained by chronic arthritis—particularly in the "type specimen" of La Chapelle-aux-Saints—and adaptation to cold like that seen in the Canoe Indians of Tierra del Fuego and the Reindeer Lapps.

Earlier than the pre-Neanderthals and Neanderthals in Europe were the skulls of the so-called pre-*sapiens* people—Swanscombe, Steinheim, and Fontéchevade—which were primitive forms of Caucasoids just as much *sapiens* as are the living Australian aborigines. Thus, as Coon points out, if all living men are *Homo sapiens,* so were these Europeans of a quarter of a million years ago, and the fact that they antedated the pre-Neanderthals and Neanderthals is simply a reflection of their marginal geographical position or climatic change, or both.

Unclassified so far by the European systematists is a series of skulls from China which form a temporal bridge between Sinanthropus and the later fully *sapiens* Mongoloids. These skulls, discovered by Communist Chinese workers in recent years, include those from Chang Yang, Ting Tsun, Mapa, Tze Yang, and Liu Kang, as well as a specimen from Tadaki in Japan, discovered by Suzuki. The first two are apparently *Homo erectus* of an advanced grade, the rest *Homo sapiens* of a grade which could be called Paleanthropic. By virtue of these discoveries, the Mongoloid subspecies is the best documented, in an evolutionary sense, of the five, and Weidenreich's prediction is fulfilled.

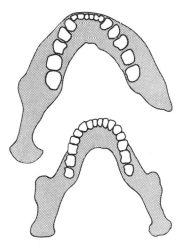

FIG. 75 Size comparison of lower jaw of *Paranthropus crassidens* (above) and *Homo heidelbergensis* (Mauer jaw) (below).

III. Modern Homo sapiens (The Neanthropines)

Like most European workers, Heberer considers the so-called *pre-sapiens* skulls (Steinheim, Swanscombe, and Fontéchevade), to be forerunners of the modern *Homo sapiens* population which first appeared in Europe during the Gottweig Interstadial of the Würm glaciation. The oldest such skeleton we have is Combe Capelle, a man of moderate stature with a long, narrow, high-vaulted skull and a long face. After him came a succession of peoples, all of whom made blade tools of various types and produced some kind of art which has survived to the present—either wall painting, wall engraving, bas-relief carving, sculpture in the round, or engraving on bone and ivory. It is this art, plus an anatomical identity with modern Europeans, that has given these people a reputation for high intelligence and other splendid qualities.

Among the half hundred skeletons found later than Combe Capelle, three have been singled out for special attention: Crô-Magnon, an old man with few teeth left and a disease which left rough areas on his face bones; the Grimaldis, a mother-boy double burial; and Chancelade, a short man with excessively flaring gonial angles.

Crô-Magnon had a short face, narrow eyesockets, a prominent nose, and a firm chin. Although credited with the stature of a giant, he stood no more than five feet ten. Men like him can be seen all over northern Europe today. The Grimaldi pair have been called Negroid, partly because of alveolar prognathism, especially in the boy. This was due partly to a poor bite and partly to faulty reconstruction. On account of his gonial angles, Chancelade has been called an Eskimo, but such protuberances can be seen among living Greeks. The Upper Paleolithic people, despite a considerable variability, were as European as any group living today.

These people had to have come from somewhere else, for they could not have simply evolved in a flash, by some kind of giant mutation, out of the local Neanderthals. They could only have come from the East. In Palestine, Lebanon, and Syria archaeologists have found blade implements, similar to those used by the Upper Paleolithic Europeans, not only in Würm II, as in Europe, but also in Würm I, when the Neanderthals reached their peak in Europe. And blade tools were also used in northern Afghanistan during the Gottweig Interstadial as early as they were in Europe. This distribution implies a diffusion from some intermediate source.

The Upper Paleolithic culture and the Upper Paleolithic people as well had their point of origin somewhere in the Near East. In Würm I of Palestine a number of skeletons have been found which show transitions from both pre-*sapiens* and Neanderthal prototypes into modern Caucasoid man. The only one of several skulls from Jebel Qafza which has so far even been illustrated is a modern Caucasoid, except that it has rather large brow ridges.

One of the Mount Carmel skeletons, that of a female called Tabun 2,

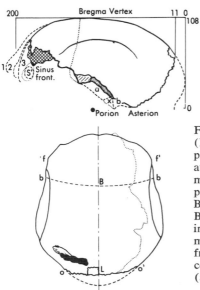

Fig. 76 Skull remnant of Fontéchevade (France). Above: lateral view. Completed forehead curve of 1 = La Chapelle aux Saints, 2 = Crô-Magnon, 3 = modern man, a, b = remnants of the right "os parietale" (mirror image), x = completed. Below: view from above, completed. B = bregma, L = lambda, b–b' = approximately "Sutura coronalis," o–o' = estimated posterior skull line, f–f' = line in front of which the contour no longer corresponds to natural circumstances (after Vallois).

is patently Neanderthaloid both above and below the neck. Others, notably Skhul 4, indicate a transition between the eastern Neanderthals and modern Nordics. This is achieved mainly by a reduction in face size and the retreat of the jaws from a forward position. Still another, Skhul 5, is both fully *sapiens* and curiously Australoid in facial features. Palestine was a busy place in Würm I.

An adolescent skull from Ksar Akil in Lebanon, called "Egbert" by its discoverer, J. F. Ewing, S.J., is completely modern, as is the skull of an infant from the same period at Starosel'e in the Crimea. It would seem, therefore, that the ancestors of the Upper Paleolithic Europeans had evolved in Würm I somewhere in western Asia from a combination of pre-*sapiens,* local Neanderthals, and perhaps some non-Caucasoid elements into a more or less homogeneous population.

The succession from Sinanthropus to *Homo sapiens* of the Mongoloid race in China has already been reviewed. At the end of the Pleistocene it led to three skeletons found in the Upper Cave of Chou Kou Tien, one male and two females, which were Mongoloid. The male was of a long-faced type common among American Indians.

In Indonesia the earliest *sapiens* Australoid skull yet found is that of a youth, in the Niah Caves of northern Borneo, dated at 40,000 years ago. Two others from Wadjak in Java are not only *sapiens* but also closely similar to those of modern Australian aborigines. Southeast Asia was probably the original home of the Australoids, who were pushed out by Mongoloids expanding from the north just as the ancestors of the Australian aborigines and Papuans were beginning to enter their present

193

homes, and eventually other Australoids moved into east-central India.

In Africa we have no certainly dated *sapiens* skulls at all which are of Pleistocene age, but four fragmentary specimens from Kanjera in Kenya may possibly be as much as 50,000 years old, and they seem to have belonged to Negroes. The Negroes probably evolved in West Africa, where no ancient skulls at all have been found, and it is possible, even likely, that the Ternefine-Tangier folk of North Africa crossed the Sahara and occupied East and South Africa after the end of the Pleistocene, having been pushed out by Caucasoid invaders, first Mouillians and then Capsians, coming probably from western Asia, or, less likely, from Spain (or from both places) about 12,000 years ago. These invaders were the ancestors of the present-day Berbers. The Capsians also crossed the Sahara to settle in the Kenya Highlands and neighboring plateaus, where their narrow-nosed descendants may still be seen in many tribes. The Bushmen, located in South Africa, began to grow small and infantile, for reasons still unknown, as most of their descendants surviving today still are.

Thus five subspecies of man originated in Eurasia and Africa, and the two northern ones, the Caucasoid and Mongoloid, invaded the lands to the south of their points of origin, causing considerable movements among the three southern ones. Meanwhile Mongoloids settled America in the guise of American Indians and Eskimos, and later still Caucasoids crossed the oceans to establish themselves in the two Americas (where they also brought Africans), South Africa, Australia, New Zealand, and elsewhere.

FIG. 77

 I. a) *Australopithecus (Plesianthropus) transvaalensis,* Sterkfontein (Transvaal), front view

  b) *Australopithecus (Plesianthropus) transvaalensis,* Sterkfontein (Transvaal), side view

  c) *Homo erectus (IV) modjokertensis,* Sangiran (Java)

  d) *Homo erectus soloensis,* Ngandong (Java)

  e) *Homo erectus pekinensis,* Chou Kou Tien (China)

  f) *Homo rhodesiensis,* Broken Hill (Africa)

 II. a) *Homo neanderthalensis,* La Chapelle aux Saints (France),
front view

  b) *Homo neanderthalensis,* La Chapelle aux Saints, side view

  c) *Homo neanderthalensis,* Saccopastore (Italy)

  d) *Homo neanderthalensis/sapiens* (?), Mt. Carmel (Palestine)

  e) *Homo (Prae) sapiens,* Steinheim, (Germany)

  f) *Homo prae sapiens,* Swanscombe (England)

 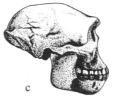 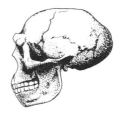

I. a
c
e

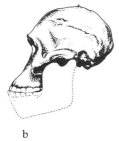 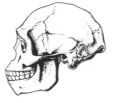 

b
d
f

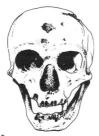

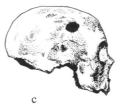 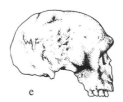

II. a
c
e

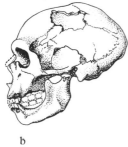 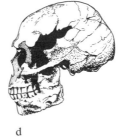 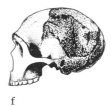

b
d
f

THE MOST IMPORTANT FOSSIL HOMINID DISCOVERIES

PLEISTOCENE	AUSTRALO-PITHECINES	AUSTRALOIDS	MONGOLOIDS	CAUCASOIDS	CAPOIDS	CONGOIDS
Gottweig Interstadial (40,000 yrs.) LATE UPPER		Niah Cave (HS)		(P-HS) { Neanderthals Skhul Starosel'e Tabun Qafza Egbert }	Taforalt ?	(P-HE) { Broken Hill, Saldanha }
Würm I (75,000 yrs.)			Tadaki ? (Japan)		Tangier ?	
EARLY UPPER		Solo (PR-HE)	Liu Kang, Tze Yang (P-HS) Mapa (P-HS) Ting Tsun, Chang Yang (P-HE)	Krapina (P-HS) Ehringsdorf (P-HS)	(PR) Rabat ?	
End Riss (150,000 yrs.)				Saccopastore (P-HS)	Sidi-Abd er-Rahman Temara } (PR)	
MIDDLE			(PR-HE) Sinanthropus	Fontéchevade (PS-HS) Montmaurin Steinheim (PS-HS)	(PR-HE??) Ternefine	(PR-HE) Chellian 3

			Swanscombe (PS-HS) (PR-HE??) Heidelberg			
Begin Mindel (500,000 yrs.)	Olduvai Teeth					
LATE LOWER	Kromdraai, Telanthropus Swartkrans, Zinjanthropus Olduvai Child Makapansgat Sterkfontein Taung, Meganthropus	(PR-HE) Pithecanthropus 1,2,3 (PR-HE) Pithecanthropus 4				
End Villafranchian (700,000 yrs.)	Tchad ?					

European System
PR = Protoanthropine
P = Paleanthropine
PS = pre-sapiens
S = sapiens

Coon's System
HE = Homo erectus
HS = Homo sapiens

(After Carleton S. Coon)

197

PATERNITY DIAGNOSIS

One of the most important fields of applied physical anthropology is the anthropological and genetic determination of kinship—particularly paternity diagnosis. In cases of questionable paternity, as many genetic criteria as possible are used to find out whether two persons—usually a child and an assumed father—are genetically enough alike to be actually parent and progeny. The method is basically similar to the method by which identical and fraternal twins are distinguished (see Human Genetics).

Especially in Europe, and more particularly in Germany, experts in paternity diagnosis are called on to testify in court cases where the financial support of a child may be at issue. This testimony may be called for in one of the following situations:

1. Support payments for illegitimate children.
2. When a husband disclaims a child.
3. More rarely, when a man claims paternity of a child.
4. Delinquency in alimony payments.
5. Perjury, especially in connection with alimony.
6. Incest.
7. Falsification of personal identity.

Determination of paternity outside the courtroom was especially important after World War II, for the identification of war foundlings and in occasional cases of substitution of babies or mistaken identity.

The choice of genetic traits to be used in a given paternity diagnosis varies, depending on a knowledge of particular mechanisms of inheritance, and whether single or multiple allelic loci are involved. Evidence based on single loci is chiefly drawn from comparisons of blood groups, and certain combinations permit the exclusion of potential fathers by serology alone. Generally, it is assumed that if a child shows a dominant allele which is absent in the mother, this gene has to be carried by the father— thus all men who do not possess it are excluded. If the gene is carried in the mother, no male can be excluded on that basis. In a diallelic or polyallelic system where some heterozygotes may be recognizable in the phenotype, as in the ABO and MN blood groups, exclusions of certain parental phenotypes are quite often possible.

More recently, aside from the ABO and MN systems, the Rh factors with their three gene pairs (Cc, Dd, Ee) have become of practical importance. The P factor is used more rarely, as are the exclusion factors Ss and the Lewis and Kell traits. The occurrence of rare or defective genes can occasionally obscure the determination of a genotype and can lead to errors. An elimination based on the ABO system alone is the most reliable procedure, but it is not possible in the majority of cases. Aside from the serological methods, few others can qualify. Criteria of pigmentation of hair, skin, or eyes, by which dominance is apparent for the darker colors, can be of help where great racial differences are suspected in the parents (as in children of Negro fathers and mothers of lighter races). The ability to taste phenylthiocarbamide (PTC) (see Genetics and Race) can also be considered.

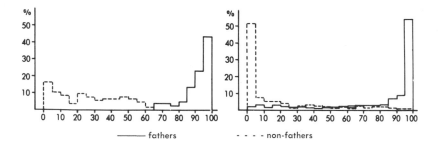

——— fathers   - - - - non-fathers

F<small>IG</small>. 78 Distribution of probabilities of paternity for fathers (solid line) and non-fathers (dotted line) according to the Essen-Möller formula. At the left in 120 ascertainments (Wichmann, 1941) on the basis of 31 traits. Right, in 370 children from 100 families, based on 36 traits (after Schwidetzky, 1956).

Where exclusion is not possible on the basis of these genetically simple comparisons, detailed morphological studies of the persons involved are used. The criteria here have a very complex genetic basis, undoubtedly involving many genes. Among the most useful traits for this purpose are the following:

1. Dermatoglyphics (prints of the fingers, toes, palms and soles). One observes the number of ridges on fingerprints, the type of print, the main lines on the palms and soles, and the patterns of the interdigital spaces.

2. Structure of the iris (form of the stroma of the iris, density of the anterior layer, width of the pupillary zone, and distribution of pigment).

3. Cranium (size, circumference, shape of the back of the head, depressions of bregma or lambda, sagittal gabling, etc.).

4. Facial form (mass, profiles, form of the zygomatic arch and chin).

5. Eye region (breadth, form, and position of the eyelid, degree and shape of the eyefold, height of the palpebral fissure, and width, relief, course, and distribution of the hairs in the eyebrows, etc.).

6. Nose (mass, breadth, and profile of nasal root, dorsum, and tip, height and form of the nostrils, form of septum, etc.).

7. Mouth and chin (height and shape of the lips, form of the philtrum, eversion of the labial mucosa, depression between lips and chin, and form of the chin).

8. Ear (mass, outline, position, curl, and course of the helix, breadth and convexity of the antihelix, convexity of the tragus and antitragus, form of the incisura intertragica, attachment and prominence of the ear-lobe).

9. Oral cavity and teeth (convexity of the gums, palatine rugae, and shape of the tongue).

10. Hands and feet (size, rank of fingers and toes in order of length, form and shape of the nails, flexion creases of the palms and digits).

11. Hairline and orientation of hairs (nuchal and forehead hair, hair whorls).

12. Other characteristics (special features of all kinds should be noted, such as anomalies and constitutional peculiarities; occasionally X-rays, physiological, or psychological studies are advisable).

The various characteristics do not carry equal weight; a great deal depends on how well the traits can be assessed and measured. For hair and eye color, dermatoglyphics, and somatic measurements of size, standardized scales and procedures are available (see Methods of Anthropology). The physiognomic and other minute traits cannot so easily be standardized. Features that change little with age, such as dermatoglyphics and the structure of the iris and ear, are especially important. Anthropometric measurements are reduced to age- and sex-specific values in terms of appropriate means. The same transformations are applied to characteristics of different sexes, since the investigations involve not only different age groups (parents and progeny) but often opposite sexes. Characteristics which are not greatly affected by the environment, such as skin prints, eye color, shape of ear, and many physiognomic features, are more valuable than modifiable traits such as body measurements (see Constitution). The rarer the characteristic, the more important and conclusive is the agreement between father and child.

In the analysis of somatic similarity, traits which differ in mother and

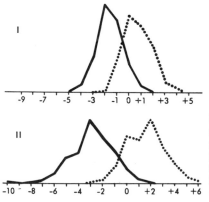

FIG. 79 Distribution of paternity logarithms after Keiter for father-child pairs (solid line) and non-father-child pairs (dotted line) using 370 children from 100 families; (I) on the basis of 25 traits, and (II) based on 70 traits (after Schwidetzky, 1956).

Child	Mother	Father may have	Father cannot have
A	A	A, B, AB, O	—
	B	A, AB	B, O
	AB	A, B, AB, O	—
	O	A, AB	B, O
B	A	B, AB	A, O
	B	A, B, AB, O	—
	AB	A, B, AB, O	—
	O	B, AB	A, O
AB	A	B, AB	A, O
	B	A, AB	B, O
	AB	A, B, AB, O	—
Phenotype of child AB, mother O not possible				

O	A	A, B, O	AB
	B	A, B, O	AB
	O	A, B, O	AB
Phenotype of child O, mother AB not possible.				

M	M	M, MN	N
	MN	M, N, MN	—
Phenotype of child M, mother N not possible.				

N	MN	N, MN	M
	N	N, MN	M
Phenotype of child N, mother M not possible.				

MN	M	N, MN	M
	N	M, MN	N
	MN	M, N, MN	—

child are the most important ones. A paternity diagnosis can be made much more easily in cases of two or more men than in those where only one man is involved. Diagnosis is rendered much more difficult if the mother and father, or potential fathers, are blood relatives. A borderline case is presented when two potential fathers are identical twins; no decision is possible on genetic grounds in this case. If the twins are not identical, however, paternity diagnosis is still possible. Another complication is that twins may have different fathers. One such "superfecundation" has been proven by H. Geyer through exhaustive anthropological tests.

Special problems arise in summarizing all of the evidence in a case in one conclusive report. A scale of probabilities has been recommended: non-decidable; paternity probable or improbable; paternity very probable or very improbable; paternity obvious or impossible. Where known genetic inheritance or blood groups do not conclusively exclude a father, the probability scale corresponds to a similarity scale.

A number of workers have proposed and used mathematical and statistical summaries of similarities and dissimilarities, and there continues to be progress in the improvement of these methods.

1. In the Essen-Möller method, a so-called "critical value" is calculated for each trait. Where X represents the frequency of similarity or agreement between children and their respective "true" fathers, and Y is the frequency of agreement between children and "wrong" fathers (i.e., the frequency of the trait in the average population), the critical value is then Y/X. The probability of the paternity of a man on the basis of traits 1, 2, 3, ... n would then be:

$$P = \cfrac{1}{1 + \cfrac{Y_1 \cdot Y_2 \cdot Y_3 \cdots Y_n}{X_1 \cdot X_2 \cdot X_3 \cdots X_n}}$$

2. The paternity logarithm of Keiter represents a modification of the Essen-Möller method. The critical values are not multiplied. Instead, their logarithms are added and the distribution of values for father-child and non-father-child pairs is represented as discordance-test curves.

3. Interpretations which abandon the concept of probability lean heavily on methods known to statisticians as discriminant functions and distance functions. Although these procedures were not originally designed for paternity diagnosis, they are applicable to them. For example, in a set of father-child pairs and non-father-child pairs, one may calculate a discriminant function which serves to separate the two groups with

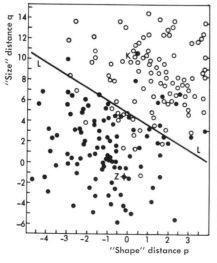

FIG. 80   Separation of father-child pairs ($\bigcirc$) and non-father-child pairs ($\bullet$) by two distance functions based on 80 traits.
K = above line L: claimants of paternity as compared to children.
L = below line L: witnesses disclaiming paternity as compared to children.
L = line of discrimination
(After Baitsch and Schwarzfischer, 1958).

maximal efficiency by means of a single over-all score, which is computed by weighting the constituent somatic similarities and dissimilarities. For any new pair of child and questionable father, the new score will assign them with maximal efficiency to the father-child or the non-father-child array, respectively. Objections have been raised to this method on the grounds that the scores are based on only part of the evidence available from similarity studies. For example, agreements or disagreements in rare traits are not properly weighted. These and other objections will have to be taken into account. The method should also be tested further on large samples of children with known fathers. In addition, its general usefulness could be tested on mother-child pairs; such data are more generally available. Current paternity litigations can also supply material for testing this method.

Anthropological and genetic diagnoses of paternity have been accepted in Denmark, Norway, Sweden, and more recently in Poland, Switzerland, Czechoslovakia, and Hungary as well as in Germany and Austria. Diagnoses based on serology and other evidence of genetically simple traits, as opposed to physiognomy and anthropometry, have been accepted in many other countries.

Other than paternity diagnosis, few applications of physical anthropology have been developed in Germany. Elsewhere, however, many other studies have been conducted. Military supply organizations have ascertained the correct size schedules of uniforms, boots, helmets, and oxygen and gas masks by means of anthropometric surveys. Various manufacturers have conducted surveys on the distribution of clothing sizes, and studies have been made for the purpose of standardizing school furniture. The armed forces of the United States have initiated anthropometric studies and psychological and physiological tests to arrive at the most suitable assignments for recruits.

POPULATION GENETICS

Population genetics can be regarded as a branch of experimental phylogenetics (see The Descent of Man). The hominids existed from the very beginning in populations, or breeding communities. In the course of their phylogenetic history they grew in number from small groups (small bands and family groups) to large populations. Today mankind, composed of many individual populations of greatly varying sizes, is a giant population with a web of sexual interrelationships too complex for detailed analysis. From the standpoint of genetics, populations are made up of groups of individuals propagating themselves within certain geographical limits. A population qualifies specifically as a Mendelian population if its members are subject to the same genetic changes, such as mutability and selection, at the same time and within the same geographical area. Each individual of such a population has at his disposal a part of the population's gene pool. The largest Mendelian populations are represented by species, which can be subdivided into series of smaller and smaller populations. This definition applies also to the hominids.

Population genetics, using statistically quantitative methods, examines the changes to which the genetic structure of a population (of a given gene pool) is subjected. Going beyond simple counts of gene frequencies, it also attempts to determine the causes of genetic structural changes. From a methodological point of view, it is essential to conceive of an ideal population, even though it represents an unrealizable model. Such a population is of infinite size, and all individuals within it have an equal probability of mating ("panmixia"); there is no mutability, and no adaptive differences among individuals with respect to their environment, which is thought of as unchanging. In such a population and its gene pool there is a genetic equilibrium, provided there is normal sexual reproduction. This equilibrium is established within one generation regardless of the frequency with which two alleles Aa were present at the beginning. If the frequency of a dominant gene or allele A equals q and the frequency of the recessive a equals $1 - q$, then the genotype frequency q^2AA : $2q(1 - q)Aa$: $(1 - q)^2aa$ (the Mendelian combination F_2) is obtained. The allele frequencies thus remain constant qA and $(1-q)a$. In such an ideal population no evolution can occur. This formula is the theoretical basis for calculating gene frequencies within populations and is referred to as the Hardy-Weinberg model.

Evolution can often be defined as change in the gene frequencies. Such changes, however, are possible only if the ideal state of the population is somehow affected. This can happen in numerous ways. A real population, which does not exhibit the ideal infinite size and is too small to constitute a statistically significant sample, will suffer a random change in gene frequencies (the Sewall Wright effect). The ensuing genetic drift may cause certain genes to become lost, to be eliminated, or to increase in number without regard to adaptive values. This is especially true of small populations, in which drift can lead to evolutionary changes in a relatively short space of time. In this way, new taxonomically unique groups of small proportions can originate. Genetic drifts alone do not produce evolutionary effects on larger populations. Important for drift effects are quantitative variations (of an accidental or rhythmic nature) in the size of populations. The changes in the concentrations of gene or allele thus brought about can gain evolutionary significance and can provide appreciable accumulations of some genes for selection to work upon.

Analysis has indicated that genetic drift does not lead to important evolutive effects—that, at any rate, no non-selective and unadaptive evolution will result. This also applies to man. If previously isolated populations of the same species are brought together, one will begin to penetrate the other; this is called gene flow. This gene flow can lead in extreme cases to a complete amalgamation of populations and races in a new gene pool.

Mutability extends the genetic variability of the populations or their gene pools through mutations (gene, chromosome, and chromosome-number mutations). In isolated populations, segments of the total gene pool can be cut off and can thus become starting points for new evolution. In this way the variability of the gene pool is built up again slowly through mutations. Generally speaking, mutations generate adaptive differences between alleles, providing the elementary material for the selective pressures. Selection causes the fittest to survive more easily, and thus quantitatively changes the gene frequencies within the gene pool of the population. Certain selective advantages of mutated genes have been accurately measured in samples that were open to analysis. These advantages are defined as an increase in the relative number of offspring of one genotype versus another. This is the way in which selection pressure is exerted; it can be accurately measured as a change in gene frequency per generation. The selection coefficient moves from $+1$ to 0 to -1; that is, from a completely positive selection through a neutral, no-change status to a completely negative selection. Thus the selective value of a gene lies somewhere between these extremes. The frequency of a gene is increased through mutation pressures along with a corresponding selection pressure. Each gene has a certain mutation rate, which ranges from 10^{-4} to 10^{-7}. It should not be forgotten that the selection pressure of a gene depends a great deal upon its genotype and the polygene system to which it belongs.

The quantitative changes in the allelic concentrations (gene frequencies) within populations are the basis for the differentiation of races, which in turn is the basis for the formation of species and thus evolution in general (see The Formation of Races).

Population genetics has achieved its most striking successes experimentally with the *Drosophila* (fruit fly). Various analyses have led to impressive experimental confirmation of the modern form of Darwin's theory of the survival of the fittest.

Under favorable circumstances, it is possible to demonstrate selective effects by means of a relatively simple population analysis. The quantitative changes in gene frequencies of adaptive genes can be demonstrated by a particularly clear example from the animal kingdom. The phenomenon of industrial melanism has been observed in regions where the atmosphere is impure. The impurity of the air can lead to a discoloration of the bark of birch trees, which is inhabited by the peppered moth (*Biston betularia*). The peppered moth in turn is adapted to the lichen growth and the light color of the birch bark. In industrial areas, since about 1850, a variant (*carbonaria*) has been found which is characterized by a darker coloration of body and wings. Today we know that a single dominant gene is responsible for the melanistic discoloration and the slightly stockier body build. This gene first occurred in low concentration; it was repeatedly eliminated although the dark-colored moths were slightly stronger than the normal-colored ones. The activity of the eliminating factor (birds) was observable. The melanism, however, always recurred mutatively, and with increasing industrialization the dark-colored variety became more numerous and has now reached 99 per cent in highly industrialized areas. In other words, in those areas there are only dark moths. The variety *carbonaria* is better protected against birds in industrialized areas than the original light form, *betularia,* and has now become the "normal" one. Ford and Kethlewell have analyzed this phenomenon very carefully, for in earlier days it led to misguided Lamarckian speculations. They found that the variety *carbonaria* survives 10 per cent better in industrial regions and that the light-colored form survives 17 per cent better in non-industrial regions. The intensity of the dark color has increased through the years. Different circumstances provide similar examples. They give an insight into the conditions under which quantitative variations in gene frequency will occur, and they show that adaptive genes which are positively selected will result in increasing gene frequencies.

Little is known about gene variations in human populations; no direct observations of any such process have been made so far. Often, however, there are close analogies to analyzed cases from the animal kingdom, so that for man too we can assume an increasing gene concentration, that is, a gene flow (a penetration of genes into populations not previously touched), as a consequence of selective pressures upon adaptive genes and their combinations. This is so, even though nothing precise can be said about their special characteristics. There are exceptions. In the case of sickle-cell anemia (see Human Genetics), the heterozygote is malaria-resistant and thus has adaptive advantages in a malarial environment; positive selection increases its concentration. The normal homozygotes are eliminated by malaria. If there is no malaria, the frequency of the sickle-cell gene decreases, because homozygous sickle-cell zygotes are not viable and are eliminated.

Quantitative and regional conditions are best studied in some of the blood-factor systems, especially the ABO system. Thus, in Australia the blood type B is normally not found, but it occurs in low concentration in the northern part of the continent. This is believed to be due to the penetration of the Neo-Melanesian racial elements, which arrived from across the sea (the Torres Straits). In Australia, the gene *B,* however, has penetrated southward farther than the Papuan cultural influences. (Birdsell attributes the introduction of this gene to mixture with Indonesian Trepang fishermen, rather than to Papuan influence, because the highest frequency of the gene is in Arnheim Land, where the Trepang fishermen come most often, and not in the Cape York region of Queensland, which lies closest to New Guinea.) The gene has spread southward independently (bound to carriers, of course), but far ahead of the cultural crest. This is only one example of what seems to be a very promising beginning for human population genetics. A great number of racial characteristics can be assumed to be genetic, and some can be so demonstrated. Thus we are implying a selective value, even though it cannot be measured exactly and only a few characteristics have been directly labeled as adaptive. At any rate, the mechanisms subsumed under population genetcis have been at work in the formation of human races, and the selection of adaptive genes no doubt played a most important role (see The Formation of Races). Genetic drift might have been particularly important in the very early stages of the racial and phylogenetic differentiation of the hominids, for it is possible that only very small populations existed at that time. The smaller the number of individuals in a population, the greater the Sewall Wright effect.

Population genetics is a branch of evolutionary genetics, and within the space of a few decades has become the basis for the study of evolutionary processes. Although its fundamental findings were obtained from animal populations, its mathematical and statistical models have universal significance. Even human gene pools and their quantitative changes can be studied in the light of models based on general population genetics, when qualified by a knowledge of local systems of mating. Darwin and his successors have demonstrated that evolution does not proceed through individuals, but through populations.

RACIAL PSYCHOLOGY

The situation in regard to the methods used in studying racial psychology is even more complicated than that in regard to genetics and race. There are, in addition to the factors of physiological modification, the factors that derive from the cultural and ethnic aspects of the environment, which for all practical purposes cannot be eliminated in research testing. While it has been possible, on the basis of tests with twins and families, to establish a hereditary component that is valid for a great variety of character traits and characteristics of mental ability, no single Mendelian factor that could be regarded as representing a norm has been identified in the sphere of the psyche, and none at all that is completely stable in relation to the environment. The extent to which modification of the psyche is possible is more marked in intellectual than in vital and vegetative functions.

In the beginning the great majority of tests were used to determine mental ability, primarily general intelligence. The largest accumulation of material on this aspect grew out of U. S. Army tests given to draftees during World War I. It was found that the scores attained by Negro draftees were considerably below those of white draftees. However, the results of the tests also reflected the differences in education and social and economic status which operated in favor of the whites: the more extensive the comparison of groups of similar social status, the more obvious the similarity in the results of the tests. Hence the performances of

Northern Negroes were superior to those of Negroes from the South. The same gradient applied to the performances of the whites, and in Canada, where discrimination has been relatively mild, the whites have scored above the Negroes. In the case of three Southern cities (Birmingham, Nashville, and Charleston) there was no tangible difference in aptitude between the Negroes who had moved to the Northern states and those who had stayed behind and attended the separate schools for colored children. The differences in test scores of various European immigrant groups—the performances of the Italians, among others, were inferior to those of the British and Scandinavians—ran parallel to the cultural and educational curves of the countries of origin or corresponded to the level of the social group from which the immigrants had come; thus no racial differences were manifest. Some people place great reliance on these tests and others consider them worthless. The truth probably lies somewhere in between. The real trouble with intelligence tests is that there is no very efficient way to handle the data statistically. For example, the speed in response is given a high value along with the correctness and completeness of answers. In other words, intelligence tests are little more than educated guesses into the intellectual potential of an individual or a race.

A more fruitful area of investigation is that of special aptitudes. Children of Scandinavian parentage excel those of Jewish descent in spatial orientation and in co-ordination of sensory perceptions and movements, but trail behind in verbal ability. The Chinese have been shown to have a better auditory memory than the Japanese, but have performed less well than the latter in tests designed to measure manual dexterity. In Mozambique, native children were found to have a more retentive memory for signs and symbols, but a less retentive memory for verbal constructs, than Portuguese children of the same age. All these results are in need of confirmation by independent multiple tests.

We also have some indications regarding differences in artistic talent. Negroes in Jamaica were found to have a more highly developed sense of rhythm and a more acute ear for pitch and intensity of tone than the whites. These findings have not been confirmed by tests with Negroes in the United States, but, as has been pointed out from a racial-sociological point of view, the most important contribution that the Negro has made to American culture has been in music, while American Indians have been credited with a special aptitude for the fine arts, notably painting.

The psycho-physical correlations established by research into constitutional factors may also have implications for psycho-racial differences, since the various races do after all show differences in physique and in the extent to which they are liable to gynandromorphism and a concurrence of other hormonal factors (see Constitution). The cultural pattern of the Negroes and American Indians and their mode of adaptation to European civilization reflect certain characteristic features that can be linked to the existence of a predominant type of physique. Some of the schizothymic traits of Negroes, which go with their predominantly lepto-

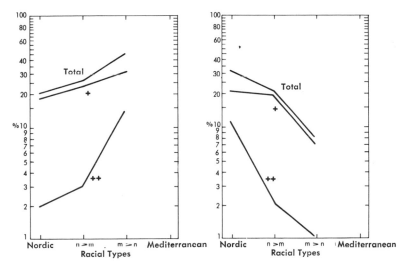

FIG. 81 Racial differences in psychological make-up. Proportion of positive reactions (+ and ++) in Nordic and Mediterranean types to the sentences: "I spend much of my time in the street and in the open" (left); and "I wish that my home were far away from others" (right) (after Arrowsmith).

somic physique, are emphasis on form rather than on color (the plastic arts as the distinctive folk art of African Negroes) and a good capacity for discrimination in dealing with over-all impressions. Side by side with these characteristics we find some of the phenomena associated with Basedow's disease (exophthalmic goiter): among the physical symptoms, wide-open, glittering, moist eyes; among psychological symptoms, marked nervous irritability. The predominant type among American Indians is the athletic type. The character traits that experts on Indians and Indian cultural forms emphasize conform to what has been described as the sluggish (viscous) temperament of athletes: tenaciousness; passivity even when assuming an attitude of bravery, manifesting itself as perseverance and self-discipline in its positive form; emotional sluggishness; lack of associative drive; a relatively crude and unvaried motor sphere which finds expression in music, among other things.

These general observations refer to the behavior pattern of whole populations or even clusters of populations as a form of cultural achievement (see Cultural Anthropology). However, as far as racial traits are concerned, there have been very few findings to date for any psycho-physical correlations within given population ranges. The weak correlations that have been established between intelligence and the body-height factor seem to have nothing to do with racial types; at any rate, there are no correlates for the cephalic index (the ratio of breadth to length of head), the nasal index, or racial characteristics of physiognomy. There are only a few positive indications with respect to pigmentation: in a village situated on the elevated land above a North German coastal region, 7 per cent of the poor peasants and, by contrast, 32 per cent of the rich peasants were found to be dark-eyed; the differences were significant. There is a positive correlation between the degree of pigmentation and Jaensch's integrated types: individuals with darker pigmentation tend to be more integrated and more extroverted in temperament, the light-skinned less integrated and tending toward greater psychic detachment. The correlations pertaining to the behavior and cultural patterns of the northern and southern European types (Nordic and Mediterranean types) are obvious. Diagnosis of racial types also shows the Nordic types to be less well integrated and more introverted, and the darker Mediterranean types to be more integrated and extroverted, even given the same leptosomic physique, the same cultural environment and socio-economic level.

As the results of research into the psychological factors of constitution and inheritable traits would lead us to expect, it would seem more fruitful to seek correlations indicating distinctive racial traits in the cognitive, vital, and vegetative functions rather than in the intellectual superstructure. Both areas are of equal importance for the cultural development and adaptation of underdeveloped ethnic groups. But the current trend among British and American social anthropologists is not favorable for the pursuit of psycho-racial investigations. Much greater stress is laid on the social than on the biological conditioning of behavior, and, given the prevailing view that intelligence studies yield no meaningful results, the tendency is to regard the school of psycho-racial orientation as theoretical and of no practical significance.

SOCIAL BIOLOGY

Social biology deals with the reciprocal relationships between man's biological nature and his social processes. The older students of this subject emphasized the anthropometric and morphological differences between social groups (urban and rural, social strata, stationary and mobile groups, criminal and non-criminal types) and the interpretation of them through the study of natural and social selection. More recently, investigations have shifted somewhat toward selective mechanisms as such, and individual and group differences such as body build, abilities, age, and sex have been studied to an increasing extent for the express purpose of evaluating and tracing these selective processes.

Concepts in Social Biology

The first process to be recognized as significant for social biology was that of natural selection. According to Spencer and Haeckel, the doctrine of "the survival of the fittest" applies as well in the field of social competition, and success in society is a criterion for biological quality. This older conception, which takes an optimistic view of progress, is known as Social Darwinism. However, when birth rates began to decline, and were accompanied by differences in fertility among the social strata (with parents of low social status having, in general, the most children—see Demography), this simple carry-over of Darwinian concepts to human society was no longer tenable. It had become obvious that the ability to survive and reproduce in society was no longer a universally valid criterion of "fitness." Hence there was coined the concept of counter-selection—i.e., the selection of the "unfit"—a process which was taken to be a characteristic of highly civilized societies. Here, "fitness" presupposes at least a subjective standard of values. But since many processes of socio-biological differentiation occur independently of traits which can be evaluated by such a subjective standard, in social biology it is advisable to interpret selection simply as applying to the differential fertility of groups of differing heredity.

A related concept, introduced by Thurnwald in 1924, may be called "genotypic assortment," or, simply, "assortment." This concept denotes the sorting of certain genotypes of a polymorphic population into specific

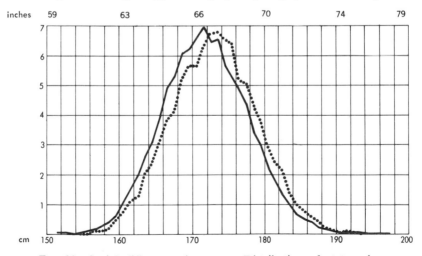

FIG. 82 Social differences in stature. Distribution of stature in the lower stratum (solid line) and in the upper stratum (dotted line) based on examination of recruits in Sweden (after F. J. Linders, 1930).

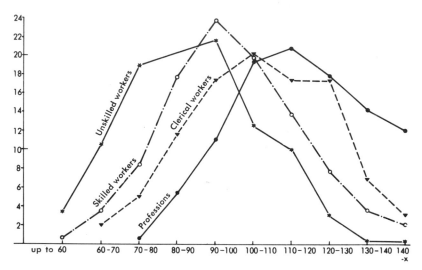

Fig. 83 Social differences in intelligence. Distribution of intelligence quotients for social groups in the United States (after Haggerty and Nash, 1924).

environmental or social niches. Territorial assortment distributes the genotypes over various geographic environments, such as mountains and valleys, field and forest, loess and sandy soil, or urban and rural areas, so that the total population is shown as a composite of population segments of varied hereditary background. In occupational or hierarchical assortment, the occupations or social classes act as the various environments into which the hereditary variants are assorted. In the actual social situation these two forms of assortment cannot be kept strictly apart, for changes in social status are frequently accompanied by changes in residence (for example, migration from rural to urban areas or, a more recent phenomenon, migration from urban to suburban areas). When a comparison is made between the emigrants and those remaining at the old location, the term "assortative migration" is employed. In preferential mating, it is the partner, and the marriage partner in particular, who acts as the assortative factor. When both partners deviate phenotypically in the same direction from the population mean, we speak of homogamy. If the partners deviate in opposing directions from the population mean, we speak of heterogamy. Thus assortative mating structures human societies, but unlike natural selection it does not necessarily alter their gene frequencies. Homogamy for specific genes can, however, act in much the same way as inbreeding to increase the frequency of the relevant homozygotes in a population. Heterogamy can correspondingly increase the frequency of heterozygotes. However, since both reproduction and length of life in human beings are strongly affected by social and cultural factors, the groups in which the assortative process operates frequently represent groups of differential reproduction rates, and hence groups in which the process of selection is at work.

The assortative process can occur only in a mobile society in which the various strata are not rigorously separated by marriage taboos, as in the caste system. However, even in societies with high social mobility assortment of hereditary variants into corresponding environmental spheres is not complete. It is counterbalanced by assortative inertia, which holds individuals in the social groups to which they belong by origin, even if they do not correspond to their potential for achievement. Moreover, there are many social processes that have no anthropological significance, since they are regulated by entirely extra-biological factors such as supply and demand. How far the assortative process proceeds is dependent on the resultant of these forces for stability and change in the social system.

Hereditary differences between social groups may derive from social stratification by territorial conquest, if in their newly composed population the victors occupy positions of dominance over the vanquished. In time, however, barriers to marriage usually become less rigid and finally disappear altogether. Then biological intermixture and cultural assimilation will homogenize the population, but remnants of hereditary differences may still linger on for a considerable period of time due to assortative inertia. Whether persistent hereditary differences between social groups are truly relics of a conquering aristocracy can be determined only from the history of that population and not merely from anthropological findings.

Somatic Differences Between Social Groups

Sexual Division of Labor. The division of labor between the sexes is the most elementary differentiation in social biology. It derives from their different reproductive functions and from the differences in physical strength and mobility. Among primitive peoples the occupations most typically regarded as man's work are the waging of war, metalworking, and hunting. Domestic pursuits, such as the preparation of food and work with textiles and pottery, are usually viewed as the province of the female. The two poles of sexual specialization in social roles, "the pole of strength" on one hand and the "pole of domesticity" on the other, have survived through all the phases of cultural development down to modern industrial society. Machine labor and social mobility have obliterated sexual specializations in many occupations, but they have not abolished them. Thus metalworking and heavy industry in particular are still primarily considered male occupations, while the textile industry preponderantly employs females. Our own social pattern, which is much more varied today than it was in the past, has given rise to new differences associated with sex, and the considerable variations in time, place, and culture indicate that these are not wholly derived from biological factors.

Social Strata and Occupations. It is accepted as a general rule that the higher a group is in the social hierarchy, the greater will be the average stature, intelligence, and precocity in that group. Moreover, the intellectual upper strata are leaner in physique than the population mean. Within the rural social hierarchy of Germany, the landowning stratum of farmers is more apt to be broad than narrow in build and shows a preponderance of light eyes. Both the social assortative process and somatic responses to environment are factors in these differences. The following facts would point to the influence of environment: (1) The course of maturation and growth show a high degree of correlation with the standard of living, particularly with the fat and protein content of food eaten. Moreover, fat and protein consumption show the same relationship to social status as body size and the onset of maturation (see Growth). (2) Achievements on intelligence tests are influenced not only by the hereditary components of talent but also by educational factors, which, again, correlate directly with intelligence. The following findings in particular point to the influence of the assortative process, i.e., to the influence of hereditary differences: (1) There is a gradation of stature not only in accordance with social origin but also within groups of the same social origin where stature varies with social status. Individuals rising or descending in the social hierarchy frequently are closer in this respect to the group toward which they are moving than to the group from which they originated. (2) The observed variability of stature and intelligence in entire populations is greater than the environmental component of variability suggested by studies on twins. (3) The light eyes in the farmers are a trait that is not influenced by environmental factors. It is probable that there is a relationship between social assortment on stature and its influence on intelligence (see Consti-

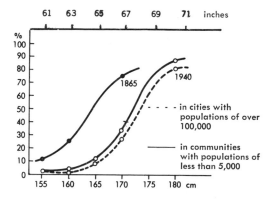

Fig. 84   Urban-rural differences in stature in Dutch recruits, 1940 (total percentage curve). The social differences are less than the changes through increase in stature since 1865 (after W. Lenz, 1951).

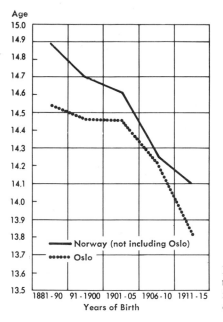

Age

15.0
14.9
14.8
14.7
14.6
14.5
14.4
14.3
14.2
14.1
14.0
13.9
13.8
13.7
13.6
13.5

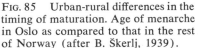

Norway (not including Oslo)
Oslo

1881-90 91-1900 1901-05 1906-10 1911-15
Years of Birth

FIG. 85   Urban-rural differences in the timing of maturation. Age of menarche in Oslo as compared to that in the rest of Norway (after B. Škerlj, 1939).

tution). In this relationship the primary role may belong to intelligence, while stature, correlated with intelligence, coexists with it in the same individuals.

In addition to the rank-related social assortative process, there is some assortment by occupations as well. Thus, within the same social level, the individual occupational groups in part are ranged in many different ways, depending on the specific requirements of the occupation. Among college graduates, future medical specialists rank higher in test achievement than those who intended to be general practitioners, dentists, and veterinarians; top rank in the achievement scale is occupied by students who name scholarly research as their vocational goal. Moreover, certain occupational groups do not range themselves in accordance with their social rank; cobblers and tailors rank behind unskilled laborers in stature (Saxony, Silesia, Denmark, Switzerland). In the United States such studies would be impracticable because these occupations are practiced by people of widely divergent national groups.

Urban and Rural Population. In Germany city-dwellers, particularly those who live in metropolitan areas, tend to be taller than the surrounding rural population; they also show a greater incidence of dark hair and dark eyes and a larger head form; as a rule, sexual maturation and the pubertal growth spurt (see Growth) set in at an earlier age, and they are almost always superior in intelligence test achievements and in scholastic ability.

215

Social assortment and environmental influences on physique interact also in the formation of urban populations; in part the two processes work in the same direction, so that the results are cumulative. Facts such as the following would be indicative of modification in the urban environment (through such factors as less ultraviolet radiation, more time spent indoors, and less need to perform heavy physical work): (1) Children born in urban areas of parents who were born in rural areas have narrower heads than their parents. (2) The younger the migrants to urban areas were at the time of their migration, the more pronounced will be the measurement traits characteristic of urban types. (3) Differences in intelligence between children of rural areas and those from urban areas are less during pre-school age and increase during school age. (4) During periods of food shortage the urban-rural differences in maturation and growth are reversed; at such times the children of rural areas mature sooner than those in the city, since they receive better nourishment.

If there are differences not merely between the urban and the rural population but even between those migrating from the rural areas and those remaining in the country, selection may be assumed to be a factor. This has been proven in several areas: (1) Pigmentation traits, which are relatively uninfluenced by environment, must necessarily be presumed to derive from hereditary differences between urban and rural populations; however, they may also be derived from another gene distribution; i.e., a stronger heterozygosity of the urban population, which is more heterogeneous in origin than the rural population. (2) In the case of stature and cephalic index, but only for migrants to metropolitan areas, not for migrants to smaller cities. (3) Not only children born in urban areas of rural-born parents but even their mothers show an acceleration in development; i.e., precocious tooth eruption. (4) Whereas points (1) to (3) thus far have been demonstrated in random samples only, results are available from a number of studies conducted in Germany of the migration of the talented from the villages. However, no generalizations can be made on the basis of these findings. Thus, on the basis of corresponding sample studies, urban sociologists in the United States assume that both extremes of ability—those of above-average ability as well as those below the average—will tend to migrate to the cities, while a stratum of average ability remains more evident in rural areas.

In Tasmania, however, extensive studies of intelligence quotients of schoolchildren have revealed marked differences in intelligence, with the brighter people moving to the cities of that island and of Australia.

Ethnically Stratified Societies. Ethnic superimposition can best be seen where there are population segments of different races. During the era of European expansion a dominant white minority was superimposed upon native colored populations in certain regions (for example in Indonesia, South Africa, Kenya, and South America) and such stratification also resulted from the importation of Negro slaves (as in the United States,

Brazil, the West Indies, and Arabia). In many parts of Africa it was shown that the higher the social stratum among the native peoples, the lighter and more Caucasoid the type became; this was the result of the migratory pressure from the Caucasoid North African region which imposed more distinctly Caucasoid groups upon more distinctly Negroid groups (Ashanti, Yoruba, Kanuri, Katoko, Asande, Mangbetu, etc.). Probably the somatic differences between the castes in India—the relatively tall stature, narrow nose, and light skin in the higher castes—are of similar origin; in India, Indo-Aryan conquerors from the North superimposed themselves upon an aboriginal society which itself was probably already stratified. Ethnologists know of numerous instances of peasants having been conquered by nomadic shepherds who, as a rule, are leaner in physique and more warlike.

Endogamy and Assortative Mating

The structuring of population by means of social assortment continually changes. However, here assortative mating in the form of homogamy acts as a stabilizing factor; it has been proven for such traits as stature, pigmentation, educational levels, and intelligence (see Figure 87); thus, mar-

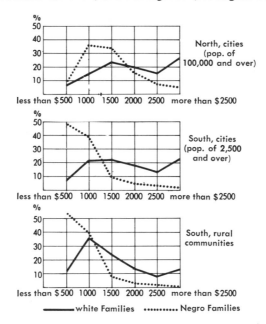

FIG. 86   Ethnic stratification. Distribution of income for whites and Negroes in the U.S.: higher proportion of whites in higher income groups throughout. Differences are smaller in the North than in the South (after M. F. Nimkoff, 1947).

217

riage partners tend to deviate from the population mean in the same direction in higher than random frequencies. Since these are hereditary traits in which the children scatter about the median value represented by the parents, the social strata tend to complement one another through the sifting out of appropriate variants not only from other strata but also from their own offspring. Thus the higher social strata have not only an above-average level of ability but also a greater number of talented children than would be in keeping with the proportion they represent in the total population. Often certain specific talents will occur in great frequency over several generations in families with appropriate assortative mating—for example, high musical aptitude in the families of Bach, Strauss, and Wagner, and literary and philosophical talents in a group of related Swabian families of scholars and clergymen which produced such men as Gerok, Hegel, Hauff, Hölderlin, Kerner, Mörike, Schiller, and Uhland. Galton documented many such families in England, such as the Darwin-Wedgwood kindred. In the United States comparable families include the Adamses, Lowells, Eliots, and Roosevelts.

On the other hand, in traits and personality features correlated with sex, heterogamy is more common. Even before the discovery of potential bisexuality and of the individual variability in the production of sex hormones (see Constitution), it was assumed by many that the hetero-sexual personality traits in marital partners are of equal magnitude. The analysis of handwriting samples in which polar pairs of traits specific to either sex were tested (such as abstraction–directness, slight feeling–intense feeling—the first in each pair belonging to the male and the second to the female pole) confirmed that contrast and complementation of behavior was more prominent in happy marriages than in unhappy ones.

The choice of persons from among whom a marriage partner may be selected is limited by a number of factors. The most elementary of these is proximity. A great many marriages take place between men and women from within the residential community represented by the village in rural areas and by the neighborhood and the block in urban areas. In one American town 62 per cent of the marriages were between partners who lived within a radius of no more than four miles; in 34 per cent of marriages in Philadelphia, the partners lived within a radius of no more than four blocks. The degree to which marriages are limited by proximity varies with the size of the locality, density of population, communications, and also educational level. Natural barriers to communication such as major rivers, forests, mountains, and oceans also act as barriers to the selection of a mate. Where population is sparse and communications not well developed, such breeding isolates will become more compact and more completely isolated than might be assumed to occur even in many primitive peoples. If isolation is extended over a sufficiently long period, such isolates may become cells for the formation of races (see The Formation of Races).

In addition to natural barriers, human groups, in some cases, are also

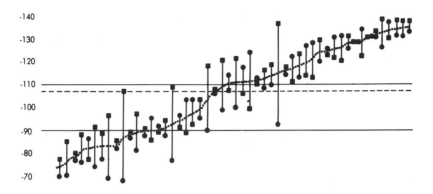

FIG. 87 Assortative mating according to intelligence. Intelligence quotients of husband (■) and wife (●) in 51 marriages in the United States (after M. C. Outhit, 1933).

faced with cultural and ethnic restrictions on their selection of mates. Particularly effective here are language barriers and forces that work against ethnic admixtures. In immigrant countries such as the United States and Argentina, the various immigrant groups tend toward ethnic homogamy; Italians and Spaniards, and Jews from Eastern Europe, for example, will prefer to mate among their own kind as long as they are concerned with preserving at least some of their cultural characteristics; on the other hand, in postwar migrations in Germany, the natives and refugees speaking the same language did not form isolates; the connuptial index (the relationship between the actual and the probable proportion of mixed marriages) has increasingly approached the coefficient of 1. Religious and sectarian barriers act much like language barriers, and their influence is in proportion to the strength of the religious affiliations. Political barriers act to limit communications, and thus marriage connections as well, even if they do not constitute language and cultural barriers.

Due to the modifiability of many cultural traits (see Cultural Anthropology), the boundaries of cultural areas show only slight stability. Migrations, transfers, and additions in population and the establishment of new political boundaries will change them, and the fluctuation of ethnic boundaries increases in proportion to the density of population and the level of civilization. Thus new isolates are constantly being formed, population segments are united and become breeding communities, and within the isolates a situation of random mating is approached. In this way man achieves a relatively high degree of racial intermixture. However, the limitation of proximity always remains, and retards amalgamation and the leveling of those racial differences which developed in the early phases of human history through prolonged isolation.

Intra-Ethnic Selective Processes

In a hereditary differentiation of social groups through ethnic super-imposition or assortment, social differences in reproduction and mortality act as selective processes. The following must be taken into account in studying the over-all effect of selection: mortality (i.e., mortality prior to the end of the reproductive age span), frequency and age of marriage, birth and reproduction rates. During the period when birth rates dropped (Phase III in the cycle of population development—see Demography) and in which family planning spread first through the upper strata, the later marriages and low birth rates may have decreased the prevalence of some hereditary traits specific to the strata, particularly for those of tall stature and outstanding talent. Nevertheless, the favorable mortality patterns in the upper strata counteracted this situation. Taking into account the intelligence-test scores and reproduction rates specific to the strata the following table of aptitude distributions in one generation in the United States was computed by Lorimer and Osborn.

DISTRIBUTION OF INTELLIGENCE QUOTIENTS IN TWO GENERATIONS OF AMERICANS			
Intelligence Scores	1st generation	2nd generation	Difference (in %)
140 and over	1.71	1.50	−12.3
130–139	3.25	2.88	−11.4
120–129	7.17	6.46	− 9.9
110–119	11.91	11.44	− 3.9
100–109	17.24	16.93	− 1.8
90–99	21.28	21.64	+ 1.6
80–89	18.67	19.31	+ 3.4
70–79	12.01	12.65	+ 5.4
60–69	5.30	5.61	+ 5.8
below 60	1.46	1.59	+ 8.8
Median value	95.90	95.01	− 0.89

(After Lorimer and Osborn, 1934)

However, it has not yet been possible to produce direct evidence of such selective effects, perhaps because environmental influences will compensate or even over-compensate for them phenotypically. For example, the increase in individuals of small stature during the period of declining birth rates was compensated for by an increase in height during that century (see Growth); a decrease in the number of talented individuals might have been compensated for by better educational conditions and habituation to tests. At any rate, a battery of tests conducted with school-children in Scotland revealed not a drop but rather a slight rise in test achievements. A drop in scholastic achievement, particularly in the students' ability to concentrate, which was frequently noted, does not necessarily indicate a change in gene frequencies; rather educators are inclined to attribute it to the relatively disturbing conditions of World War II and its aftermath.

Early in the Industrial Revolution, the low fertility and unfavorable mortality of urban areas tended to limit or reduce the frequencies of "urban" genotypes in the more advanced nations of the world. However, the improvements in sanitation and hygiene took full effect sooner and more rapidly in urban areas than in the rural regions, so that the urban-rural differences in mortality canceled each other to a great extent and the major effect of selection to be expected now is one deriving from fertility. Here, too, it has not yet been possible to produce direct evidence.

With the general adoption of contraceptive measures, the selective process initiated by the drop in birth rates has come to an end. As early as 1920 there was an indication, first in several large European cities, that the pendulum would swing back to the earlier differences in reproduction in which size of family was correlated positively with income and social status. This change has also appeared in the United States since World War II. There are also other major temporal and spatial differences in the extent and even in the direction of demographic differentiation and thus also of the selective processes. For example, in France, unlike many other countries, the drop in births began in the rural areas, which then continued to lag behind the cities (not including Paris). Similarly, in Sweden, up to World War I, the birth rates in agricultural communities were lower than those in industrial centers.

Earlier periods in the history of populations have left very little reliable data concerning the social differentiation of mortality, fertility, and social selection. A number of indications point to the "extinction of elites." In the Hellenistic period the frequency of marriage and average number of children, or at least the number of children raised to adulthood, fell in the cities of ancient Greece; population was limited by means of celibacy and the exposure of newborn infants to the elements. In the era of the Roman Republic many patrician families died out or survived only by adopting children; the strata of leadership (senate, knighthood) were replenished to an increasing extent from the lower social strata and from among alien immigrants. Caesar and Augustus devised various measures to encourage fertility, particularly in the upper social strata of Rome proper (see Demography). However, these processes were always limited in time, place, and extent. Many other "elites" did not become biologically extinct, but were supplanted sociologically by other strata of leadership. There is no historical proof for the existence of a general, universal trend of social selective processes as interpreted by those who hold a pessimistic view of the development of culture; i.e., a steady "consumption of elites" accompanied by a decrease in outstanding talent. In fact, an opposing trend is more likely for the major part of the history of human populations, since under primitive demographic conditions—Phase 1 of the cycle of the development of population, with high birth rates and high death rates—there is rather a positive correlation between reproduction and social status. However, the extraordinary multiplicity and the complex nature of the assortative processes and the instability of the demographic factors, particularly during the period which yields adequate statistical evidence, should caution us against making generalizations of any sort.

Inter-Ethnic Selective Processes

Like the various social strata, the various peoples, too, do not emerge simultaneously from the primitive, stationary phase of the development cycle into the phase of decreasing mortality rates (greater population growth), and thence to the phase of declining birth rates (a drop in excess births). Thus the proportions of ethnic groups in the total population of the world are altered. During the eighteenth and nineteenth centuries the population of Europe grew more rapidly than that of the other continents; today it grows more slowly (see Demography). At present, the populations of China, India, and a number of South American states show the fastest growth; in the countries of Eastern and Southern Europe reproduction rates are higher than in Northern and Western Europe, and so forth. Thus here, too, selection is at work, favoring the numerical increase enjoyed by less-developed peoples who have not yet run through the entire cycle of population development. There is no evidence, however, that the present differences in complexity of civilization in present-day nations are based on differences in intelligence level, as some believe to be the case in intra-ethnic differentiation (see Racial Psychology). On the other hand, such differentiations in growth cause a shift in the racial composition of the population of the world.

Here too, as in intra-ethnic selection, there is considerable transient variation in the extent and even in the direction of the selective process; thus an increasing number of peoples move into the third, stationary phase (low death rates and low birth rates), and even those peoples that are still in a phase of growth steadily approach stabilization on a level of lower population turnover. Given equal rates of growth and equal duration of the growth phase, the end result will be that the more numerous peoples will represent a larger proportion of the earth's total population than they did prior to the onset of growth differentiation, while the relative proportion of ethnic entities with smaller numbers will decline. The development of increasingly large ethnic units and thus increasingly large breeding areas is also reflected in statistics pertaining to language. Of the approximately 1,500 living languages, 22 represent three-fourths of mankind; there were probably at least twice as many languages spoken during the era prior to the expansion of European peoples. Here, too, even as in the case of the "extinction of elites," what has occurred is often simply a case of the social obliteration of various groups as ethnically independent isolates.

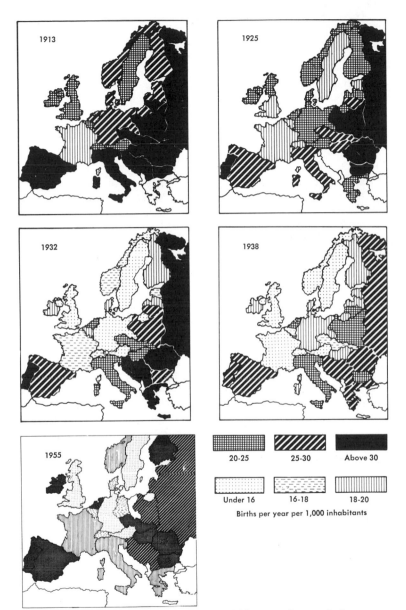

FIG. 88   Inter-ethnic selective processes. Differences in population growth according to birth figures in various census years.

However, unusually small ethnic minorities also face the danger of biological extinction. In many places the spread of Europeans has resulted in the extinction of primitive peoples (Tasmanians, some Caribbean Indians) or in their extensive decimation (many Polynesian and Melanesian tribes, North American Indians). These depopulations have usually resulted from more than one cause. Some groups have been violently exterminated by groups superior in numbers and armed strength. New epidemic diseases have often been fatal. Psychic apathy in some cases has probably produced a drop in birth rate and in the probability of survival to adulthood. Another factor has sometimes been a disintegration of tribal and family units as a result of their young men engaging in contract or migratory labor.

However, after a period of great recession in population size, many primitive peoples passed the "adjustment crisis" and reverted to an equalized or positive population balance. In every instance this phenomenon was associated with the adoption of European cultural traits—to the extent of complete abandonment of ethnic individuality (complete acculturation). In particular, European practices of hygiene and sanitation and the efforts to reduce infant mortality had immediate demographic results. Since, as a rule, these primitive groups moved into the phase of lowered birth and mortality rates later than the European colonial powers, they were able to outstrip the latter, at times, in rates of growth. Thus, at present, the Maoris of New Zealand and a number of North American Indian tribes have a higher reproduction rate than the white population in their territory. It is probable that, with progressing cultural and ethnic assimilation, the differences in growth rates will eventually become equalized.

The development of primitive peoples in the era of European expansion represents a pattern that probably was followed also by numerous other processes of which less adequate historical evidence remains. The spread of the civilized nations is effected not only through the superior growth potential of their cultural pattern but also, and probably predominantly, through the ethnic assimilation of groups that were formerly ethnically independent. Where there are differences in cultural levels, the pressure of assimilation as a rule follows the civilization gradient. Thus, through the ability of their culture to assimilate other cultures, the Chinese people, step by step from their area of origin in the Huang Ho Valley, managed to assimilate the more primitive mountain and forest tribes of what today are the southern provinces of China. The ancient Egyptian nation of the era of Pharaonic dynasties was welded together from a Lower Egyptian peasant population and a pastoral population from Upper Egypt, and then proceeded to assimilate populations of Nubian origin all the way to the fourth cataract of the Nile. The history of the Roman Empire is one of political and military expansion of a part of the population of Latium, accompanied by the Latinization of the groups which first had been politically assimilated. In a culturally complex nation the culturally assimilated populations which have a relatively efficient economy and a more lavish food supply often become more numerous. Thus the abandonment of ethnic independence and assimilation by higher civilizations constitutes a selective process in favor of those being assimilated.

Racial Politics

Wherever ethnic groups of varying racial structure come into contact, conspicuous racial traits such as skin color often give rise to awareness of difference that is at times embraced by virtually the entire community. Most frequently this takes the form of a contempt for those of other races, which represents one of the many forms of ethnocentrism: the rejection of aliens in general. The Negro problem in the United States and that in the Union of South Africa are the best-known examples of group conflict based on an awareness of racial differences. However, racial consciousness is not always a primary factor; it is possible for ethnic, social, religious, or cultural contrasts, running parallel to differences in racial structure, to be motivated secondarily by racial ideology (for example, anti-Semitism), which in recent times has based itself on arguments of racial psychology (see Racial Psychology). In such instances, the racial phenotype may play only a subordinate role in the collective evaluation of individuals; the decisive factor then will be whether or not a person is known to have been born into the rejected group (for example, Negroes "passing for white" in the United States; in Germany proof of Aryan descent).

Where groups of differing race live together, the politically or culturally superior group may take one or more of the following measures to shut out the race that is being discriminated against: (a) *Marriage taboos,* which may be established either by law or merely by convention. In the United States, many states still prohibit marriages between Negroes and whites; elsewhere extramarital sexual intercourse between the races is also subject to punishment (as in the Union of South Africa and Nazi Germany). (b) *The monopolizing of social power.* The race held in contempt will be kept in a position of social dependency; it will constitute a substratum separated from the upper strata by barriers to the assortative process. (c) *Segregation,* which may be enforced through outright legal strictures or supported by means of generally recognized social practice.

Barriers to marriage usually persist longer than barriers to social mobility, but they tend to be relaxed by extramarital liaisons. In most such relationships, the males, rather than the females, will belong to the dominant group; females, on the other hand, are more stringently guarded against sexual contact with males of the subordinate group. These rules also apply to the numerous instances throughout history in which ethnic superimposition was followed by the establishment of barriers to marriage (note, for example, the Spartans and the Perioeci; the Helots in Sparta; the caste system in India; the Arioi in Polynesia). In all these instances racial policies may have retarded the amalgamation of the various segments of the populations involved, but in the final analysis they were not able to delay them indefinitely.

TAXONOMY OF THE PRIMATES

The primates are an "order" in the class Mammalia (mammals), according to the classification that has come down from Linnaeus (1758). Presumably the primates originated in the Cretaceous period from insectivorous ancestor forms. Their direct ancestors are not known paleontologically. A prototype of the first forms with which the evolution of the primates began still survives in the Tupaioidea (tree shrews). The complexity of the problems involved in systematic classification is demonstrated, for example, in the survey made recently by W. Fiedler in the *Handbook for the Study of Primates* (1956). An arrangement of the primates within the total system of mammalia was made by G. G. Simpson in 1945. Most of the texts devoted to mammals and anthropology present systematic surveys, in varying detail, of the Primate order. From among the more comprehensive descriptions of the class Mammalia, particular mention should be made here of the German work by Weber and Abel (1928) and of the French volume *Traité de Zoologie,* which was published by Grassé in 1955. The first adequately substantiated determination of the place of the hominids (manlike creatures) in the animal system was made in 1863 by T. H. Huxley.

In this section we are following Fiedler's classification of Primates. However, G. G. Simpson's taxonomy, which is largely followed in the English-speaking world, differs from it in the following details.

Simpson recognizes the same two sub-orders, but calls them Prosimii and Anthropoidea. Simpson does not use the infra-order category, and does not recognize the terms Platyrrhina and Catarrhina. He divides the Simii (Anthropoidea) into super-families of Ceboidea, Cerpithecoidea, and Hominoidea: New World Monkeys, Old World Monkeys, and Apes and Men.

The primates, as placental mammals, are characterized chiefly by extremities with five digits each, by flat nails (clawlike nails on one or more digits occur in a few species), by grasping hands and feet, and by an arboreal way of life. The eye sockets are surrounded by a closed rim of bone. Dentition is heterodont with chisel-shaped incisors, pointed canine teeth, and molars with several cusps (bunodont). The general dental

formula is: $I\frac{2}{2}\quad C\frac{1}{1}\quad P\frac{2\ (3)}{2\ (3)}\quad M\frac{3\ (2)}{3\ (2)}$.

The Primate order is divided into two sub-orders: Prosimiae (lemurs and related animals) and Simiae (monkeys, apes, and men).

The Prosimiae are divided into four groups (infra-orders): I. Tupaiiformes (tree shrews); II. Lemuriformes (lemurs); III. Lorisiformes (lorises); and IV. Tarsiiformes (tarsiers and their extinct relatives).

The first group (Tupaiiformes) consists of the most primitive of all primates, the tree shrews, which form a link between primates and insectivores. The second are lemurs in the narrower sense of the term. The tarsiers stand apart from the rest and are closer in origin to the Simiae than are the more specialized lemurs and lorises.

The Simiae are divided into two groups:

I. Platyrrhina (flat-nosed New World monkeys), with broad external nasal septum, and a dental formula of $I\frac{2}{2}$ $C\frac{1}{1}$ $P\frac{3}{3}$ $M\frac{2\text{-}3}{2\text{-}3}$. The su-per-family Ceboidea consists of two families: (1) Cebidae (cebus monkeys) and (2) Callithricidae (marmosets). Among the genera are: *Alouatta* (howler monkey), *Cebus* (capuchin monkey), *Ateles* (spider monkey), *Leontocebus* (maned marmoset), and *Callithrix* (tufted marmoset).

II. Catarrhina (narrow-nosed Old World monkeys), with narrow external nasal septum and a dental formula of $I\frac{2}{2}$ $C\frac{1}{1}$ $P\frac{2}{2}$ $M\frac{3}{3}$.

They, in turn, are divided into super-families as follows:

A. Cercopithecoidea (frequently referred to as Old World monkeys), with the family Cercopithecidae, which is divided into two sub-families: (a) Cercopithecinae, with genera: *Macaca* (macaque), *Cynopithecus* (Celebes or black ape) and *Papio* (typical baboon, mandrill), *Cercopithecus* (guenon), *Theropithecus* (gelada), and *Erythrocebus* (Patas monkey); and (b) *Colobinae* (slender monkeys), with genera: *Presbytis, Pygathrix, Rhinopithecus,* and *Simias* (langurs), *Nasalis* (proboscis monkey), and *Colobus* (guereza).

B. Hominoidea (anthropoid apes and man), with the families: (1) Hylobatidae (gibbons), (2) Pongidae (anthropoid apes in the narrower sense of the definition), and (3) Hominidae (manlike creatures).

The hominid family will be discussed separately. Pongidae and Hominidae together form one phylogenetic unit (see The Descent of Man). The Hylobatidae are frequently classed in one family with the Pongidae.

The Hylobatidae comprise several genera. The fossil forms include: *Propliopithecus* (Oligocene), *Limnopithecus* (Miocene), *Pliopithecus* (Pliocene), and *Epipliopithecus* (Pliocene); the recent forms include: *Hylobates* (gibbon), and *Symphalangus* (siamang). Fossil forms are known from Europe and Africa; living forms from Southeast Asia.

To date the Pongidae, including the fossil groups, can be divided into three sub-families: (a) Proconsulinae (relatively primitive pongidae; structurally, these are below the level of long-armed apes). (b) Dryopithecinae. (According to their dentition, these were well-differentiated Pongidae. The skeletal structure of their extremities is not sufficiently known; in all likelihood they still did not have the structure typical of the brachiators.) Genera: *Dryopithecus* (Miocene), *Sivapithecus* (Miocene-Pliocene), *Gigantopithecus* (Pleistocene). (c) Ponginae (recent anthropoid

ORDER OF PRIMATES, LIVING GENERA
(F) Fiedler's classification   (S) Simpson's classification

SUB-ORDER	SUPER-FAMILY	FAMILY	SUBFAMILY	GENUS	ENGLISH NAME	HABITAT OR RANGE
PROSIMII	Tupaioidea	Tupaiidae	Tupaiinae	Tupaia	Tree Shrew (various)	Southeast Asia, Indonesia, South India
				Dendrogale	Smooth-tailed Tree Shrew	Vietnam and Borneo
				Urogale	Philippine Tree Shrew	Mindanao
			Ptilocercinae	Ptilocerus	Pen-tailed Tree Shrew	Malay Peninsula, Sumatra, Borneo
	Lemuroidea	Lemuridae	Lemurinae	Lemur Hapalemur Lepilemur	Common Lemur Gentle Lemur Sportive Lemur	Madagascar
			Cheirogaleinae	Cheirogaleus Microcebus	Mouse Lemur Dwarf Lemur	
		Indridae		Indri Lichanotus Propithecus	Indris Avahi Sifaka	
		Daubentoniidae		Daubentonia	Aye-aye	
	Lorisoidea	Lorisidae		Loris Nycticebus Arctocebus Perodicticus	Slender Loris Slow Loris Angwantibo Potto	South India and Ceylon India to Borneo West Africa West Africa
		Galagidae (F)	Galaginae (S)	Galago	Bush Baby	Africa south of Sahara
	Tarsioidea	Tarsiidae		Tarsius	Tarsier	Indonesia
		Callithricidae		Callithrix (including Cebuella) Leontocebus	Plumed and Pygmy Marmosets Maned Marmosets Tamarins and Pinchés	Panama to Southern Brazil

			Callimiconinae	Callimico	Callimico, or Goeldi's Marmoset	
PLATYR-RHINAE	Ceboidea	Cebidae	Aotinae (S)	Aotus	Douroucouli	Southern Mexico to Argentina
			Pithecinae (S)	Callicebus, Pithecia, Chiropotes, Cacajao	Titi, Saki, Saki, Uakari	
			Alouattinae (S)	Alouatta	Howler	
			Cebinae (S)	Cebus, Saimiri	Capuchin, Squirrel Monkey	
			Atelinae (S)	Ateles, Brachyteles, Lagothrix	Spider Monkey, Woolly Spider Monkey, Woolly Monkey	
CATAR-RHINAE	Cercopithe-coidea	Cercopithecidae	Cercopithecinae	Macaca, Cynopithecus, Cercocebus, Papio, Theropithecus, Cercopithecus, Erythrocebus	Macaque, Black Ape, Mangabey, Baboon, Gelada, Guenon, Patas Monkey	Gibraltar, Morocco, Tibet, India to Japan; Celebes; Africa; Africa and Arabia; Ethiopia; Africa; Africa
			Colobinae	Presbytis, Pygathrix, Rhinopithecus, Simias, Nasalis, Colobus	Banded Langur, Douc Langur, Snub-nosed Langur, Pagi Island Langur, Proboscis Monkey, Gueraza	India and Himalayas; East Indochina; East Tibet and Kansu; Sumatra; Borneo; Ethiopia
	Hominoidea	Hylobatidae (F)	Hylobatinae (S)	Hylobates, Symphalangus	Gibbon, Siamang	Southeast Asia and Indonesia; Sumatra
		Pongidae		Pongo, Pan, Gorilla	Orangutan, Chimpanzee (including pygmy), Gorilla	Sumatra and Borneo; Congo and West Africa; Central and West Africa
		Hominidae		Homo	Man	Global (and Spatial)

Reprinted with permission of Alfred A. Knopf, Inc. from *The Origin of Races* by Carleton S. Coon. Copyright © 1962 by Carleton S. Coon.

apes, brachiators by structure). Genera: *Pongo* (also fossil and sub-fossil; orangutan), eastern Asia; *Pan* (chimpanzee and dwarf chimpanzee), Africa; *Gorilla* (gorilla, with mountain gorilla), Africa. It might be proper to class *Pan* and *Gorilla* together as a single genus as contrasted with *Pongo* (orangutans), since there are, relatively, considerable differences between these two groups.

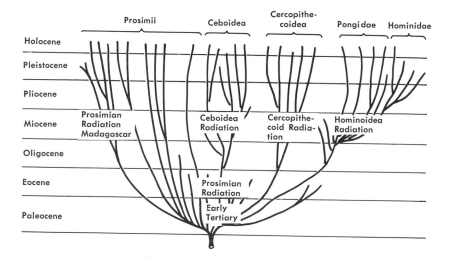

FIG. 89   Diagrammatic representation of primate phylogenetic relationships, with their radiations (after Simpson).

It should be pointed out here that the experts have not yet arrived at a uniform system of evaluation as regards hierarchical order; i.e., arrangements into super-families, families, and sub-families.

The phylogeny of the primates (Figure 89) shows an initial adaptive radiation in the Paleocene epoch (Early Tertiary Prosimian Radiation). Surviving from this radiation are the Platyrrhina and the Catarrhina, branches of the Prosimian sub-order that continued to develop. During the Miocene-Pliocene epoch the Prosimians show further radiations which gave rise to a considerable variety of forms, particularly on the isolated island of Madagascar. Surviving to this day from the Eocene epoch as a kind of living fossil is *Tarsius spectrum*. The Prosimian root of the

Platyrrhina is uncertain; it may be that they and the Catarrhina have a common ancestor. During the Miocene-Pliocene epoch the Platyrrhina underwent a radiation which was confined to South America and resulted in the present multiplicity of forms noted in South American monkeys, creatures that have attained amazing adaptive convergences with the catarrhines in the process. As for the Catarrhina, it must be assumed that they have a root common to both Cercopithecoidea and Hominoidea. It is uncertain whether this root, as G. G. Simpson, for one, assumes (Figure 89), goes back to Prosimian conditions, i.e., to the lemur level. In all probability some proto-catarrhine forms which already had become differentiated beyond the Prosimian level, may be regarded as an ancestral group. In all likelihood, this ancestral group dates from the Eocene epoch. During the Miocene and Pliocene the Cercopithecoidea and Hominoidea also underwent adaptive radiations, as did the Pongidae and Hominidae within the latter super-family. Insofar as they have not secondarily adapted themselves to life on the ground, the Pongidae today still lead a rather circumscribed existence in refuge areas as specialized brachiators of the tropical-rain-forest regions. The Hominidae, after acquiring the erect posture and with the onset of the cerebralization (an increase in brain size) typical of the hominid family, went through a radiation into several branches which, with the end of the Ice Age, climaxed in the branch of *Homo sapiens* and led to the highly polytypic make-up of present-day man.

The Hominidae evolved, probably during the first half of the Miocene epoch, from primitive *man-apes* which presumably had not yet become differentiated as brachiators; that is, their arms had not yet become specialized as organs for swinging and for horizontal locomotion. The genus *Proconsul,* which dates back to the Lower to Middle Miocene epoch, may serve as a model for the ancestral type of this family.

The Hominidae may possibly be grouped into three sub-families: (a) Oreopithecinae, (b) Australopithecinae ("Praehomininae"), and (c) Homininae ("Euhomininae").

(a) The Oreopithecinae are still not universally acknowledged to belong to the Hominidae family (see The Descent of Man). *Oreopithecus,* the sole genus known thus far, and *O. bambolii,* the only species now known, have been known since 1871. More recently, in 1958, Hürzeler, a paleontologist in Basel, discovered numerous remains from this form, including a complete skeleton. These finds date from the Lower Pliocene lignite deposits in Tuscany. Hürzeler has already reported on this material in detail. The result was a combination of hominid characteristics so complex in nature that he finds it hard to assume that this combination could have been formed independently of the human family line. However, Schultz, working on the postcranial skeleton and Butler and Mills on the teeth, conclude that Oreopithecus was too specialized to be called a hominid and should be placed in an extinct family of its own. Which opinion is right remains to be seen. Kenyapithecus: in 1961 Louis Leakey found a maxilla with parts of five teeth at Fort Ternan in Kenya. The specimen is of Pontian age, the same as Oreopithecus. Its teeth are almost indistinguishable from those of man and this animal can be called hominid with much more assurance than Oreopithecus.

(b) The Australopithecinae ("Praehomininae") have been known since 1924, the date of the first such find at Taung, Bechuanaland, South Africa. Geologically they belong to the late Lower Pleistocene (Villafranchian); some finds may date from the Middle Pleistocene. At the time of this writing, remains from more than one hundred individual specimens have been recovered and new finds are continually augmenting the available material. There can be no doubt as to the hominid character of the Australopithecinae. That these creatures already had an erect walk is confirmed by five pelvis finds. Their dentition, too, was typically hominid. Attempts to subdivide the Australopithecinae sub-family, at this time, can be regarded as provisional only. However, it now seems possible to make a distinction between two type groups, though no definite statement can be made as to their proper taxonomic position (genera, sub-genera, species: Robinson divides them into two genera—Australopithecus (Taung, Sterkfontein, and Makapan specimens) and Paranthropus (Kromdraai, Swartkrans, and Olduvai); other workers, particularly in America, consider them tentatively as one genus with two species, *Australopithecus africanus* and *Australopithecus robustus* (see Paleoanthropology).

Presumably Australopithecinae also occurred outside of Africa, in Java and in China. According to their type, the Australopithecinae were survivals from the Pliocene living in the Lower Pleistocene epoch. Forms such as *Australopithecus* ("Plesianthropus") *transvaalensis* (found at Sterkfontein) might be models for the phylogenetic ancestral form of the sub-family Homininae ("Euhomininae"). It is still uncertain whether further studies will confirm the assumption that there is a third group, the Gigantopithecus (Gigantanthropus), which we have learned of through numerous teeth and three lower jaws found thus far in southern China; a more thorough study of the lower jaws is needed. It seems likely that Gigantopithecus was a particularly robust member of the Pongidae family.

(c) The Homininae ("Euhomininae" or genus *Homo*). Here we shall place all Homininae into only one genus—that of *Homo*. This genus, in turn, has been divided in two different ways. European workers usually recognize three divisions: (1) Archanthropinae or Protoanthropinae (Pithecanthropus, Sinanthropus, etc.); (2) Paleanthropinae (Neanderthals and others of the same general evolutionary grade; and (3) Neanthropinae ("sapiens" types with fossil forerunners). Americans particularly limit the genus to two successive species, *Homo sapiens* and *Homo erectus,* with the "Paleanthropinae" divided between them. (For the racial grouping of recent hominids, see The History of Races.)

BIBLIOGRAPHY

GLOSSARY

INDEX

BIBLIOGRAPHY

The present bibliography is a selection of the leading periodicals and general works in biological anthropology, from which the reader may continue into many relevant source materials. The listings in the original German edition have been greatly changed, so that the present emphasis is on literature in English rather than in German. The subject matter, however, corresponds as closely as possible to the original citations.

In social biology and racial psychology, scholarly works are included which represent both sides of the current controversy on inborn intellectual differences between human races.

General

Biasutti, R.: *Le Razze e Popoli della Terra*. Torino: Unione Tipografico-Editrice; 1953–57, 2nd ed.
Boule, M., and Vallois, H. V.: *Fossil Men* (translated by M. Bullock). New York: Dryden; 1958.
Boyd, W.: *Genetics and the Races of Man*. Boston: Boston University Press; 1958.
Clark, W. E. Le Gros: *The Antecedents of Man*. Edinburgh: University of Edinburgh Press; 1959.
Coon, C. S.: *The Origin of Races*. New York: Knopf; 1962.
Dobzhansky, T.: *Evolution, Genetics and Man*. New York: Wiley; 1957.
——: *Mankind Evolving*. New Haven: Yale University Press; 1962.
Eickstedt, E. v.: *Die Forschung am Menschen*. Stuttgart: Enke; 1937ff.
Hill, W. C. Osman: *Primates: Comparative Anatomy and Taxonomy* (5 Vols.). New York: Interscience Publishers; 1953–62.
Hofer, H., Schultz, A. H., and Starck, D., eds.: *Primatologia* (3 Vols.). Basel: Karger; 1956.
Hooton, E. A.: *Up From the Ape*. New York: Macmillan; 1946, 2nd ed.
Howells, W. W.: *Mankind in the Making*. New York: Doubleday & Co.; 1959.
Kroeber, A. L.: *Anthropology*. New York: Harcourt, Brace; 1948, 2nd ed.
Montagu, M. F. A.: *An Introduction to Physical Anthropology*. Springfield, Illinois: Thomas; 1960, 3rd ed.
Piveteau, J.: *Traité de Paléontologie, VII, Traité de Paléontologie Humaine, Les Primates et l'Homme*. Paris: Masson et Cie; 1957.
Rensch, B.: *Evolution Above the Species Level*. New York: Columbia University Press; 1960.
Schwidetzky, I.: *Grundzüge der Völkerbiologie*. Stuttgart: Enke; 1950.
Simpson, G. G.: *The Major Features of Evolution*. New York: Columbia University Press; 1953.
Stern, C.: *Principles of Human Genetics*. San Francisco: W. H. Freeman; 1960, 2nd ed.

Vallois, H. V., and Movius, H. L., eds.: *Catalogue des Hommes Fossiles.* Algiers: 19th International Geological Congress; 1952.

Periodicals

Acta Genetica et Statistica Medica, Basel
American Anthropologist, Baltimore
American Journal of Human Genetics, Baltimore
American Journal of Physical Anthropology, Philadelphia
Annals of Human Genetics, London
Anthropos, Vienna
Antiquity, London
Antropologiya, Moscow
Anthropologischer Anzeiger, Stuttgart
Archiv der Julius-Klaus Stiftung für Vererbungforschung, Zurich
Biometrika, London
Biotypologie, Paris
Current Anthropology, Chicago
Evolution, Lancaster, Pennsylvania
Genetics, Austin, Texas
Hereditas, Lund
Homo, Göttingen
Human Biology, Detroit
Journal of the Royal Anthropological Institute, London
L'Anthropologie, Paris
Man, London
Archives de l'Institut de Paléontologie Humaine, Paris
Mitteilungen der Anthropologischen Gesellschaft, Vienna
Population, Paris
Przeglad Antropologiczny, Poznan
Revista de Antropologia, São Paulo
Rivista di Antropologia, Rome
Zeitschrift für Tierpsychologie, Berlin, Göttingen, Hamburg
Zeitschrift für Vergleichende Konstitutionsforschung, Berlin, Göttingen, Heidelberg

Anthropology

Kluckhohn, C.: *Mirror for Man.* New York: Whittlesey; 1949.
Martin, R., and Saller, K.: *Lehrbuch der Anthropologie in systematischer Darstellung.* Jena: Fischer; 1958, 3rd ed.
Roberts, D. F., and Weiner, J. S., eds.: *The Scope of Physical Anthropology and Its Place in Academic Studies.* London: Institute for Biology; 1958.

The Concept of Race / The Formation of Races (See also Population Genetics)

Anonymous: *The Race Question in Modern Science.* New York: UNESCO Publications; 1956.
Coon, C. S., Garn, S. M., and Birdsell, J. B.: *Races: A Study of the Problems of Race Formation in Man.* Springfield, Ill.: Thomas; 1950.

Count, E. W., ed.: *This Is Race.* New York: Schuman; 1950.
Garn, S. M., ed.: *Readings on Race.* Springfield, Ill.: Thomas; 1960.
Hulse, F. S.: "Race as an Evolutionary Episode." *American Anthropologist,* Vol. 64 (1962), pp. 929–945.
Hunt, E. E., Jr.: "Anthropometry, Genetics, and Racial History." *American Anthropologist,* Vol. 61 (1959), pp. 64–87.
Lundman, B.: *Umriss der Rassenkunde des Menschen in geschichtlicher Zeit.* Copenhagen: Munksgaard; 1952.
Mayr, E., Linsley, E. G., and Usinger, R. L.: *Methods and Principles of Systematic Zoology.* New York: McGraw-Hill; 1953.
Simpson, G. G.: *Principles of Animal Taxonomy.* New York: Columbia University Press; 1961.

Constitution

Bauer, J.: *Constitution and Disease.* New York: Grune and Stratton; 1945.
Brozek, J.: "The Measurement of Body Composition," in Montagu, M. F. A.: *Introduction to Physical Anthropology.* Springfield, Ill.: Thomas; 1960.
Draper, G., Dupertuis, C. W., and Caughey, J. C., Jr.: *Human Constitution in Clinical Medicine.* New York: Hoeber; 1944.
Heath, C. W.: *What People Are: A Study of Normal Young Men.* Cambridge, Mass.: Harvard University Press; 1945.
Hooton, E. A.: *Young Man, You Are Normal.* New York: Putnam; 1945.
Kretschmer, E.: *Physique and Character.* London: Routledge and Kegan Paul; 1936.
Lessa, W. A.: "An Appraisal of Constitutional Typologies." *American Anthropological Association Memoir,* No. 62 (1943).
Lindegård, B.: "Variations in Human Body Build, a Somatometric and X-ray Cephalometric Investigation on Scandinavian Adults." *Acta Psychiat., Neurol. Suppl.,* No. 86 (1953), pp. 1–163.
Lindegård, B., ed.: *Body Build, Body Function and Personality.* Lund: C. W. K. Gleerup; 1956.
Parnell, R. W.: *Behaviour and Physique: An Introduction to Practical and Applied Somatometry.* Baltimore: Williams and Wilkins; 1958.
Sheldon, W. H., Stevens, S. S., and Tucker, W. B.: *The Varieties of Human Physique.* New York: Harper; 1940.
Sheldon, W. H., and Stevens, S. S.: *The Varieties of Temperament.* New York: Harper; 1942.
Tanner, J. M.: "Growth and Constitution," in Kroeber, A. L., ed.: *Anthropology Today.* Chicago: University of Chicago Press; 1953.
Tucker, W. B., and Lessa, W. A.: "Man: A Constitutional Investigation." *Quarterly Review of Biology,* Vol. 15 (1940), pp. 265–289.

Sex and Constitution

Mead, M.: *Male and Female.* New York: Morrow; 1949.
Montagu, M. F. A.: *The Natural Superiority of Women.* New York: Macmillan; 1953.
Scheinfeld, A.: *Women and Men.* New York: Harcourt Brace; 1944.

BIBLIOGRAPHY

Terman, L. M., and Miles, C. C.: *Sex and Personality*. New York: McGraw-Hill; 1936.

Thieme, F. P., and Schull, W. J.: "Sex Determination from the Skeleton." *Human Biology,* Vol. 29 (1957), pp. 242–273.

Plasticity

Hunt, E. E., Jr.: "Human Growth and Body Form in Recent Generations." *American Anthropologist,* Vol. 60 (1958), pp. 118–131.

Kaplan, B.: "Environment and Human Plasticity." *American Anthropologist,* Vol. 56 (1954), pp. 780–800.

Shapiro, H. L.: *Migration and Environment*. New York: Oxford University Press; 1939.

Woodworth, R. S.: "Heredity and Environment: A Critical Study of Recently Published Material on Twins and Foster Children." *Soc. Sci. Res. Council Bull.,* No. 47 (1941).

Cultural Anthropology

Coon, C. S.: *The Story of Man*. New York: Knopf; 1961, 2nd ed.

Gehlen, A.: *Urmensch und Spätkultur*. Bonn: Athenäum; 1956.

Kroeber, A. L.: *Anthropology*. New York: Harcourt Brace; 1948, 2nd ed.

——, and Kluckhohn, C.: "Culture: Critical Review of Concepts and Definitions." *Peabody Museum Papers* (Harvard University), Vol. 47 (1952).

Lorenz, K. Z.: *King Solomon's Ring*. New York: Crowell; 1952.

——: "The Evolution of Behavior." *Scientific American,* Vol. 199 (1958), pp. 67–74, 76, 78.

Roe, A., and Simpson, G. G., eds.: *Behavior and Evolution*. New Haven: Yale University Press; 1958.

Yerkes, R. M.: *Chimpanzees*. New Haven: Yale University Press; 1943.

Domestication

Fischer, E.: "Racial Characters of Man as Phenomena of Domestication," in Count, E. W., ed.: *This Is Race*. New York: Schuman; 1950.

Klatt, B.: *Haustier und Mensch*. Hamburg: Hermes; 1948.

Snyder, L. H.: "The Effects of Selection and Domestication of Man." *J. National Cancer Institute,* Vol. 15 (1954), pp. 759–769.

Sex and Family

Count, E. W.: "The Biological Basis of Human Sociality." *American Anthropologist,* Vol. 60 (1958), pp. 1049–1085.

Ford, C. S., and Beach, F. A.: *Patterns of Sexual Behavior*. New York: Harper and Hoeber; 1951.

Thurnwald, R.: *Economics in Primitive Communities*. Oxford: Oxford University Press; 1932.

Washburn, S. L., ed.: "Social Life of Early Man." Viking Fund Publ. in *Anthropology,* Vol. 31 (1961).

Tools

Dart, R. A.: "The Osteodontokeratic Culture of *Australopithecus africanus." Transvaal Museum Memoir,* No. 10 (1957).
Köhler, W.: *The Mentality of Apes.* New York: Harcourt Brace; 1925.
Singer, C., Holmyard, E. J., and Hall, A. R., eds.: *A History of Technology* (5 Vols.). Oxford: Oxford University Press; 1954–58.

Speech

Du Brul, E.: *Evolution of the Speech Apparatus.* Springfield, Ill.: Thomas; 1958.
Hockett, C. F.: *A Course in Modern Linguistics.* New York: Macmillan; 1958.
Hockett, C. F.: "Animal 'Languages' and Human Language." *Human Biology,* Vol. 31 (1959), pp. 32–39.
Penfield, W., and Roberts, L.: *Speech and Brain Mechanisms.* Princeton: Princeton University Press; 1959.

Demography

Dublin, L. I., Lotka, A. J., and Spiegelman, M.: *Length of Life.* New York: Ronald Press; 1949.
Hauser, P. M., and Duncan, O. D., eds.: *The Study of Population: An Inventory and Appraisal.* Chicago: University of Chicago Press; 1959.
Krzywicki, L.: *Primitive Society and Its Vital Statistics.* New York: Macmillan; 1934.
Lorimer, F., *et al.: Culture and Human Fertility.* Paris: UNESCO; 1954.
Pearl, R.: *The Biology of Population Growth.* New York: Knopf; 1925.
Schwidetzky, I.: *Das Problem des Völkertodes, Eine Studie zur historischen Bevölkerungsbiologie.* Stuttgart: Enke; 1954.
Spengler, J. J., and Duncan, O. D., eds.: *Demographic Analysis: Selected Readings.* Glencoe, Illinois: Free Press; 1956.
Spengler, J. J., and Duncan, O. D., eds.: *Population Theory and Policy.* Glencoe, Illinois: Free Press; 1956.
Thompson, W. S.: *Population Problems.* New York: McGraw-Hill; 1953, 4th ed.
United Nations Statistical Office: *Demographic Yearbook.* New York: United Nations; 1948, ff.

The Descent of Man

Clark, W. E. Le Gros: *The Fossil Evidence for Human Evolution.* Chicago: University of Chicago Press; 1955.
——: *History of the Primates: An Introduction to the Study of Fossil Man.* London: British Museum (Natural History); 1958, 6th ed.
——: *The Antecedents of Man.* Chicago: Quadrangle; 1960.
——, and Leakey, L. S. B.: *The Miocene Hominoidea of East Africa.* London: British Museum (Natural History); 1951.
Cold Spring Harbor Symposia on Quantitative Biology: *The Origin and Evolution of Man.* Vol. 15, 1950.
Colloques Internationaux du Centre National de la Recherche Scientifique: *Les Processus de l'Hominisation.* Paris; 1958.

BIBLIOGRAPHY

Darwin, C.: *The Origin of Species.* London: Murray; 1859.
——: *The Descent of Man.* London: Murray; 1871.
Dobzhansky, T.: *Genetics and the Origin of Species.* New York: Columbia University Press; 1951, 3rd ed.
Hürzeler, J.: *Oreopithecus bambolii* Gervais." *Verh. Naturf. Ges. Basel,* Vol. 69 (1958), pp. 1–48.
Huxley, J.: *Evolution: the Modern Synthesis.* New York: Harper; 1942.
Huxley, T. H.: *Evidence as to Man's Place in Nature.* London: William and Norgate; 1863.
Mayr, E.: *Systematics and the Origin of Species.* New York: Columbia University Press; 1942.
Rensch, B.: *Evolution Above the Species Level.* New York: Columbia University Press; 1960.
Simpson, G. G.: *The Major Features of Evolution.* New York: Columbia University Press; 1953.
Straus, W.: "The Riddle of Man's Ancestry." *Quarterly Review of Biology,* Vol. 24 (1949), pp. 200–223.

The Formation of Races   (See the Concept of Race and Population Genetics)

Genetics and Race

Baker, P. T.: "Racial Differences in Heat Tolerance." *American Journal of Physical Anthropology,* Vol. 16 (1958), pp. 287–305.
——: "American Negro-White Differences in Thermal-Insulative Aspects of Body Fat." *Human Biology,* Vol. 31 (1959), pp. 316–324.
——: "Climate, Culture and Evolution." *Human Biology,* Vol. 32 (1960), pp. 3–16.
Boyd, W. C.: *Genetics and the Races of Man.* Boston: Boston University Press; 1958.
Hammel, H. T.: "Thermal and Metabolic Responses of the Alacaluf Indians to Moderate Cold Exposure." *Wright Air Development Command Technical Report,* No. 60-633 (Dec. 1960).
——, Elsner, R. W., LeMessurier, D. H., Andersen, K. L., and Milan, F. A.: "Thermal and Metabolic Responses of the Australian Aborigine Exposed to Moderate Cold in Summer." *Journal of Applied Physiology,* Vol. 14 (1959), pp. 605–15.
Montagu, M. F. A.: *An Introduction to Physical Anthropology.* Springfield, Ill.: Thomas; 1960, 3rd ed.
Mourant, A. E.: *The Distribution of Human Blood Groups.* Springfield, Ill.: Thomas; 1954.
Newman, M. T.: "The Application of Ecological Rules to the Racial Anthropology of the Aboriginal New World." *American Anthropologist,* Vol. 55 (1953), pp. 311–327.
——: "Adaptation of Man to Cold Climates." *Evolution,* Vol. 10 (1956), pp. 101–105.
——: "Man and the Heights." *Natural History,* Vol. 67 (1958), pp. 9–19.
Race, R. R., and Sanger, R.: *Blood Groups in Man.* Oxford: Blackwell; 1958, 3rd ed.

240

Scholander, P. F., Hammel, H. T., Hart, J. S., LeMessurier, D. H., and Stern, J.: "Cold Adaptation in Australian Aborigines." *Journal of Applied Physiology,* Vol. 13 (1958), pp. 211–218.

Steinberg, A. G.: *Progress in Medical Genetics* (Vols. 1 and 2). New York: Grune and Stratton; 1961–62.

Growth

Altman, P. L., and Dittmer, D. S.: *Growth: Including Reproduction and Morphological Development.* Washington, D.C.: Federation of American Societies for Experimental Biology; 1962.

Binning, G.: "Health in the School." *Health,* March-April 1948; July-August 1949.

Büchi, E. C.: *Änderungen der Körperform beim erwachsenen Menschen.* Vienna: Horn; 1950.

Clark, W. E. Le Gros, and Medawar, P. B., eds.: *Essays on Growth and Form Presented to D'Arcy W. Thompson.* Oxford: Clarendon Press; 1945.

Garn, S. M., and Shamir, Z.: *Methods for Research in Human Growth.* Springfield, Ill.: Thomas; 1958.

Harris, J. A., Jackson, C. M., Patterson, D., and Scammon, R. E.: *The Measurement of Man.* Minneapolis: University of Minnesota Press; 1930.

Krogman, W. M.: *Growth of Man. Tabulae Biologicae Vol. XX.* The Hague: W. Junk; 1941.

Lansing, A. I.: *Cowdry's Problems of Ageing.* Baltimore: Williams & Wilkins; 1952, 3rd ed.

Montagu, M. F. A.: *Parental Influences.* Springfield, Ill.: Thomas; 1962.

Mussen, P. H., ed.: *Handbook of Research: Methods in Child Development.* New York: Wiley; 1960.

Schultz, A. H.: "Fetal Growth of Man and Other Primates." *Quarterly Review of Biology,* Vol. 1 (1926), pp. 465–521.

——: "Ontogenetic Specializations of Man." *Arch. Julius Klaus-Stift,* Vol. 24 (1949), pp. 197–216.

——: "Postembryonic Age Changes." *Primatologia,* Vol. 1 (1956), pp. 887–964.

Shock, N. W., ed.: "Ageing: Some Social and Biological Aspects." *Am. Assn. for the Advancement of Science Publication,* No. 65 (1960).

Steggerda, M.: "Maya Indians of Yucatan." *Carnegie Institute of Washington Publication,* No. 531 (1941).

Stuart, H. C., and Prugh, D. A.: *The Healthy Child: His Physical, Psychological and Social Development.* Cambridge, Mass.: Harvard University Press; 1960.

Tanner, J. M.: *Human Growth* (Symp. Soc. Study of Human Biology, 3). New York: Pergamon Press; 1960.

——: *Growth at Adolescence.* Springfield, Ill.: Thomas; 1962, 2nd ed.

Thompson, D. W.: *On Growth and Form.* Cambridge: Cambridge University Press; 1951.

Vallois, H. V.: "La durée de la vie chez l'homme fossile." *Anthropologie,* Vol. 47 (1937), pp. 499–532.

Watson, E. Y., and Lowrey, G. A.: *Growth and Development of Children.* Chicago: Year Book; 1962, 4th ed.

BIBLIOGRAPHY

Zubek, J. P., and Solberg, P. A.: *Human Development.* New York: McGraw-Hill; 1954.

The History of Anthropology

Haddon, A. C.: *History of Anthropology.* London: Watts; 1934, 2nd ed.
Kluckhohn, C.: "Developments in the Field of Anthropology in the Twentieth Century." *Journal of World History,* Vol. 3 (1957), pp. 754–777.
Montagu, M. F. A.: *An Introduction to Physical Anthropology.* Springfield, Ill.: Thomas; 1960, 3rd ed.
Mühlmann, W. E.: *Geschichte der Anthropologie.* Bonn: Bonn Universitäts Verlag; 1948.
Penniman, T. K.: *A Hundred Years of Anthropology.* New York: Macmillan; 1952.

The History of Races

Allen, J. A.: "The Influence of Physical Conditions in the Genesis of Species." *Radical Rev.,* Vol. 1 (1877), pp. 108–140.
Allison, S. D., and Wong, K. L.: "Skin Cancer." *Arch. Dermatol.,* Vol. 76 (1957), pp. 737–739.
Bergmann, C.: "Über die Verhältnisse der Warmeökonomie des Thiere zu ihrer Grösse." *Göttinger Studien,* Vol. 3 (1947), pp. 595–708.
Bielicki, T.: "Some Possibilities for Estimating Inter-population Relationship on the Basis of Continuous Traits." *Current Anthropology,* Vol. 3 (1962), pp. 3–8.
Coon, C. S.: *The Races of Europe.* New York: Macmillan; 1939.
——: *The Origin of Races.* New York: Knopf; 1962.
——: Garn, S. M., and Birdsell, J. B.: *Races: A Study of the Problems of Race Formation in Man.* Springfield, Ill.: Thomas; 1950.
Cowles, R. B.: "The Black Skin and Human Protective Coloration." *Journal of Entomology and Zoology,* Vol. 42 (1950), pp. 1–4.
Dorn, H. F., and Cutler, S. J.: "Morbidity from Cancer in the U.S." *Public Health Monograph,* No. 56 (1959), U.S. Dept. of Health, Education, and Welfare.
Ewing, J. F.: "Hyperbrachy as Influenced by Cultural Conditioning." *Peabody Museum Papers* (Harvard), Vol. 23 (1950), pp. 10–99.
Gloger, C. L.: *Das Abändern der Vögel durch Einfluss des Klima's.* Breslau: Schulz; 1833.
Heuse, G. A.: *Biologie du Noir.* Brussels: Lielens; 1957.
Hunt, E. E., Jr.: "The Continuing Evolution of Modern Man." *Cold Spring Harbor Symp. Quant. Biol.,* Vol. 24 (1959), pp. 245–254.
——: "Malocclusion and Civilization." *Am. J. Orthodontics,* Vol. 47 (1961), pp. 406–422.
Newman, M. T.: "The Application of Ecological Rules to the Racial Anthropology of the Aboriginal New World." *American Anthropologist,* Vol. 55 (1953), pp. 311–327.
Newman, R. W., and Munro, E. H.: "Climate and Body Size in U.S. Males." *American Journal of Physical Anthropology,* Vol. 13 (1955), pp. 1–17.

Rensch, B.: "Umwelt und Rassenbildung bei warmblütigen Wirbeltieren." *Arch. f. Anthropol.*, Vol. 23 (1935), pp. 326–333.

——: "Typen der Artbildung." *Camb. Phil. Soc. Biol. Rev.*, Vol. 14, pp. 180–222.

Ridgway, W.: "The Application of Zoological Laws to Man." *Report of the Meeting, Brit. Assn. Advancement of Science, 1908*, pp. 832–847.

Walcher, G.: "Über die Entstehung von Brachy- und Dolichocephalie durch willkürliche Beeinflussung des kindlichen Schädels." *Zentralbl. f. Gynakol.*, Vol. 29 (1905), pp. 193–196.

Weidenreich, F.: *Anthropological Papers of Franz Weidenreich, 1933–1948* (compiled by S. L. Washburn and D. Wolffson). New York: Viking Fund; 1950.

Human Genetics

Burdette, W. J., ed.: *Methodology in Human Genetics*. San Francisco: Holden-Day; 1962.

Fuller, J. L., and Thompson, W. R.: *Behavior Genetics*. New York: Wiley; 1960.

Li, C. C.: *Human Genetics: Principles and Methods*. New York: McGraw-Hill; 1961.

Osborne, R. H., and De George, F. V.: *Genetic Basis of Morphological Variation*. Cambridge, Mass.: Harvard University Press; 1959.

Steinberg, A., ed.: *Progress in Medical Genetics* (Vols. 1 and 2). New York: Grune and Stratton; 1961–62.

Stern, C.: *Principles of Human Genetics*. San Francisco: Freeman; 1960, 2nd ed.

Verschuer, O. Fr. von: *Genetik des Menschen*. Munich and Berlin: Urban and Schwarzenberg; 1959.

Methods of Anthropology

Comas, J.: *Manual of Physical Anthropology*. Springfield, Ill.: Thomas; 1960.

Hooton, E. A.: *Up From the Ape*. New York: Macmillan; 1946, 2nd ed.

Hrdlička, A.: *Practical Anthropometry* (edited by T. D. Stewart). Philadelphia: Wistar Institute; 1957, 4th ed.

Martin, R., and Saller, K.: *Lehrbuch der Anthropologie in systematischer Darstellung*. Jena: Fischer; 1958, 3rd ed.

Montagu, M. F. A.: *Introduction to Physical Anthropology*. Springfield, Ill.: Thomas; 1960, 3rd ed.

Simpson, G. G., Roe, A., and Lewontin, R.: *Quantitative Zoology*. New York: McGraw-Hill; 1960, 2nd ed.

Paleoanthropology

Boule, M., and Vallois, H. V.: *Fossil Men* (translated by M. Bullock). New York: Dryden; 1957.

Clark, W. E. Le Gros: *The Fossil Evidence for Human Evolution*. Chicago: University of Chicago Press; 1955.

——: *History of the Primates: an Introduction to the Study of Fossil Man*. London: British Museum (Natural History); 1958, 6th ed.

———: *The Antecedents of Man.* Edinburgh: University of Edinburgh Press; 1959.

Coon, C. S.: *The Origin of Races.* New York: Knopf; 1962.

Howell, F. C.: "Pleistocene Glacial Geology and the Evolution of 'Classic Neanderthal' Man." *Southwest. J. Anthrop.,* Vol. 8 (1952), pp. 377–410.

———: The Age of the Australopithecines of Southern Africa." *Am. J. Phys. Anthrop.,* Vol. 13 (1955), pp. 635–662.

———: "Upper Pleistocene Men of the Southwest Asian Mousterian," in Koenigswald, G. H. R. von, ed.: *Hundert Jahre Neanderthaler* (Neanderthal Centenary). Utrecht: Kemink; 1958.

———: "Upper Pleistocene Stratigraphy and Early Man in the Levant." *Proc. Am. Philosophical Soc.,* Vol. 103 (1959), pp. 1–65.

———: "The Villafranchian and Human Origins." *Science,* Vol. 130 (1959), pp. 831–44.

———: "European and Northwest African Middle Pleistocene Hominids." *Current Anthropology,* Vol. 1 (1960), pp. 195–232.

Howells, W. W.: *Mankind in the Making.* New York: Doubleday; 1959.

———, ed.: *Ideas on Human Evolution.* Cambridge, Mass.: Harvard University Press; 1962.

Keith, A., and McCown, T. D.: *The Stone Age of Mt. Carmel* (Vol. 2). Oxford: Clarendon; 1939.

Koenigswald, G. H. R. von: "Fossil Hominids from the Lower Pleistocene of Java." *International Geological Congress,* Vol. 9 (1948), pp. 51–69.

———: "Gigantopithecus blacki von Koenigswald, a Giant Fossil Hominid from the Pleistocene of South China." *Anthrop. Papers American Museum of Natural History,* Vol. 43 (1952), pp. 295–325.

———: *Meeting Prehistoric Man.* New York: Harper; 1956.

Kurth, G., ed.: *Evolution und Hominisation.* Stuttgart: Fischer; 1962.

Patte, É.: *Les Néanderthaliens: Anatomie, Physiologie, Comparaisons.* Paris: Masson et Cie; 1955.

Piveteau, J.: "Primates. Paléontologie Humaine," in Piveteau, J., ed.: *Traité de Paléontologie.* Paris: Masson et Cie; 1957.

Symposium Commemorating the Hundredth Anniversary of the Discovery of Neanderthal Man: *Quarterly Review of Biology,* Vol. 32 (1957), pp. 323–369.

Vallois, H. V., and Movius, H. L.: *Catalogue des Hommes Fossiles.* Algiers: 19th International Geological Congress; 1952.

Weidenreich, F.: "The mandibles of Sinanthropus Pekinensis." *Paleontologia Sinica New Series D,* Vol. 7 (1936).

———: "The Dentition of Sinanthropus Pekinensis." *Paleontologia Sinica New Series D,* Vol. 1 (1937).

———: "The Skull of Sinanthropus Pekinensis." *Paleontologia Sinica New Series D,* Vol. 3 (1943).

———: "Giant early man from Java and South China." *Anthrop. Papers American Museum of Natural History,* Vol. 40 (1945).

Wormington, H. M.: *Ancient Man in North America.* Denver: Denver Museum of Natural History, Popular Series No. 4; 1957.

Zeuner, F.: *Dating the Past.* New York: Longmans; 1957, 4th ed.

Paternity Diagnosis

Cummins, H., and Midlo, C.: *Finger Prints, Palms and Soles: An Introduction to Dermatoglyphics.* New York: Dover; 1961.
Schwidetzky, I.: "Forensic Anthropology in Germany." *Human Biology,* Vol. 26 (1954), pp. 1–20.

Population Genetics

Birdsell, J.: "Some Implications of the Genetical Concept of Race in Terms of Spatial Analysis." *Cold Spring Harbor Symposia on Quantitative Biology,* Vol. 25 (1950), pp. 259–314.
Blumberg, B. S., ed.: *Proceedings of the Conference on Genetic Polymorphisms and Geographic Variations in Disease.* U. S. Dept. of Health, Education and Welfare, National Institutes of Health, 1960.
Cold Spring Harbor Symposia on Quantitative Biology: *Population Genetics: The Nature and Causes of Genetic Variability in Populations.* Vol. 20, 1955.
——: *Population Studies: Animal Ecology and Demography.* Vol. 22, 1957.
——: *Genetics and Twentieth Century Darwinism.* Vol. 24, 1959.
Dahlberg, G.: *Mathematical Methods for Population Genetics.* New York: Interscience Publishers; 1948.
Dobzhansky, Th.: *Genetics and the Origin of Species.* New York: Columbia University Press; 1951, 3rd ed.
——: *Mankind Evolving.* New Haven: Yale University Press; 1962.
Dunn, L. C.: *Heredity and Evolution in Human Populations.* Cambridge, Mass.: Harvard University Press; 1959.
Fisher, R. A.: *The Genetical Theory of Natural Selection.* New York: Dover; 1959, 2nd ed.
Lasker, G. W., ed.: *The Processes of Ongoing Human Evolution.* Detroit: Wayne State University Press; 1960.
Lerner, I. M.: *Genetic Homeostasis.* Edinburgh: Oliver and Boyd; 1954.
Li, C. C.: *Population Genetics.* Chicago: University of Chicago Press; 1955.
Sheppard, P. M.: *Natural Selection and Heredity.* London: Hutchinson; 1958.
Wright, S.: "Evolution in Mendelian Populations." *Genetics,* Vol. 16 (1931), pp. 97–159.

Racial Psychology

Anastasi, A.: *Differential Psychology.* New York: Macmillan; 1958, 2nd ed.
Anonymous: *The Race Question in Modern Science.* New York: UNESCO Publications; 1959.
Eels, K., Davis, A., Havighurst, R. J., Herrick, V. E., and Tyler, R. W.: *Intelligence and Cultural Differences.* Chicago: University of Chicago Press; 1951.
George, W. C.: "The Biology of the Race Problem." *Report by Commission, Governor of Alabama, 1962.*

BIBLIOGRAPHY

Klineberg, O.: *Race Differences*. New York: Harper; 1935.
Porteus, S. D.: *The Porteus Maze Test and Intelligence*. Palo Alto: Pacific Books; 1950.
Shuey, A. M.: *The Testing of Negro Intelligence*. Lynchburg, Virginia: Bell; 1958.

Social Biology (See also Demography)

Andrewartha, H. G., and Birch, L. C.: *The Distribution and Abundance of Animals*. Chicago: University of Chicago Press; 1954.
Berry, B.: *Race and Ethnic Relations*. Boston: Houghton Mifflin; 1958, 2nd ed.
Darlington, C. D.: *The Facts of Life*. London: Allen and Unwin; 1953.
Hooton, E. A.: *Crime and the Man*. Cambridge, Mass.: Harvard University Press; 1939.
Lenz, F.: *Menschliche Auslese und Rassenhygiene*. Munich: Lehmann; 1923.
Lewis, J. H.: *The Biology of the Negro*. Chicago: University of Chicago Press; 1942.
Mühlmann, W. E.: "Sociology in Germany: A Shift in Alignment," in Becker, H., and Boskoff, A., eds.: *Modern Sociological Theory in Continuity and Change*. New York: Dryden; 1957.
Myrdal, G.: *An American Dilemma: The Negro Problem and American Democracy* (2 Vols.). New York: Harper; 1944.
Schwidetzky, I.: *Grundzüge der Völkerbiologie*. Stuttgart: Enke; 1950.
Walter, P. A. F.: *Race and Culture Relations*. New York: McGraw-Hill; 1952.
Weyl, N.: *The Negro in American Civilization*. Washington: Public Affairs Press; 1960.

Taxonomy of the Primates

Clark, W. E. Le Gros: *The Antecedents of Man*. Edinburgh: University of Edinburgh Press; 1959.
Gavan, J. A., ed.: "The Non-Human Primates and Human Evolution." *Human Biology*, Vol. 26 (1954), pp. 179–312.
Hill, W. C. Osman: *Primates: Comparative Anatomy and Taxonomy* (5 Vols.). New York: Interscience Publishers; 1953–62.
Hofer, H., Schultz, A. H., and Starck, D., eds.: *Primatologia* (3 Vols.). Basel: Karger; 1956.
Hooton E. A.: *Man's Poor Relations*. New York: Doubleday; 1942.
Mayr, E., Linsley, E. G., and Usinger, R. L.: *Methods and Principles of Systematic Zoology*. New York: McGraw-Hill; 1953.
Simpson, G. G.: "The Principles of Classification and a Classification of the Mammals." *Bull. American Museum of Natural History*, No. 85, 1945.
Vallois, H. V.: "Ordre des Primates," in Grasse, P. P., ed.: *Traité de Zoologie: Mammiferes, Systematique* (Vol. 17). Paris: Masson et Cie; 1955.

GLOSSARY

ADAPTIVE   Tending to promote the survival of an organism or species.

ADAPTIVE RADIATION   The ramification of a phylogenetic tree into evolving lines of organisms, each in a distinctive habitat.

ALLELE   One of two or more slightly dissimilar variants of a gene which coexist in a population or species.

ALLOMETRY   The principle which governs the relative sizes of different organs or parts of an organism in animals of different sizes in the same or related species: e.g., a small dog has a relatively large brain.

ALLOPATRIC   Occupying dissimilar habitats.

ANAGENESIS   The evolution of one species out of another by succession.

ANTHROPOMETRY   The measurement of the size and shape of the human body or skeleton.

ASSORTMENT (ASSORTATIVE PROCESS)   The process by which certain genetic types tend to form racial groups and mate.

AUSTRALOPITHECINES   Upright, small-brained, nearly human primates which inhabited Africa (and possibly parts of Eurasia) during the Lower Pleistocene.

BIOTOPE   The animals, plants, and environment of a locality, considered as a unit.

BRACHIATION   A form of locomotion used by apes and some South American monkeys in which the animal swings through the trees with its arms.

BRACHYCEPHALIC   Of a head, relatively broad, the breadth being 82 per cent or more of its length.

BRECCIA   Rock containing angular stone and bone objects that have been naturally cemented.

BREGMA   A point near the top of the skull where the frontal bone and the two parietal bones meet.

CATARRHINES   Old World monkeys, apes, and men.

CENOZOIC   The present geological era.

CHROMOSOME   A structure in the nuclei of cells, usually most conspicuous at cell division as a rod, which transmits a finite and usually fixed linear order of genes.

CLINE, CLINAL   A progressive gradation in a racially variable characteristic found in intermediate populations lying between primary geographic regions.

DIASTEMA   Space between teeth.

DIMORPHISM (SEXUAL)   The anatomical differentiation of males and females, which is greater in some races than in others.

DRYOPITHECINES   Miocene apes, known mainly from teeth and jaws; some probably quadrupedal.

ECOLOGY   A scientific discipline concerned with the interaction of plant and animal species with one another and their environment.

ECOTYPE   A taxonomic unit more or less equivalent to a subspecies.

ENDOGAMY   The practice of mating within one's own group.

EPIPHYSES   The separate bony centers in children which are encased in growing cartilage and which eventually fuse with major bones.

EUHOMINID   A term used by some European anthropologists to refer to man as distinguished from the Australopithecines.

EXOGAMY   The practice of mating outside one's own group.

FONTANELLE   A gap between the corners of certain bones of the cranium in newborn babies.

GENE   A complex of protein molecules forming a portion of a chromosome and, it is believed, serving as a unit of heredity.

GENE FLOW   The transmission of genes from one population to another, usually in a measurable direction, by the migration or interbreeding of individuals.

GENE POOL   The totality of genes in a genetically distinct population.

GENETIC DRIFT   Random, unpredictable changes in the genetic composition of a population; characteristic of small populations.

GENOTYPE   The specific gene or genes present in an individual.

GENUS   The taxonomic unit above "species," being a group of closely related species, as the genus *Homo*.

GRADE   A stage in an evolutionary line.

GÜNZ   The first major glacial advance of the Pleistocene, especially the local glaciation of Switzerland.

HETEROGAMY   The mating of individuals who are more unlike genetically than is usual between members of a population.

HETEROZYGOUS   Designating the coexistence of two different alleles of a given gene in an individual, one from each parent.

HOMINID   A family of primates including the Australopithecines and *Homo*.

HOMININE   A proposed subfamily having only one genus, *Homo*.

HOMINOID   A bipedal, nearly human or human primate.

HOMO ERECTUS   The parent species from which all living races of man are descended.

HOMO SAPIENS   Living man, and all fossil men not designated as *Homo erectus*.

HOMOGAMY   The mating of genetically similar persons.

HOMOLOGOUS, HOMOLOGY   Pertaining to organs in different but related species which have similar embryological origins but may or may not be alike in function. A good example is the wing of a bird and the arm of a man.

HOMOZYGOUS   Having both alleles of a given gene alike.

HYLOBATIDAE   Gibbons and siamangs.

INTERGLACIAL   A period between glacial advances in the Pleistocene characterized by warm climate and minimal amounts of ice on the earth's surface.

INTERSTADIAL   A period of partial retreat of glacial ice between the several maxima of each glaciation.

LORDOTIC   Having a lumbar region which curves markedly forward; sway-backed.

MALAR   The cheekbone.

MEIOSIS   The cell division by which sperm and eggs are formed with half a parental endowment of chromosomes.

MELANISM   The presence of dark or black mutant individuals in an evolving population.

MENARCHE   The first menstruation.

MINDEL   The second major glacial advance of the Pleistocene.

MIOCENE   The fourth epoch of the Cenozoic, from which many apes and monkeys are known.

MONOGENY   The descent of a group of organisms directly from its source, without branching into one or more evolutionary lines.

MONOMERY   A situation in which the genetic effect of a locus is distinguishable from all others.

MORPHOLOGY   The study of body structure.

MOUSTERIAN   A Middle Paleolithic flake industry of Europe and western Asia, closely identified with Neanderthal man.

MUTATION   The biochemical alteration of a gene (or, less often, a chromosome) to yield a new allele or aberrant chromosomal type.

NEANDERTHAL   Pertaining to an early form of *Homo sapiens,* characterized by large brains and massive faces and noses, which inhabited western Eurasia during the Upper Pleistocene.

NEOLITHIC AGE   The period after the Pleistocene in which man began to raise crops and livestock but did not yet smelt or work metals.

NOTOCHORD   The axial rod underlying the future spinal cord in a vertebrate embryo.

OLIGOCENE   The third epoch of the Cenozoic.

ONTOGENESIS   The development or life cycle of an individual.

ONTOGENY   The cycle of physical development or changes in the life cycle of the individual.

OREOPITHECUS   A swamp-dwelling, aberrant, apelike primate of the Lower Pliocene of Italy.

ORTHOGRADE   Pertaining to upright locomotion, as in man.

ORTHOSELECTION   Regular, uninterrupted, and seemingly "directional" natural selection.

OSTEODONTOKERATIC   A term used by Raymond Dart for an alleged use of animal horns, teeth, and bones as tools by the Australopithecines.

PALEOLITHIC AGE   The period from the Early to the Late Pleistocene in which hominids made chipped stone tools.

PHENOTYPE   The observable or ascertainable effects of an individual's genotype.

PHYLETIC   Pertaining to an evolving line.

PHYLOGENY   The evolutionary line of a species, or the evolutionary histories of many related species.

PITHECANTHROPUS   A generic name often used for *Homo erectus,* or, more specifically, the earliest men in Java.

PLATYRRHINES   New World monkeys.

PLEISTOCENE   The sixth epoch of the Cenozoic, between the Pliocene and recent times.

PLEITROPY   Multiple physiological effects of a single gene.

PLIOCENE   The fifth epoch of the Cenozoic, just before the Pleistocene, during which hominids may have become bipedal.

PLUVIAL   A period of high rainfall and overflowing rivers in the non-glaciated parts of the earth, probably contemporaneous with glacial periods.

POLYGENY   The result of small but additive individual actions of many genes on a hereditary trait.

POLYMERY   The combining of small molecules into strings of larger ones.

POLYPHYLETIC   Divided into more than one evolutionary line.

POLYTYPIC   Designating a species which has more than one geographical subspecies.

PONDERAL (GROWTH)   Pertaining to weight.

PONGIDAE (PONGIDS)   The anthropoid apes.

PRIMATES   The order of placental mammals to which tree shrews, lemurs, tarsiers, monkeys, apes, and men belong.

PROCONSULINES   Quadrupedal, small-jawed anthropoid apes from the Lower Miocene of Africa.

PRONOGRADE   Pertaining to locomotion on all fours in higher vertebrates.

PROSIMIANS   Lemurs and tarsiers, primates less advanced than monkeys, apes, or men.

RACES   Subspecies.

RISS   The third major glacial advance of the Pleistocene.

SALTATION   An abrupt evolutionary change.

SALTATION HYPOTHESIS   The theory that abrupt and drastic evolutionary changes can occur in an evolutionary line.

SECULAR   Occurring over a span of time.

SEROLOGY   The study of blood groups and other inherited properties of the blood.

SHOVELING   A hollowed or shovel-shaped outline of the anterior teeth on the lingual aspect.

SINANTHROPUS   The subspecies of *Homo erectus* from the Middle Pleistocene in China.

SPECIES   A population, or, more commonly, a group of related populations, of organisms which do not interbreed with other such units.

STEATOPYGIA   The condition of having large deposits of fat on the buttocks, as in Capoids.

STRATIGRAPHY   The study of layers of deposits of soil or sedimentary rock.

SYMPATRIC   Designating the coexistence of two or more related species in one environment.

TARSIOIDS   Primitive, nocturnal primates with large eyes, which hop through the trees.

TAURONDONTISM   Enlargement of the pulp of molar teeth, with partial or complete fusion of the roots.

VILLAFRANCHIAN   The earliest division of the Pleistocene, lasting until about 700,000 years ago.

WÜRM   The fourth major glacial advance of the Pleistocene.

INDEX

Abbevillian culture, 183
  dated, 182
Abiotic-biotic transition, 57
ABO blood-group system
  agglutination traits of, 166–67
  heredity of, 168
  in paternity diagnosis, 198, 201
  racial distribution of, 90–91, 93
    spread of gene *B* into Australia,
      206
Abortion, 46, 51
Acheulian culture, 145, 183
  dated, 182
Adaptations of man
  to climate, *see* Climate
  to social living, 81
Additive typogenesis, 62
Aeta (pygmies), 157
Afalou-bou-Rhummel, Algeria, 156
Afghanistan, 151
Africa
  population of
    historical trend, 46
    life expectancy in Roman Africa,
      45
    1961 estimate, 40
  racial history of, 137–43, 144, 187–
    88, 194
  racial stocks in, 120, 129
  See also East Africa; South Africa
African Negritos, described, 120, 142–
  43
Africanthropus, 140
Age, determination of, *see* Growth
Age pyramid, 41, 43
Agglutination in blood groups, 166–67
Agriculture, origin of, 155
AHT (animal-hominid threshold), 64–
  65, 67, 69–73, 79
Ainu, described, 128
Aitape, New Guinea, 134
Alakaluf Indians, basal metabolic rate
  of, 22
Algeria, anthropological finds in, 138,
  142, 156, 186, 187

Aliçar Hüyük, Mesopotamia, 156
Alkaptonuria, 161
Alleles, 162, 168, 204, 205
Allen, J. A., rule of, 159
Allometric growth changes, 20–21
  formula for, 100–1
  stature vs. extremities, 104
Alpines, described, 120
American Indians, 14, 224
  blood groups of, 90–92
  Central, described, 128–29
  Marginal, 157
    described, 128
  Mongoloid features of, 137
  psychology of, 208–9
  See also specific tribes
American Negroes, *see* North Ameri-
  can Coloreds
Anagenesis, 57, 60
Ancestry, determination of, *see* Pater-
  nity diagnosis
Andaman Islands, 128, 157
Androgens, 18
  daily production of, 11
Anemia
  Cooley's, 94
  sickle-cell, 94, 168–69, 206
Anorexia nervosa, 109
"Anthropobiology," 2
Anthropoid apes, *see* Ponginae
Anthropology
  applied, 203
    defined, 2
  cultural, **22-37**
    scope of, 22
    see also Behavior; Cultures; Fam-
      ily; Psychology
  defined, **1-2**
  history of, **113-18**
  methods of, *see* Methods of Anthro-
    pology
  origin of term 1, 113–14
  scope of, 2
  societies of, founding, 114–15
Anthropometer, 177

253

Acknowledgments of the Illustrations

Photographs

Figs.

18   R. Pettazoni, *Der allwissende Gott*. Frankfurt am Main: Fischer Bücherei; 1960.

29   G. Heberer, *"Fosselgeschichte der Hominoidea,"* in *Primatologia*, Vol. 1. Basel: S. Karger; 1956.

31, 39   British Museum (Natural History).

32   A. H. Schultz.

50b   W. C. Ripley, *The Races of Europe*. London; 1900.

50d, 50e, 53b, 53c, 53f, 54d, 54e, 55a   R. Biasutti, *Le Razze e Populi della Terra*, Vol. 2. Turin: Unione Tipografico-Editrice; 1953–57, 2nd ed.

50c, 51a, 51d, 52f, 53b, 54a, 56a   E. von Eickstedt, *Die Forschung am Menschen*, Vol. 1. Stuttgart: Enke; 1937.

51b, 51c, 51e, 52a, 52b, 52c, 52e   R. Biasutti, Vol. 3.

51f   E. von Eickstedt.

52f   Lidio Cipriani.

53e   Carleton S. Coon.

53a   L. F. Clauss, *Von Seele und Antlitz der Rassen und Völker*. Munich: Lehmann; 1929.

54b, 54c, 54f   E. von Eickstedt, *Rassendynamik von Ostasien*. Berlin: Gruyter; 1944.

55b, 55c   Heberer-Lehmann, *Die Inland Malaien von Lombock und Sumbawa*. Göttingen: Musterschmidt; 1952.

55e   Carleton S. Coon.

55d, 55f, 56b, 56c, 56d, 56e   R. Biasutti, Vol. 4.

56f   Carleton S. Coon.

59a   Lundborg-Linders, *The Racial Character of the Swedish Nation*. Upsala: Almquist; 1926.

59f   G. Sauser, *Die Otztaler*. Innsbruck: Naturw.-mediz.; 1938.

69   G. Heberer.

71   Wayland Minot.

Drawings   Adapted by Ruth and Harald Bukor

Figs.

2   P. R. Hofstätter, *Psychologie*. Frankfurt am Main: Fischer Lexikon (Vol. 6); 1957.

4, 6, 8, 63   Wolfgang Bender.

44   W. Lenz, *"Körpergewicht und Körperlänge,"* in *Daten f.d. Kinderartzt* (J. Brock). Berlin: Springer; 1954, 2nd ed.

61, 64, 67, 68, 71   Heinz Radloff.